1875 EE
/

Thermal
Characterization
Techniques

Techniques and Methods of
POLYMER EVALUATION

EDITORS

Philip E. Slade, Jr.

Technical Center
Monsanto Company
Pensacola, Florida

Lloyd T. Jenkins

Chemstrand Research Center
Research Triangle Park
Durham, North Carolina

THERMAL CHARACTERIZATION TECHNIQUES

Philip E. Slade, Jr., and Lloyd T. Jenkins

TECHNICAL CENTER
MONSANTO COMPANY
PENSACOLA, FLORIDA

CHEMSTRAND RESEARCH CENTER
RESEARCH TRIANGLE PARK
DURHAM, NORTH CAROLINA

MARCEL DEKKER, INC.   New York   1970

Preface

One of the most significant aspects of materials characterization by thermal analysis is that these techniques have become standard in many laboratories. They are regarded, especially in the study of macromolecules, as a basic tool for the evaluation of new or modified polymeric systems and in many situations are used as frequently as solution property measurements and spectroscopy as an aid to the chemist. A number of quality control laboratories are also using thermoanalytical techniques as part of their routine procedures in assessing the state of their products. This recognition by the scientific and technological community that thermal analysis can be used to solve problems signifies its coming of age.

This book, the second volume of a review of polymer thermal analysis by outstanding contributors, is concerned with a number of techniques that are of more specialized interest than the broad treatment of differential thermal analysis and thermogravimetric analysis contained in Volume I of this series. These methods greatly expand our knowledge of the composition and structure of polymer systems, and it is the hope of the editors that these discussions will stimulate the reader to broader applications of thermal analysis in his own laboratory.

Unfortunately, one cannot be all inclusive in assembling a treatise on any subject, but we have attempted to select topics that would be of value to the working chemist. We have endeavored to adopt a format to present the material in an organized manner so that it could be read and studied from both a theoretical and a practical position. All of the distinguished authors have followed this format and have presented a most comprehensive treatment of their subjects.

Grateful acknowledgment is made to the Chemstrand Research Center and the Textiles Division of the Monsanto Company for the services made available in assembling this publication. Technical material from industry, government, and educational institutions has been used and the cooperation of the following is sincerely appreciated: Chevron Research Company, Dental Research Section— National Bureau of Standards, Rutgers University, Pennsylvania State University, Rensselaer Polytechnic Institute, and Xerox Corporation.

P. E. SLADE
Pensacola, Florida

L. T. JENKINS
Durham, North Carolina

Contributors

EDWARD M. BARRALL, II, IBM Research Laboratory, San Jose, California

G. M. BRAUER, National Bureau of Standards, Washington, D.C.

J. K. GILLHAM, Polymer Materials Program, Department of Chemical Engineering, Princeton University, Princeton, New Jersey

DAVID HANSEN, Materials Research Center, Rensselaer Polytechnic Institute, Troy, New York

JULIAN F. JOHNSON, Department of Chemistry and Institute of Materials Science, University of Connecticut, Storrs, Connecticut

DONALD E. KLINE, Department of Materials Science, Pennsylvania State University, University Park, Pennsylvania

J. A. SAUER, Department of Mechanics and Materials Science, Rutgers – The State University, New Brunswick, New Jersey

D. A. SEANOR,* Chemstrand Research Center, Durham, North Carolina

A. E. WOODWARD, Department of Chemistry, The City College of the City University of New York, New York

Present address: Chemical Research Laboratories, Xerox Corporation, Webster, New York.

Contents

Chapter 4 Torsional Braid Analysis: A Semimicro Thermomechanical Approach to Polymer Characterization 225

J. K. Gillham

Chapter 5 Thermal Conductivity of Polymers 247

Donald E. Kline and David Hansen

Chapter 6 Electrothermal Analysis of Polymers 293

D. A. Seanor

*Thermal
Characterization
Techniques*

CHAPTER 1

Differential Scanning Calorimetry Theory and Applications

EDWARD M. BARRALL, II

IBM RESEARCH LABORATORY
SAN JOSE, CALIFORNIA 95114

JULIAN F. JOHNSON

DEPARTMENT OF CHEMISTRY
AND INSTITUTE OF MATERIALS SCIENCE
UNIVERSITY OF CONNECTICUT
STORRS, CONNECTICUT 06268

1-1   INTRODUCTION

Differential scanning calorimetry (DSC) is a technique of non-equilibrium calorimetry in which the *heat flow* into or from a sample and reference is measured as some function of time or temperature. This is separated from differential thermal analysis (DTA) where the *temperature difference* between a sample and reference is measured as some function of time or temperature. In presently available DSC equipment, the heat flow is measured by keeping the sample and reference thermally balanced by changing a current passing through the heaters under the two chambers. This practice closely resembles classical calorimetry. In most cases, only the time scale of the studies provides a real differentiation between DSC and classical adiabatic methods.

The desirability of obtaining calorimetric data on polymer systems is obvious and has been the subject of considerable research using various classical techniques. Much of this work is characterized by very precise results. The methods usually are very time consuming which prohibits their widespread use. This is especially true for polymer characterization where frequently many samples must be compared.

In 1964 Watson et al.(*63*) and O'Neill(*45*) described a differential scanning calorimeter and analyzed its performance. This instrument became commercially available (Perkin-Elmer Corporation, Norwalk, Connecticut) and has been widely used. Other workers had previously reported on differential calorimeters, see for example (*18, 59*), but the design of Watson et al. has been by far the most popular.

This chapter will be concerned primarily with applications of differential scanning calorimetry, a brief description of the theory, and some comments on interpretation of results. Instrumentation will not be considered in detail. The choice of *differential scanning calorimetry* as the name of the technique is based on the fact that it was used in the original publications and has been widely accepted. *Dynamic differential calorimetry* and *differential enthalpic analysis* have also been proposed.

The symbols used in the field of calorimetry show considerable variance. Those used in this chapter are given in Table 1-1 and in general follow those proposed by O'Neill(*45*).

TABLE 1-1

Symbols

T_0	Temperature of sample platform; °C
R_0	Thermal resistance between the sample and the sample holder; °C. sec cal^{-1}
T_p	Temperature of temperature source; °C
T_T	Transition temperature; °C
W	Measured heat flow rate; cal sec^{-1}
t	Time; sec
A	Area of platform; cm^2
ρ	Sample density; g cm^{-3}
η	Specific transition energy; cal g^{-1}
r	Sample resistivity
$\dot{T}_p$	Rate of temperature scan; °C, sec^{-1}
Δt	Peak width; sec
ΔH	Transition energy; cal
W_p	Maximum value of measured heat flow rate for a sharp transition; cal sec^{-1}
W_n	Noise level; cal sec^{-1}
M	Figure of merit; °C^{-1}

1-2 THEORY

Figure 1-1 shows a block diagram of a differential scanning calorimeter and a typical chart record. The abscissa is temperature, the ordinate differential power. Following the treatment of O'Neill(45) we consider the case of a sharp transition. The sample may be represented by Fig. 1-2. The calorimeter is shown as a platform, at temperature T_0, on which the sample rests. By analogy to an equivalent electrical circuit the platform is connected through a resistance R_0, (which is the thermal resistance between the sample and sample holder) and a thermal ammeter to a temperature source at a temperature T_p. For a sharp endothermic transition the transition starts when T_p equals the transition temperature T_T. At this point a solid–liquid interface forms in contact with the platform at the bottom of the sample. The interface moves toward the top of the sample as T_p increases. Figure 1-3 shows a plot of the measured heat flow rate W versus time t. The differential equation describing the motion of the solid–liquid interface in the x direction as a function of the source temperature is

$$AR_0\rho\eta\frac{dx}{dt} + r\rho\eta\frac{dx}{dt} = T_p - T_T \qquad (1\text{-}1)$$

where A is the area of the platform, ρ is the sample density, η is the specific transition energy, and r is the sample resistivity. For the case

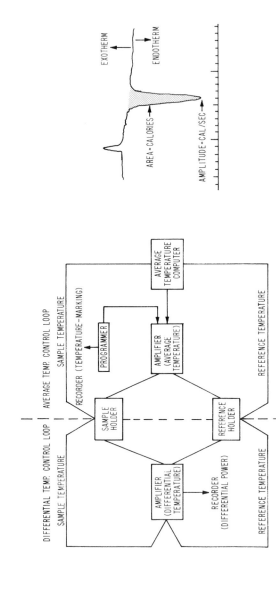

Figure 1-1. Block diagram of a differential scanning calorimeter and a typical chart record(63).

4

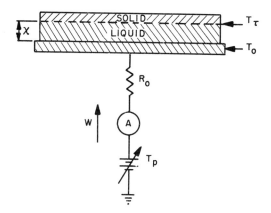

Figure 1-2. Sample geometry(45).

of linear temperature programing if $\mathring{T}_p$ is the scanning speed

$$T_p = T_T + \mathring{T}_p t \tag{1-2}$$

Substituting Eq. (1-2) in Eq. (1-1), integrating, and solving for x yields

$$x = \left[\frac{A^2 R_0^2}{r^2} + \frac{\mathring{T}_p t^2}{r \rho \eta} \right]^{1/2} - \frac{A R_0}{r} \tag{1-3}$$

As the measured heat flow rate is given by

$$W = A \rho \eta \frac{dx}{dt} \tag{1-4}$$

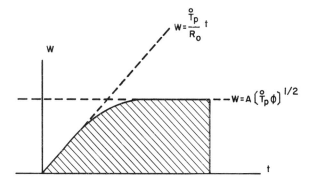

Figure 1-3. Analysis of a fusion endotherm(45).

W is then found to be

$$W = \frac{\mathring{T}_p t / R_0}{[1 + (\mathring{T}_p r t^2 / A^2 R_0^2 \rho \eta)]^{1/2}} \tag{1-5}$$

Equation (1-5) provides a relationship between the value of the ordinate and the instrument and sample parameters.

O'Neill has also suggested a method for assigning a "figure of merit," M, for scanning calorimeters (45). The peak width Δt is given by

$$\Delta t = \left[\frac{\Delta H}{\mathring{T}_p} \left(2 R_0 + \frac{r \Delta H}{A^2 \rho \eta} \right) \right]^{1/2} \tag{1-6}$$

where ΔH is the transition energy. Ideally for a sharp transition the ratio of the temperature interval Δt to the maximum value of W, designated by W_p, should approach zero. This ratio is found to be

$$\frac{\Delta t}{W_p} = R_0 + \frac{\Delta H r}{A^2 \rho \eta} \tag{1-7}$$

from Eqs. (1-5) and (1-6). Equation (1-7) shows that the shape of the peak is independent of scan rate and, additionally, if the second term is small with respect to the first, the shape is independent of sample size. The figure of merit is defined by using the ratio of $W_p / \Delta t$ and the noise level W_N.

$$M = \frac{W_p}{W_N \Delta t} \tag{1-8}$$

The figure of merit represents a convenient parameter to compare instrument performance and is independent of the rate of temperature programing and sample size. Currently values are in the $100–150°C^{-1}$ range but will doubtless improve with more sophisticated instrumentation.

1-3 APPLICATIONS

Prior to consideration of specific examples of DSC studies, a general discussion of what can and cannot be studied by DSC is in order. DSC has been successfully used to measure temperatures and heats of transition, specific heat, thermal emissivity, and certain isothermal functions. Within these general headings fall the measurement of glass transition temperature, crystallinity, purity, rate of reaction, rate of crystallization and rate of decomposition, and the analysis of active material.

A. Transition Temperatures

The most frequent application of DSC has been to the measurement of transition heats and temperatures. Any transition in the range of $-100°C$ to $+600°C$ which involves the absorption or liberation of heat is amenable to study. Some systems require special precautions. Greatest accuracy in temperature measurement is attained by observing the following four considerations: (1) calibration of the instrument, (2) small sample size, (3) proper encapsulation of the sample, and (4) slow scanning rate (not greater than 5°C/min). Transition temperatures in reasonably pure materials are most accurately reflected by the vertex of the endotherm or exotherm of the transition[4]. Hereafter, melting point and vertex temperature will be considered to be the same except where noted otherwise.

Due to the thermal resistance R_0 between the sample and the sample holder, the recorded vertex is not indicated at the exact temperature at which it occurred in the instrument. It is possible, and necessary for accurate temperature measurement, to evaluate the lag, $\mathring{T}_p/R_0$, and remove it from experimental measurement. The lag can be determined by melting 2–4 mg of very pure material, such as semiconductor-grade indium, encapsulated in the same manner as the samples, at the temperature and scanning rate to be used in the future measurement. Since the melting of high-purity indium is essentially a step function, any lag, i.e., slope, will be due to the instrument sample $\mathring{T}_p/R_0$. This factor is sensitive with respect to heating rate and encapsulation. This slope can be applied to any point, especially the vertex of an experimental melting curve determined under the same conditions as the indium melt, and the true temperature read at the intersection of the $\mathring{T}_p/R_0$ line with the true base line. The determination of a vertex temperature with the aid of an indium melting curve and the true base line is shown in Fig. 1-4. The actual melting temperature is at B, not at A. In most cases, the true base line is close enough to the isothermal base line and no severe error is introduced if it is substituted for the reading at B.

For precise temperature measurement, $\pm0.2°C$ absolute, it is necessary to calibrate currently available instrumentation for DSC. The temperature error of a DSC varies in a complex manner with respect to the indicated temperature, due to the nonlinearity of the platinum-resistance temperature sensors and of the temperature-compensation electronics. However, it is possible to minimize this error over a certain range by proper adjustment of the average and differential control on the DSC. This setting will vary between instruments and between calorimeter cells. Calibration is most conveniently carried out by melting

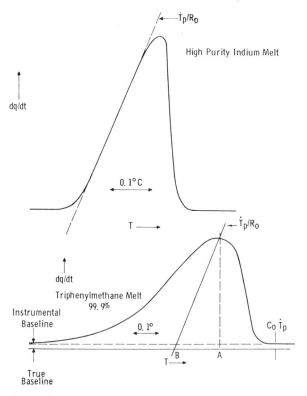

Figure 1-4. The use of an indium melting curve to remove thermal lag (61).

pure materials with sharply-defined melting points. A separate calibration is needed for each heating rate. Materials which the present authors and others have found useful are given in Table 1-2. A typical calibration plot is shown in Fig. 1-5. The curve has been optimized for the organic polymer melting range by setting the average control at 387, the differential control at 504, and the slope control at 494.5 at a scanning rate of 5°C/min. These settings will differ between instruments and cells.

The most frequent source of error in temperature measurement is a variation of R_0. This is usually due to improper encapsulation or dirty cells. It is very important that the bottom of the sample capsule is as flat as possible, that the sample is tightly sealed, and that no dust or dirt lies between the bottom of the cell and the sample capsule. At least three types of sample encapsulation have been described. These are illustrated in Fig. 1-6. The most widely used encapsulation is the simple flat-bottomed planchet with crimped-on lid, Fig. 1-6c. The geometry of

TABLE 1-2

Materials Used for the Calibration of a Differential Scanning Calorimeter

Temperature °C	Material	Melting (M) or inversion (I)	Enthalpy change cal/g
−38.9	Mercury	M	2.74
29.8	Gallium	M	19.9
69.4	Stearic acid	M	47.6
125.2	Ammonium nitrate	I	12·6
169.6	Ammonium nitrate	M	16.2
122.4	Benzoic acid	M	33.9
156.6	Indium	M	6.79
231.9	Tin	M	14.2
264	Lithium nitrate[a]	M	88.4
273	Sodium nitrate	I	9.5
327.4	Lead	M	5.89
419.5	Zinc[a]	M	27.0
588	Potassium sulfate	I	12.3

[a]Place between mica strips prior to encapsulation.

this particular encapsulation is very stable, and it is quite easy to see if the bottom of the cell has been deformed by unusual pressure. The ultra-high pressure cell described in the literature (20), Fig. 1-6a, is somewhat less satisfactory for precise temperature-of-transition measurements. The ultrahigh pressure cell has a mass which is somewhat too high for

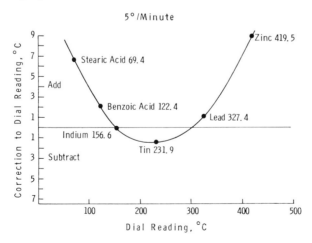

Figure 1-5. Typical temperature calibration correction curve, high temperature plug-in (61).

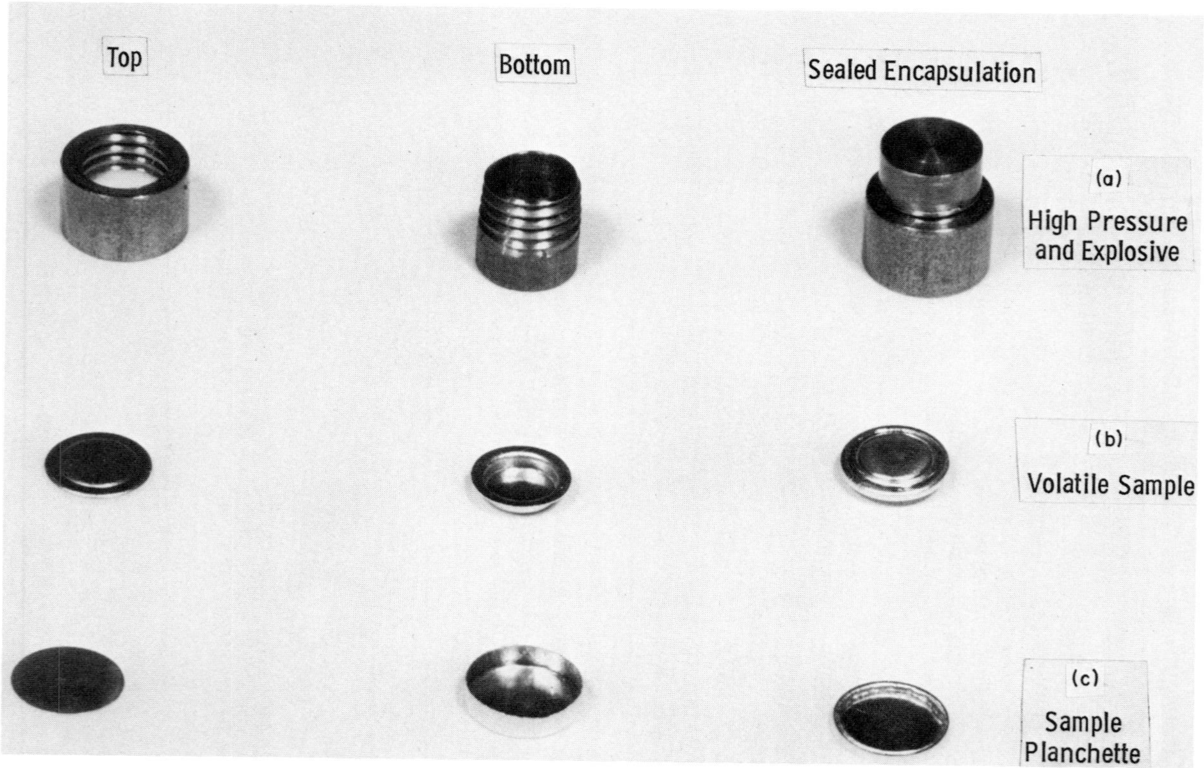

Figure 1-6. Sample encapsulations for DSC.

precise temperature scanning. Except in very limited situations, capping of the sample cell is mandatory for precise temperature measurement and for obtaining true calorimetric traces. Problems of thermal emissivity, change of the sample shape, etc., complicate the picture of the scanning calorimeter when samples are in uncapped cells. The volatile sample cell (Fig. 1-6b), cold-welded under nitrogen, should be used in all cases where sample volatility or oxidation is suspected, see Fig. 1-7. Each encapsulation type requires a different temperature calibration curve. Some of the problems encountered can be decreased considerably by using a slow scanning rate and by using aluminum domes to cover the individual sample and reference platform. This adds some thermal lag to the system, but the equalization of the temperature gradients over the sample and the removal of a portion of the R_0 factor by the aluminum dome more than compensates for the thermal lag.

It is not an infrequent observation that the temperatures measured from the vertex of a differential scanning calorimeter trace or a differential thermograph trace do not correspond closely to the indicated melting temperatures obtained by other techniques, such as hot-stage microscopy and capillary melting point (5a). This is usually due to the fact that optically observed phenomena need not coincide with the maximum melting rate of the system. As has been previously pointed out, the maximum melting rate and the vertex of a differential scanning calorimeter trace usually coincide. Specific difficulties are encountered

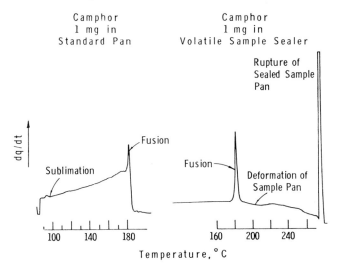

Figure 1-7. Effect of the volatile sample sealer on a sublimation process (61).

with polymeric systems where the melting range is more important than the temperature at which the crystals are melting at maximum rate (*15*). Small traces of impurities cause broadening of the differential scanning calorimeter trace and a flattening of the vertex, making it very difficult to locate with precision the temperature of the vertex. This phenomena will be dealt with later when purity measurements are considered. Systematic and instrumental errors which have been discussed can be minimized by the formulation of a precise procedure for the measurement of transition temperatures and then rigid adherence to this procedure in all future work with a particular system or systems. It is also important to remember that the thermal and physical history of the sample can affect the temperature of the transition [see ref. (*15*)]. Unusual crystalline transitions can be induced by subjecting a number of materials to pressure or to previous thermal transition. Precipitation of material from solution and formation of the crystalline state from the melt can give widely varying melting points due to the formation of a different solid state or a slightly different degree of aggregation in the solid state. It is extremely difficult to obtain the melting point of a finely divided powder scattered in the bottom of the planchet (see Fig. 1-8). The total heat of melting, however, is usually not affected within the limits of experimental error.

B. Heats of Transition

The precautions given above for the precise measurement of temperatures of transition, using the DSC, apply to a lesser extent for the measurement of heats of transition. This is due to the lesser importance of R_0, which is removed by integration with respect to time. However, for precise measurements of heats of transition, it is necessary to add two further precautions. The first is precise weighing. The second is precise measurement of the area lying under the endotherm or exo-

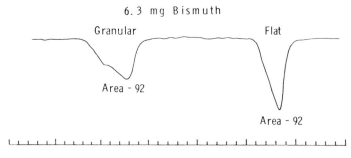

6.3 mg Bismuth

Granular   Flat

Area - 92

Area - 92

Figure 1-8. Effect of sample configuration on peak shape (*63*).

therm caused by the transition. Precise weighing is necessary to at least four significant figures in order that three significant figures may be obtained with confidence. In the experience of the authors, it is possible to obtain with an extremely reproducible transition a precision of better than ± 1%. However, such measurements are usually vitiated by poor weighing procedures.

The measurement of the area underneath the endotherm or exotherm requires the construction of a base line which permits the entry of a certain degree of selectivity by the experimenter. Two base line types are customarily employed, the isothermal base line and the scanning base line. The isothermal base line is constructed by drawing the best straight line between isothermal points before and after the transition. These points are obtained by permitting the instrument to come to balance at some isothermal temperature below the transition temperature. A chart tracing is obtained of this line. The programer is then turned on and the transition scanned. At a temperature well above the conclusion of the transition, the programer is turned off, and a new isothermal point is obtained. If the isothermal base line is used, the normal specific heat or enthalpy change of the sample is integrated into the enthalpy change of the sample from the transition heat. The scanning base line is constructed between the first sensible departure from the program line of the instrument to the last sensible departure of the endotherm or exotherm from the program line of the instrument. It is at this point that a high degree of selectivity enters into the measurement. For a sharp transition, this sensible departure is easily defined. For less sharp transitions, considerable portions of the area under the curve can be neglected through oversight. Further mention of this will be made under purity determination. For very pure materials, the scanning base line is the one most customarily used.

C. Calibration

Calibration is most conveniently carried out by melting a carefully weighed sample of very pure material, such as semiconductor-grade indium, dotriacontane, and other materials mentioned under calibration for transition temperature, Table 1-2. The scanning base line is constructed. The area between the curve and the scanning base line is determined by some suitable integrating technique. Planimetry, while usually satisfactory, can give results precise to no more than three significant figures. Quite frequently a variation of at least 5% is introduced by the usual planimeter used for gas chromatographic analysis. More precise integrating techniques have been described(21).

The information obtained from the melting of the highly purified material is applied in

$$\Delta \tilde{H}_a = \frac{\Delta \tilde{H}_b W_b A_a C_b r_a}{A_b C_a r_b W_a}$$

where $\Delta \tilde{H}_a$ = specific heat of melting of the sample, cal/g
  $\Delta \tilde{H}_b$ = specific heat of melting of the standard, cal/g
     (see Table 1-1)
  W_b = weight of the standard, g
  W_a = weight of the sample, g
  A_a = area of the standard peak, in.^{2}
  A_b = area of the sample peak, in.^{2}
  C_b = chart speed of the standard, in./min
  C_a = chart speed of the sample, in./min
  r_a = range setting of the sample, mcal/sec
  r_b = range setting of the standard, mcal/sec

The "calibration factor" K is

$$K = \frac{\Delta \tilde{H}_b W_b}{A_b r_b} \quad \text{cal/unit area} \tag{1-9}$$

It is important that the relationship K in cal/unit area be obtained at several temperatures. There is a sensible variation in this relationship depending upon temperature (see Fig. 1-9). Generally, the cal/unit area increases as temperature increases. This is due to instrumental changes within the scanning calorimeter. It is also important for precise work to reproduce the heating rate of the standard and the sample exactly.

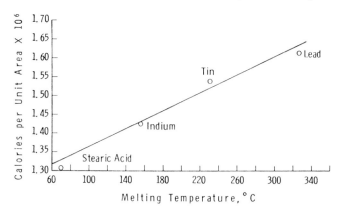

Figure 1-9. Variation in calibration factor, calories per unit area, with temperature.

Small variations in heating rate caused by instrumental parameters are usually not important. However, high precision calorimetry cannot be obtained if the sample is scanned at, for example, 4°C per min while the calibration was carried out at 2°C per min. For general operation, differences in scanning rate less than 2°C are not important. This is in contrast to differential thermal analysis where small variations in scanning rate, as little as one degree per minute, can cause large errors in the determination of heats of transition under certain conditions.

Two principal errors are encountered in the determination of transition heats by the DSC. The first is due to neglecting area on the chart in the construction of the scanning base line. There are techniques for offsetting this error, which will be described under purity determination. The second error is in the weighing of the sample into the planchet. Although this may be minimized by the use of a microbalance, very close attention must be paid to handling procedures due to the small sample size. It is important that a small sample size, consistent with good recording, be used so that the instrument can precisely follow the transition and register the true heat.

Extremely large heats of transition and heats of explosion can be measured either by choosing small samples or by using one of the reinforced encapsulations shown in Fig. 1-6. As R_0 is removed to a certain extent by integration with respect to time, extremely reproducible thermal contact between the sample encapsulation and the cell are not as important as with temperature measurement. With gas producing reactions and detonations, it is important that all gases be maintained in the immediate vicinity of the sample by suitable encapsulation. Loss of the gas will subtract from the exothermal heat which these reactions usually exhibit due to the latent heat of vaporization and heat capacity of the escaped gases.

Sublimation of a solid is another source of error (see Fig. 1-7). It is not uncommon for polymeric materials to decompose partially during heating. Such decomposition decreases the total crystalline order and introduces impurities in the system. This can cause a decrease in heat of melting as observed by the instrument. Suitable atmospheres over the sample can generally prevent this situation. Stabilizers can also be employed. It is important to remember that the atmosphere over the sample is the atmosphere in which the sample was encapsulated. It does not correct the situation to flush the apparatus with nitrogen if the sample has been encapsulated in an airtight container under atmospheric conditions. Therefore, the use of a nitrogen-filled dry box for the encapsulation is recommended.

Evaporation of solvent from a solid material due to faulty recrystallization and insufficient drying generally causes a drifting or unstable scanning base line. It is advisable, where this is observed, to separate solvent effects from decomposition effects by running a thermogravimetric analysis on the sample. Solvent effects are generally characterized by a relatively gradual loss in weight by the sample which can be changed by changing the heating rate. Decompositions generally proceed at a more rapid rate and they have a correspondingly more rapid rate of weight loss. However, this technique is not infallible. Frequently, it is desirable to observe the sample as it is being heated. Since differential scanning calorimetry is difficult in an open cell, it is advisable to run two samples on suspect material, one to observe color changes in the sample, which quite frequently indicate decomposition or chemical reaction, and the second to obtain precise calorimetric results. Usually some system of sample atmosphere and encapsulation technique can be used to overcome difficulties encountered with intractable samples. However, melting with decomposition can be a serious error in scanning calorimetry as with classical adiabatic calorimetric studies. Since the amount of material dealt with in scanning calorimetry is generally somewhat smaller than in adiabatic calorimetry, this error becomes proportionately larger in many cases.

D. Specific Heat Measurement

Specific heats can be measured with a scanning calorimeter with rapidity and reasonably good accuracy over the temperature range $-100°$ to $+600°C$. The measurement is a dynamic one based upon the power expenditure required to heat the sample container without the sample compared to that required for the sample container with the sample. These two measurements are then compared to a third measurement over the same temperature range made on a material of known heat capacity. Most workers have used vitrious alumina or sapphire as a standard. The heat capacity of sapphire is known over a broad temperature range with a high degree of precision. The ordinant displacement of the DSC is proportional to $\dot{T}C_p m$, where $\dot{T}$ is the scanning rate in degrees/second, C_p is the specific heat, and m is the mass of the sample in grams. The ordinant displacement due to the heat capacity of the sample during a temperature-scanning increment is measured with respect to the base line before and after this increment is obtained under isothermal conditions(23). In practice, the instrument is calibrated each time a sample is run since it is necessary to account for small heat capacity differences due to the varying weight of the planchet used to contain the sample or the reference material.

A specific heat measurement consists of three separate determinations (see Fig. 1-10). The first, curve ABC, is the empty pan calibration. An isothermal base line is established below the lowest temperature of the temperature interval of interest. After the base line has stabilized, and a few inches are displayed on the chart, the heating program is commenced. Heating ranges of wider than 100°C are normally not advisable. After the temperature increment range of interest has been covered, the programer is turned off and a new isothermal base line is established. The best straight line is constructed between the initial isothermal base line and the final isothermal base line and the height or depth of the departure of the pan program base line is determined at appropriate temperatures by measuring with a vernier rule. This same process is repeated with the sapphire standard in place, curve AEC. The isothermal base line is established, the program started, the program carried through the necessary temperature increments and a second isothermal base line is established. The same process is repeated a third time with 20–40 mg of sample present in the pan in place of the sapphire, curve ADC. For most normal organic samples and polymers, scanning rates of 5°–20°C per minute are satisfactory. The sample size should be adjusted so that the deflection of the pan during the scanning interval is approximately the same as the deflection of the pan during the scanning interval on the standard. Relatively high sensitivity is employed, 1–4 mcal/sec. The calculation of heat capacity or

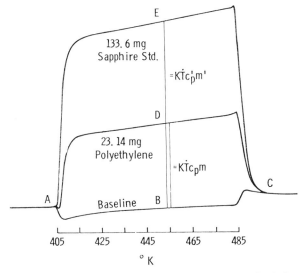

Figure 1-10. Typical specific heat determination, molten linear polyethylene 405–485°K
(*23*).

specific heat as a function of temperature is carried out as indicated in the following formula:

$$\tilde{C}_s = \frac{H_s}{H_a}\frac{W_a}{W_s}\tilde{C}_a \qquad (1\text{-}10)$$

where $\tilde{C}_s$ = specific heat of the sample at T_1
  H_s = amptitude of the sample at T_1
  H_a = amptitude of the sapphire at T_1
  W_a = weight of sapphire
  W_s = weight of sample
  C_a = specific heat of sapphire at T_1.

DSC heat capacity measurement is subject to several systematic and experimental errors. The method is a dynamic method, unlike the classical techniques. Slow phase transformation caused by recrystallization of the sample on heating can cause serious errors in the heat capacity as determined by the DSC. Careful annealing of samples at temperatures near known phase transitions can be a considerable aid in removing this particular variable ($42,44$). It is also important that the sample pan be in extremely good contact with the sample base heater. Dust, dirt, or nonplanar bottoms on the planchet can cause considerable variation between the power expenditure required to heat the sample and the power expenditure required to heat the reference material. Such error causes displacement in the ratio H_s/H_a shown in Eq. (1-10). This usually results, if conditions are stable, in a general shifting of the whole heat capacity curve to some value other than the true value.

It is desirable to make more than one scan on each sample and reference. In order to remove variation in thermal emissivity between the sample and the reference, it is necessary to cover the DSC cell with aluminum domes. These domes must be replaced in exactly the same position for each determination within a sequence of three scans. Many workers have found it desirable to remove the metal framework which shields the DSC cell heaters and resistance thermometer. This tends to equalize the heat dissipation in all directions.

For very precise work it is desirable to form the sample in the same shape as the sapphire standard. Excellent agreement between specific heat measurements made by the scanning calorimeter and by classical techniques has been reported ($23,33,46,65$). When proper precautions are taken to avoid recrystallization of the sample during determination, decomposition of the sample during the heating program, and nonidentical conditions during the sample and calibration run, the DSC can produce results equivalent in accuracy and precision to many of the classical techniques. However, it must be borne in mind at all times that the technique is a dynamic one, and, therefore, cannot approach the ultimate precision and accuracy of the better classical methods. In speed, however, there is no comparison between the classical and DSC methods. A complete specific-heat curve over a temperature range of 200°C can be obtained on a reasonably stable compound in a period of two hours. Equivalent classical techniques normally require days for the same determination.

E. Thermal Emissivity

Changes in the thermal emissivity of an uncovered sample in the scanning calorimeter have been regarded as a disturbing source of error in the measurements of heats of transition for colored materials. Rogers and Morris(55) have worked out a system for overcoming this source of error and have devised an excellent method for the determination of thermal emissivity of various surfaces using a known reference surface. Figure 1-11 shows the effect of temperature on the heat correction of a scanning calorimeter. At 127°C, energy can be lost in the scanning calorimeter pan at a rate of 10^{-2} cal/sec. This is more than the full-scale instrument deflection in the lowest ranges of the DSC-1B for a

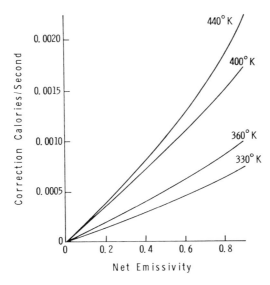

Figure 1-11.   Effect of temperature and net emissivity on the caloric correction of a scanning calorimeter(55).

pan area of 0.3167 cm². In order to remove this error it is only necessary to heat the surfaces facing the sample and reference cell at a rate which is equivalent to that at which the sample and reference cells themselves are being heated. This reduces the effective thermal gradient to zero and the thermal emissivity correction to a term very near zero. The same arrangement can put known thermal gradients into the apparatus permitting it to be used as an instrument for the determination of thermal emissivity.

Such a shield has been described (55) as follows:

> The low-temperature cover of the Perkin–Elmer scanning calorimeter is modified by removing the foamed plastic insulator on the inside of the cover. The interior surface of the cover is then polished and painted with optical black paint. Inside the Dewar compartment of the cover, an aluminum block large enough to slip over the cell for a distance of approximately ¼ in. is placed. Holes are drilled in the aluminum block and cartridge heater, control thermocouple and readout thermocouple are inserted. This arrangement is attached to an appropriate temperature programer. For the determination of thermal emissivity a ¼ in. disk is cut from the sample material and placed in a standard aluminum sample planchet. A reference disk of aluminum foil in a sample planchet is placed on each pan support. The assembly is covered and the instrument brought to balance as indicated by the recorder zero. The recorder is turned off and the reference disk and the pan in the sample pan support is replaced by the sample. The balance setting of the instrument should not be changed. The assembly is covered again with the temperature control compartment cover. The temperature of the cover is adjusted to the temperature of the sample, i.e., the temperature at which the emissivity is to be determined. The energy difference between the reference and sample is read from the recorder. The temperature control block is then removed from the Dewar compartment of the cover and the chamber filled with crushed ice and distilled water. The instrument is brought to balance again with the two reference foils in the sample and reference container. The difference in energy between the sample and reference platforms is then read. The temperature set into the calorimeter is not changed between these two groups of readings. The first reading combines all corrections or differences and the characteristics of the two real surfaces being studied.

The second reading measures differential emission between the two surfaces. The emissivity coefficient is calculated as follows:

$$\epsilon_n = \frac{S(C + R_i) + R_r}{Z} \qquad (1\text{-}11)$$

where ϵ_n = total normal emissivity at the specified temperature

   S = the sensitivity factor for the instrument and recorder for the range being used in the measurement, the units being cal/cm sec

   C = the result from the correction run, in centimeters of recorder deflection

R_i = the result from the second run in centimeters of the recorder deflection

R_r = emission of the reference surface in cal/sec at the specified temperature which would be 0.00036 cal/sec for a 0.3167 cm² aluminum foil reference at 400°K

Z = emission of a black body at the specified temperature

Note that all emissions must be adjusted to the same surface area and all apply to the specified temperature only.

Excellent agreement, considering the unusual range of variations and values, has been obtained between DSC values and those in the literature (see Table 1-3). The DSC method for determining thermal emissivity has several advantages not found in other methods for determining emissivity. It requires only an extremely small sample and can be used as a null method to compare the characteristics of two surfaces. It is very rapid and requires very little skill on the part of the operator to obtain reasonably precise values.

F. Isothermal Functions

REACTION RATES AND ENERGY OF ACTIVATION

The differential scanning calorimeter is uniquely suited for studies of reaction rates. Fava(19) has presented an excellent study of the differential scanning calorimetry of the epoxy resins. The scanning calori-

TABLE 1-3

Total Thermal Emissivities as Measured by Perkin–Elmer DSC-1(55)

Surface	Found	Literature
Lead, rolled surface as received	0.069	0.057
Brass, rolled surface as received	0.095	0.07
Copper, polished on 600 grit	0.038	0.03–0.04
Molybdenum	0.07	0.07
Monel, smooth, not polished	0.13	0.16
Aluminum, 0.25-micron electrolytic oxide	0.11	0.06
Aluminum, 0.35-micron electrolytic oxide	0.12	0.09
Aluminum, 0.5-micron electrolytic oxide	0.20	0.11
Aluminum, 0.65-micron electrolytic oxide	0.27	—
Aluminum, 1.0-micron electrolytic oxide	0.41	0.30
Aluminum, 3.0-micron electrolytic oxide	0.63	0.70
Aluminum, 5.0-micron electrolytic oxide	0.60	0.70
Aluminum, 7.0-micron electrolytic oxide	0.62	0.75
Black optical paint	0.98	0.98

meter was used not only in the isothermal mode but also in the program mode at different scanning rates. In addition, scans were carried out on partially cured resins.

The isothermal operation is most closely comparable to classical isothermal calorimetry. In practice, a sample is placed in the scanning calorimeter cell and the temperature of the instrument is increased manually as quickly as possible to the desired test temperature. A time record of the rate at which heat is generated in the sample by the exothermic curing reaction is made until the curve levels off to a base line, indicating that the reaction has been completed. Figure 1–12 shows a typical isotherm. The isothermal cure curve is obtained by stepwise integration of the thermogram as a function of time. Fava found it necessary to express heats of reaction in reduced form, that is, as a fraction H/H_0 of the total heat H_0. This is because the total heat of reaction varies with the cure temperature. The same behavior would be expected of any thermosensitive reaction which can be stopped by lowering the temperature.

In epoxy systems at cure temperatures below a certain value there is always some unreacted material present; that is, the reaction does not approach completion at certain temperatures. Further treatment at higher temperatures will show a residual reaction. This should also be the case with any other applicable system. It is possible that the mechanism of reaction changes as a function of the temperature, causing an equilibrium shift. A typical scan of 28 mg of uncured sample at 16°C per min. is shown in Fig. 1-13.

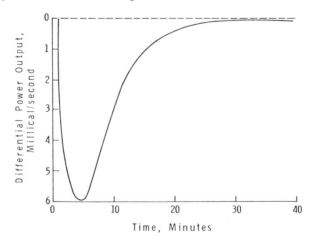

Figure 1-12.   A typical epoxy isotherm 42 mg sample cured at 400°K (*19*).

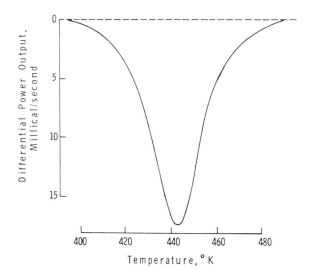

Figure 1-13. A typical epoxy DSC scan, 28 mg uncured resin scanned at 16°C/min(*19*).

Fava found, in contrasting the scanning method to the isothermal method, some points which should be generally applicable.

(1) At low temperatures where the reaction is proceeding slowly, the isothermal method gives reliable results while the scan method provides insufficient data from which to construct a reliable cure curve.

(2) The two methods give results which agree quite well at about 400°K. Above this temperature, the isothermal method gives unavoidable temperature lags due to the finite heating time of the sample and the test cell so that the curve is shifted along the time axis by about 1 min.

(3) Above 435°K the peak of the exotherm is clipped off by the heat-up time, which distorts the shape of the curve. Thus, the two methods are complementary.

(4) For fast cures, the scan method yields information on the state of cure for isothermal times of the order of 1 sec, which cannot possibly be done by the direct isothermal method because of the thermal lags in the system and reference sample.

Thermographic scans on partially cured resins are the technique usually followed in differential thermal analysis. The method is useful when the rate of heat evolution is too small for isothermal detection. The disadvantage of this method is that a very large number of samples must be partially cured and subsequently thermographed. For the epoxy systems, excellent agreement has been obtained between the isothermal system and the partially cured systems. When the extent of cure was compared to the duration of cure, the scanning calorimeter techniques discussed above completely avoided the application of the Arrhenius equation. However, Fava(19) did discover that there was excellent agreement between the Arrhenius equation calculations and the scanning calorimeter determination based on straightforward thermodynamic correlations. Thermodynamic data from the scanning technique indicated that the mechanism of cure did in fact change as the cure temperature was increased. However, a linear Arrhenius plot was obtained. Therefore, any changes in the curing mechanism with curing temperature did not affect the over-all reaction rate as would have been expected. It is highly probable that just such fortuitous events have permitted the application of the Arrhenius equation on systems as complex as explosives, rubber vulcanization, and epoxy resin cures.

G. Kinetic Parameters

In addition to the above technique, several methods for obtaining kinetic parameters directly from the DSC curve have been published. Rogers, Morris, and Smith(56, 57) have given a method for obtaining activation energies and the preexponential factor from the DSC thermal decomposition curve of an unweighed sample. The necessary data are present in a DSC curve run at constant heating rate in covered cells. The data are distances measured between the reaction curve and the base line (scanning) at associated absolute temperatures. The distance measured is proportional to the rate of heat evolution or absorption at that temperature. This rate is proportional to the rate constant. As many distances as possible are measured between the onset and maximum of the curve. The log of the distance is plotted versus $1/T°K$. The best straight-line portion is chosen; and distances at the extremes, d_1 and d_2, with corresponding temperatures, $1/T_1$ and $1/T_2$, are put into the equation,

$$-E = \frac{4.58 \log (d_1/d_2)}{1/T_1 - 1/T_2} \tag{1-12}$$

The distances enter only as a ratio, so that proportionality constants cancel. Neither weight nor heat of reaction needs to be known. The Arrhenius plot should be linear over a reasonable range. E will appear in kcal/mole. Caution must be exercised not to exceed the dynamic range of the DSC and to contain the reaction and products within the sample cell. Some consideration of the sample phase during the reaction must also be made when the data are compared to literature values.

Given E from the previous calculation, the heating rate B, and the temperature at maximum, T_{max}, it is possible to calculate the pre-exponential factor A with

$$A = \frac{BEe^{E/RT_{max}}}{RT_{max}^2} \qquad (1\text{-}13)$$

where R and e have the usual values and T_{max} is in $°K$. Excellent agreement between values obtained by other means and by DSC has been noted for several explosives, diazo salts, and $KMnO_4$(57). The method seems to be totally independent of sample weight and operable so long as the kinetic order of the reaction is not significantly different from 1 and the above precautions are observed.

Barrett(6) has employed a slightly different DSC approach to the evaluation of thermal decomposition rates in solution. The following equation was derived for the calculation of k, the rate constant.

$$k = (dH/dt)/(A - a) \qquad (1\text{-}14)$$

where $a =$ the area of the curve up to a given temperature,

$\quad\quad A =$ the remaining curve area,

$dH/dt =$ height of the curve at the temperature in mcal/sec. These are shown in Fig. 1-14.

The activation energy is obtained in the usual way from a plot of $\log k$ as a function of $1/T$ for several values of a and A. Barrett obtained excellent agreement between DSC values and the literature values on diisopropyl peroxydicarbonate and benzoyl peroxide. The primary subject of Barrett's work concerned the decomposition of polymerization initiators. Ellerstein(16) has suggested placing the sample between two 100-mesh screens prior to encapsulation. This method is very useful with samples which bubble on decomposition. Perkins et al.(49) have used DSC to evaluate the flame resistance of fabrics.

H. Rates of Crystallization

Several methods are available for the measurement of polymer crystallinity: dilatometry, microscopy, calorimetry, X-ray diffraction, and infrared spectrophotometry. With the exception of microscopy, all of the above techniques are very difficult when crystallinity must be evaluated as a function of time. DSC has made possible the much wider application of the calorimetric method to crystallinity studies.

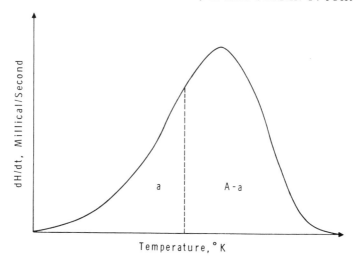

Figure 1-14.   DSC curve and quantities measured to evaluate rate constants (6).

For absolute evaluations, the heat of fusion of the 100% crystalline sample must be known. For relative measurements, only the total heat absorbed for a given sample must be known. Knox (33a) has described the application of DSC to the determination of crystallization rates and crystallization activation energy. These parameters are valuable when studying the effect of various nucleating agents on crystal growth.

In practice, the polymer sample is melted in place in the DSC. After melting, the programer is rapidly turned manually down to the crystallization temperature to be studied. The recorder is started as soon as the control light comes on, indicating that thermal equilibrium has been established. A typical record is shown in Fig. 1-15. The curve is integrated in 1 min intervals and the areas applied to

$$\% \text{ cryst.} = \frac{A \times r \times 100}{W_s \times \Delta H_f \times f} \qquad (1\text{-}15)$$

where A = area to the time, sq in.
   r = recording range, cal/sec
   W = weight of sample, g
   ΔH_f = heat of fusion of 100% crystalline material, cal/g
   f = calibration factor, sq in./sec.

A summation of per cent crystallinity, Σ_0^t cryst, may be made and an integral of crystallization as a function of log time obtained. Alternatively, the reduced crystallinity, the amount of crystallinity

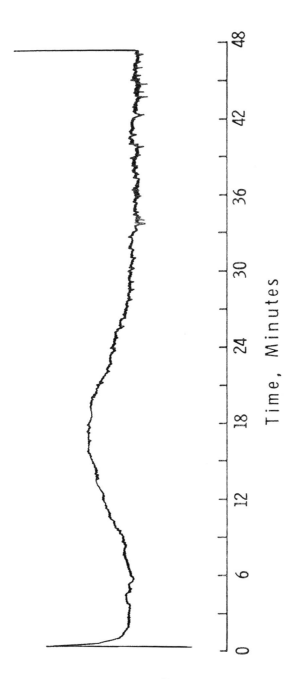

Time, Minutes

Figure 1-15. Isothermal crystallization of nucleated polypropylene; polymer melted at 200°C, crystallization at 142°C(*33a*).

developed at any time divided by the total crystallinity attained at that temperature, can be plotted in the same way, see Fig. 1-16. Rates of crystallization are obtained from the linear portion of the curves. A log plot of the rate as a function of the reciprocal of the crystallization temperature can be treated as an Arrhenius function and the activation energy of crystallization calculated in the usual way. Energies are usually of the order of 10 to 20 kcal/mole for most polymers. Knox (*33a*) found that the energy for nucleated polypropylene was 13.8 kcal/mole. For nonnucleated polymer, the nucleation process changes at about 130°C. Below 130°C, the activation energy is 21.4 kcal/mole; above 130°C, the activation energy is 42.8 kcal/mole. The lower activation energy probably represents mixed homogeneous and heterogeneous nucleation. The effect of molecular weight on heterogeneous nucleation has been studied by Beck(*8*).

I. Purity Determination

The melting of a relatively pure material is described by the van't Hoff equation as follows:

$$T_0 - T_m = \frac{R T_0^2 X_2}{\Delta H_f} \tag{1-16}$$

where T_0 = melting temperature of the 100% pure material, °K
T_m = melting temperature of the impure material, °K
R = gas constant, 1.9865 cal/°K/mole
ΔH_f = heat of fusion of the sample, cal/mole

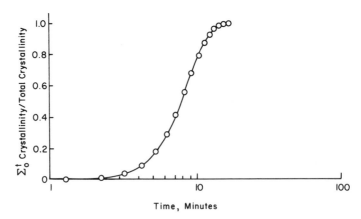

Figure 1-16.   Reduced per cent crystallinity of polypropylene; 200°C melt temperature, 126°C crystallization temperature (*33a*).

X_2 = mole fraction of impurity

$T_0 - T_m$ = melting point depression, °K

As usually applied, the melting point depression is determined by measuring T_m to a high degree of accuracy and subtracting that value from a previously known T_0. This is a very difficult determination due to the precision required in the measurement of T_m. In addition, it is necessary to know the "melting point depression constant," which is a unique function for each material. This is the basis of the Rast melting point depression method for the determination of molecular weight. Camphor, the usual material used in the Rast method, has a very large melting-point depression coefficient.

The DSC method makes the application of the van't Hoff equation much simpler in execution and more accurate in result. It can be shown that the fraction of the sample melted, F, at any particular sample temperature T_s in the melting range is given by

$$F = \frac{T_0 - T_m}{T_0 - T_s} \qquad (1\text{-}17)$$

This can be arranged to obtain

$$T_s = T_0 - \frac{(T_0 - T_m)}{F} \qquad (1\text{-}18)$$

This means that the melting point depression, $T_0 - T_m$, is the slope of a plot of sample melting temperature as a function of the reciprocal of the fraction melted at that temperature. The y intercept will be the melting point of 100% pure material, T_0. Given ΔH, the mole fraction of impurity can be readily determined. The effect of impurity on the shape of a DSC scan is shown for three samples of benzoic acid in Fig. 1-17 (60).

In practice, measurement is made at several points along the curve (see Fig. 1-18). The scanning rate in this case was 1.25 deg/min at a sensitivity of 4 mcal/min full scale. Measurements are made in the range from 10% to 50%. For example, at point A the temperature is read off at D (see Fig. 1–18, and melting point determination discussion) and the area measured up to the line AB. The area EBCD is also included since this area is equivalent to a heat of fusion even though it appears as ordinary heat capacity energy. Figure 1-18 also shows the corresponding $1/F$ plot.

Unfortunately, it is very difficult to measure all of the area due to the melting process. The onset of melting is not adequately detected when the DSC sensitivity is adjusted to register the rest of the melting peak.

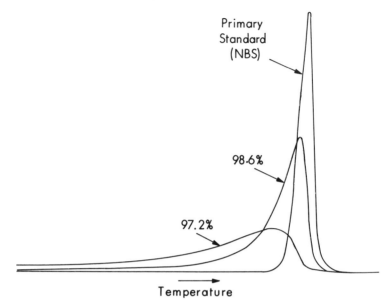

Figure 1-17. Effect of purity on DSC peak shapes, benzoic acid(*60*).

This missing area a results in a curve rather than a straight line in the T_s vs. $1/F$ plot (see Fig. 1-19). This means that each area measure is too small by an amount a. The deviation is much larger at small fractions melted than at large F and is not cumulative. The correct value for any F is

$$F_1 = \frac{A_1 + a}{A_T + a}, \qquad F_2 = \frac{A_1 + A_2 + a}{A_T + a}, \qquad F_n = \frac{A_1 + A_2 + A_n + a}{A_T + a} \qquad (1\text{-}19)$$

where A_1 = area under the curve up to a given temperature
        A_T = total area measured under the curve
        a = area missed.

The value of a is found by trial. It is known, if the technique is at all applicable, that the T_s vs. $1/F$ plot should be linear. Estimates of the value of a are made and the resulting linearity tested. Only one value of a will produce linearity. This is not an arbitrary method since the value of a is unique for linearity. A computer program to do this regression as well as other purity calculations is not overly difficult to write and is applicable to a "time share" computer service.

Where applicable, the DSC purity technique can give the purity of an unknown compound containing unresolved impurities. All that need be

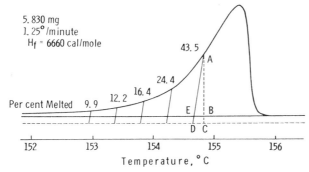

Figure 1-18A. Testosterone purity run.

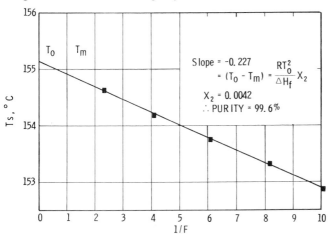

Figure 1-18B. Testosterone purity determination.

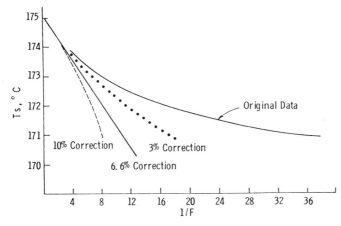

Figure 1-19. Graphical linearization of $1/F$ plot, phenolbarbitol 99.4%(60).

known is the DSC curve and the molecular weight of the material under study. The molecular weight need not be known to a high degree of accuracy and can be obtained from osmometry or mass spectrometry. The same restrictions as to cocrystal formation, solid solutions, and eutectics applies to the DSC purity as to the van't Hoff equation. The method has been applied to a large number of compounds (54).

1-4 SPECIFIC APPLICATIONS

A. Polymers

By far the largest body of DSC literature is concerned with the thermal analysis of polymers (54a). Indeed, the necessity for rapidly obtaining the thermal characteristics of polyolefins, and other polymers, has certainly been one of the prime movers behind the development of scanning calorimetry. The applications have extended over the complete range of polymer study, from fundamental studies of polymer solid state to routine process control. The application of DSC to new polymers now seems as common as the measurement of IR spectra (13,30,48,25). The following discussion is not intended to be a complete coverage of polymer DSC but an account of typical examples drawn from the current literature.

One of the earliest studies to utilize the rapid thermal response of the DSC was made by Gray and Casey (24) using a poly(ethylene-butene)copolymer, among others. The results are shown in Fig. 1-20. The sample was first heated to 180°C and held for several minutes, cooled to ambient temperature at 6°C/min, and then scanned to 160°C at 18°C/min to produce Fig. 1-20a. The sample was then cooled at 18°C/min to 104°C. At the onset of the freezing exotherm, the sample was reheated to 120°C at 18°C/min and annealed for 1 min. The sample was cooled to ambient by manual turning of the temperature program. The sample was heated quickly to 85°C and programed to 115°C at 18°C/min, where a second 1-min annealing was carried out. The procedure was repeated at successive 5°C intervals down to ambient, each scan up to the next annealing temperature being started 25°C lower where possible. Reheating at 18°C/min resulted in the most unusual curve in Fig. 1-20b. Annealing experiments of this sort have served to illustrate the effect of thermal history on polymer crystal perfection.

Karasz and O'Reilly (33) used DSC to characterize a new polymeric material, poly(2,6-dimethylphenyleneether), prior to more precise calorimetry. The heat, temperature, and range of melting were rapidly

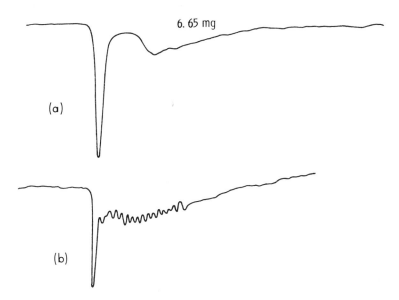

Figure 1-20. Polyethylene fusion curves, effect of thermal history(24): (a) continuously cooled at 2°C/min; (b) stepwise annealed at 2°C intervals to 90°C, then cooled continuously at 6°C/min.

determined. A glass transition in the amorphous solid was discovered, and the upper range of thermal stability was found.

Hellmuth and Wunderlich(26) used the DSC to study superheating of linear polyethylene crystals. The sample, after appropriate annealing conditions, was taken quickly by manual adjustment of the programer to the chosen melt temperature. After equilibration, the sample was heated to a higher temperature to examine possible additional melting. Use was made of the supercooled liquid phase to obtain satisfactory nonmelting base lines. Wunderlich and Cormier(66, 67) have used the DSC to measure isothermal seeding of melts cooled below the melting point of linear-extended chain polyethylene crystals. Seeding had little effect on the amount of supercooling required to initiate crystal growth. No extended chain crystal was noted. Extended chain structure in polyethylene was later studied successfully (22,25,38) and DSC has been applied to other extended chain structures(1). The effect of branching in various polymers has also been studied(7,11,12,14,28, 35).

Wakelyn and Young(62) have used DSC to determine the crystallinity index of poly(ethyleneterephthalate) by means of fusion heat.

The DSC crystallinity index was calculated as

$$\text{Index} = \frac{H_{fu} - H_{fa}}{H_{fc} - H_{fa}} \times 100 \tag{1-20}$$

where H_{fu}, H_{fa}, and H_{fc} are the heats of fusion of the specimen, the amorphous standard, and the crystalline standard, respectively. Good agreement with X-ray data was obtained. Polymer crystal polymorphy in the case of polyisobutene-1 has been subject to detailed thermal study(22). Kambour and Karasz(31) employed DSC to measure film crystallinity as have Kamide and Sarada(32), McKinney and Foltz(40), and Peterlin and Meinel(50,52).

Peterlin et al.(53) and Winslow et al.(64) have used DSC to obtain melting curves of solution-crystallized polyethylene etched with fuming nitric acid. Although no particular advantage was made of the thermal program of the DSC, the melting curves were used to separate reactions at the chain fold from simple annealing effects. Meinel and Peterlin(41) used the DSC melting curves on similarly etched samples of drawn polyethylene to determine crystal thickness. Combined with fractionation by isothermal crystallization, DSC was very helpful in demonstrating the presence of two distinct molecular weight groups after etching. Mandelkern et al.(39) have examined fractionated linear polyethylene without etching.

Huseby and Bair [see (3,29)] used the DSC melting curves to measure premelting recrystallization on polyethylene crystals prepared from stirred xylene solutions. These authors irradiated samples to cause minor crosslinks which restricted chain rotation in the fibrillar crystals. These samples were shown to melt without rearrangement. Lamellar thickening was found to cause the multiple peaks seen on unirradiated samples [see also Ref.(37)]. Other cross-linking studies have been made(36).

Bair and Salovey(2) used the same irradiation followed by scanning calorimetry on polybutene-1. They found it possible to separate lamellar thickening from true polymorphic effects.

Ellerstein(16,17) has used the DSC to obtain the kinetic parameters of the glass transition. He has shown that the methods of Borchardt and Daniels(10a) and Freeman and Carroll(20a) can be extended to include the glass transition. This work demonstrated very clearly the link between glass transition phenomena and previous thermal history.

Conciatori et al.(13) have employed DSC in the study of the crystallinity of poly(benzinidazole). Jordan et al.(30) have correlated thermal and mechanical properties of acrylamides and acrylonitrile. Schmidt

(*58*) has carried out a similar useful correlation between thermal constants and deformation in epoxy-glass fiber laminates. Morosoff et al.(*43*) have used DSC to characterize the type of polymer induced in the solid phase polymerization of vinyl stearate as opposed to solution phase polymerization.

B. Nonpolymeric Organic Systems

DSC is especially useful for studying organic solids and liquids. The small sample involved and the high sensitivity make it a particularly useful research tool for the characterization of new materials. The high thermal resolution is very useful in studying closely spaced transitions and recrystallizations. DSC purity analysis has found wide application in this area. However, the published body of data in this field is much smaller than in polymer DSC. Liquid crystal systems have been studied by several authors(*4,5,5a,17a*) with respect to both heats of transition and specific heats of solid, liquid, and mesophases. Extremely close agreement between laboratories has been reported on materials which exhibit rapid and reversible transition heats(*5*). Pacor and Spier(*47*) have applied DSC to fatty acid sodium soaps. The phase transitions in these extremely complex materials were followed by DSC and the data applied to the preparation of phase diagrams. Kubota and Spessard(*34*) have applied DSC to the metastable modifications of glutaronitrile. Studies of this sort have indicated the usefulness of DSC in exploring the thermodynamic parameters of biological materials available only in small quantities and of limited stability.

C. Inorganic Systems

DSC studies of inorganic materials have not been widely published. Part of the reason for this is the limited upper temperature range of currently available equipment which lies below many interesting inorganic transitions.

Block(*9*) has described a unique application of DSC to chloride/bromide determination in silver precipitates. Use is made of the heat of fusion of the mixed salts. The fusion heat is directly proportional to the solute ion concentration, assuming that silver chloride acts as an ideal solute in silver bromide solid solutions. In practice, a slightly acidic aqueous solution of the mixed ions is heated with a 10% excess of 0.1 M silver nitrate, boiled, filtered, washed, and dried. A 3-mg weighed portion of the precipitate is placed on a small sheet of mica (to prevent reaction of the halide melt with the DSC pans) and scanned at 20°C/min heating rate. Examples are shown in Fig. 1-21.

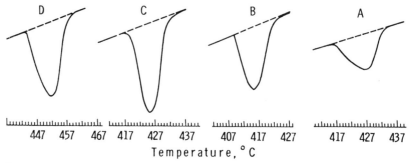

$$\text{Temperature, }^{\circ}\text{C}$$

Figure 1-21. Silver chloride–bromide mixed salt DSC(9). A, AgBr; B, 24.6% AgCl in AgBr; C, 64.0% AgCl in AgBr; D, AgCl. Sample weights: A, 3.17 mg; B, 3.61 mg; C, 3.99 mg; D, 3.23 mg. Heating rate: 20°/min.

The heat of fusion is compared to a standard curve of fusion heat as a function of weight per cent chloride. The standard curve is prepared by mixing in the correct proportions 0.1 M solutions of KCl and KBr and treating with a 10% excess 0.1 M silver nitrate followed by boiling, filtration, washing, and drying. Block's results indicate that the calibration is linear over most of the ion composition range. Theoretically, any two ions forming ideal solid solutions in all proportions will yield straight line plots. The melting point is the only limitation.

Block and Gray(10) have employed the DSC to study the thermal decomposition of lithium aluminum hydride. The decomposition was found to occur in three stages, two endothermic and one exothermic change with the evolution of hydrogen, see Fig. 1-22. In addition, a reversible-phase change and an exotherm related to sample purity were noted. The hydrogen-evolving reactions were separated from phase changes by measuring the thermal conductivity of the gas eluting from the sample compartment (EGA) in an argon carrier. The EGA curve is shown in Fig. 1-22b. The study presented by Block and Gray demonstrates the power of combined DSC and EGA in elucidating a complex reaction sequence.

1-5 FUTURE OF DIFFERENTIAL SCANNING CALORIMETRY

At present, the future of scanning calorimetry hinges on two items: improvement in instrumentation and the continued application of creative effort by the experimenters. Although the latter point lies in the realm of human curiosity and is a philosophical problem, the former point can be addressed directly.

The temperature range of DSC instrumentation must be increased

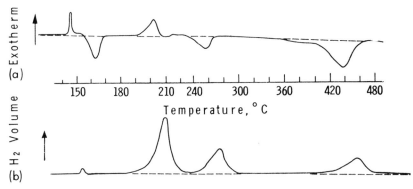

Figure 1-22. DSC and EGA of lithium aluminum hydride(*10*). Sample weight is 2.34 mg. Heating rates are (*a*) 100°–220°C at 10°/min and (*b*) 220°–500°C at 20°/min.

so that a number of interesting inorganic transitions can be studied in the same detail as lower temperature organic materials. Hill and Slessor(*27*) have suggested one possible solution to the high-temperature problems using radiant heating control. More attention must be paid to the electronic components of the existing system, so that the temperature response curve can be a linear rather than a hyperbolic function. The design of sample cells should receive more attention so that truly inert encapsulations can be used. Improved sensitivity and stability should permit slower and faster heating rates to be explored for equilibrium and kinetic studies. Undoubtedly, the near future holds all of the above and more.

ACKNOWLEDGMENTS

The authors are pleased to acknowledge the courtesy of the editors of the following journals for permission to reproduce the indicated figures.

Journal	Figures
Analytical Chemistry	1-1, 1-2, 1-3, 1-8, 1-11, 1-21
Polymer	1-12, 1-13
Journal of Polymer Science	1-20
Journal of Applied Polymer Science	1-14
Perkin-Elmer Corporation	1-4, 1-5, 1-7, 1-17 to 1-19
Inorganic Chemistry	1-8, 1-22
Am. Chem. Soc. Div. Polymer Chem. Preprints	1-10
Plenum Press	1-15, 1-16

The authors are indebted to Chevron Research, Richmond, California, for the use of library material, to Mrs. M. A. Yeaton of IBM Research, San Jose, California, for typing the final manuscript, and to Dr. Roy J. Gritter of IBM for proofreading the final manuscript.

REFERENCES

1. T. Arakawa and B. Wunderlich, *J. Polymer Sci.*, Part A-2, **4**, 53 (1966).
2. H. E. Bair and R. Salovey, *J. Polymer Sci.*, **B5**, 429 (1967).
3. H. E. Bair, R. Salovey, and T. W. Huseby, *Polymer*, **8**, 9 (1967).
4. E. M. Barrall, II, R. S. Porter, and J. F. Johnson, *J. Phys. Chem.*, **71**, 895 (1967).
5. E. M. Barrall, II, R. S. Porter, and J. F. Johnson, *J. Phys. Chem.*, **71**, 1224 (1967).
5a. E. M. Barrall, II, and M. A. Sweeney, *Molecular Cryst.*, **5**, 257 (1969).
6. K. E. J. Barrett, *J. Appl. Polymer Sci.*, **11**, 1617 (1967).
7. I. J. Bastien, R. W. Ford, and H. D. Mak, *J. Polymer Sci.*, **B4**, 147 (1966).
8. H. N. Beck, *J. Polymer Sci.*, Part A-2, **4**, 631 (1966).
9. J. Block, *Anal. Chem.* **37**, 1414 (1965).
10. J. Block and A. P. Gray, *Inorg. Chem.*, **4**, 304 (1965).
10a. H. J. Borchardt and F. Daniels, *J. Am. Chem. Soc.* **79**, 41 (1957).
11. G. Carrazzolo and M. Mammi, *J. Polymer Sci.*, **B2**, 1053 (1964).
12. B. H. Clampitt and R. H. Hughes, *Anal. Chem.*, **40**, 449 (1968).
13. A. B. Conciatori, E. C. Chenevey, T. C. Bohrer, and A. E. Prince, *J. Polymer Sci.*, **C19**, 49 (1967).
14. H. W. Coover, R. J. McConnell, F. B. Joyner, D. F. Slonaker, and R. L. Combs, *J. Polymer Sci.*, Part A-1, **4**, 2563 (1966).
15. M. Dole, *J. Polymer Sci.*, **C18**, 57 (1967).
16. S. M. Ellerstein, *J. Phys. Chem.*, **69**, 2471 (1965).
17. S. M. Ellerstein, *Appl. Polym. Symp.*, **2**, 111 (1966).
17a. R. D. Ennulat, *Analytical Calorimetry, Applied Polymer Symposia* (R. S. Porter and J. F. Johnson, eds.), p. 219, Plenum Press, New York, 1968.
18. C. Eyraud, *Compt. Rend.* **238**, 1511 (1954).
19. R. A. Fava, *Polymer*, **9**, 137 (1968).
20. F. E. Freebergand and T. G. Alleman, *Anal. Chem.*, **38**, 1806 (1966).
20a. E. S. Freeman and B. Carroll, *J. Phys. Chem.*, **62**, 304 (1958).
21. K. W. Gardiner, R. F. Klaver, F. Baumann, and J. F. Johnson, *Gas Chromatography* (N. Brenner, J. E. Callen, and M. D. Weiss, eds.), Chap. 24, pp. 349–361, Academic Press, New York, 1962.
22. C. Geacinov, R. B. Miles, and H. J. L. Schuurmans, *J. Polymer Sci.*, Part A-1, **4**, 431 (1966).
23. A. P. Gray and N. Brenner, *Am. Chem. Soc., Div. Polymer Chem.*, Preprints **6**, 956 (1965).
24. A. P. Gray and K. Casey, *J. Polymer Sci.*, **B2**, 381 (1964).
25. F. Hamada, B. Wunderlich, T. Sumida, S. Hayashi, and A. Nakajima, *J. Phys. Chem.*, **72**, 178 (1968).
26. E. Hellmuth and B. Wunderlich, *J. Appl. Phys.*, **36**, 3039 (1965).
27. R. A. W. Hill and R. P. Slessor, *Trans. Faraday Soc.*, **65**, 340 (1969).
28. P. J. Holdsworth and A. Keller, *J. Polymer Sci.*, **B5**, 605 (1967).
29. T. W. Huseby and H. E. Bair, *J. Polymer Sci.*, **B5**, 265 (1967).
30. E. F. Jordon, G. R. Riser, W. E. Parker, and A. W. Wrigley, *J. Polymer Sci.*, Part A-2, **4**, 975 (1966).
31. R. P. Kambour, F. E. Karasz, and J. H. Danne, *J. Polymer Sci.*, Part A-2, **4**, 327 (1966).
32. K. Kamide and M. Sanada, *Kobunshi Kagaku*, **24**, 662 (1967).
33. F. E. Karasz and J. M. O'Reilly, *J. Polymer Sci.*, **B3**, 561 (1965).
33a. J. R. Knox, *Analytical Calorimetry*, *op. cit.*, p. 45.

34. M. Kubota and G. O. Spessard, *J. Phys. Chem.*, **70**, 941 (1966).

35. W. R. Licht and D. E. Kline, *J. Polymer Sci.*, Part A-2, **4**, 313 (1966).

36. C. H. Mack and S. R. Hobart, *Appl. Polymer Symposia*, **2**, 133 (1966).

37. L. Mandelkern and A. L. Allou, *J. Polymer Sci* , **B4**, 447 (1966).

38. L. Mandelkern, A. L. Allou, and M. Gopalan, *J. Phys. Chem.*, **72**, 309 (1968).

39. L. Mandelkern, G. Fatou, R. Denison, and J. Justin, *J. Polymer Sci.*, **B3**, 803 (1965).

40. P. J. McKinney and C. R. Foltz, *J. Appl. Polymer Sci.*, **11**, 1189 (1967).

41. G. Meinel and A. Peterlin, *J. Polymer Sci.*. **B5**. 197 (1967).

42. G. Meinel and A. Peterlin, *J. Polymer Sci.*, **B5**, 613 (1967).

43. N. Morosoff, H. Morawetz, and B. Post, *J. Am. Chem. Soc.*, **87**, 3035 (1965).

44. P. R. Morrow and G. C. Richardson, *J. Polymer Sci.*, Part A-2, **5**, 493 (1967).

45. M. J. O'Neill, *Anal. Chem.*, **36**, 1238 (1964).

46. M. J. O'Neill, *Anal. Chem.*, **38**, 1331 (1966).

47. P. Pacor and H. L. Spier, *J. Am. Oil Chem. Soc.*, **45**, 338 (1968).

48. S. Papette, B. B. Schaeffer, A. P. Gray, and T. L. Heying, *J. Polymer Sci.*, Part A-1, **4**, 1623 (1966).

49. R. M. Perkins, G. L. Drake, and W. A. Reeves, *J. Appl. Polymer Sci.*, **10**, 1041 (1966).

50. A. Peterlin and G. Meinel, *J. Polymer Sci.*, **B3**, 783 (1965).

51. A. Peterlin and G. Meinel, *J. Appl. Phys.*, **36**, 3028 (1965).

52. A. Peterlin and G. Meinel, *Appl. Polym. Symp.*, **2**, 85 (1966).

53. A. Peterlin, G. Meinel, and H. G. Olf, *J. Polymer Sci.*, **B4**, 399 (1966).

54. C. Plato and A. R. Glasgow, Jr., *Anal Chem.*, **41**, 330 (1969).

54a. R. S. Porter and J. F. Johnson, *Analytical Calorimetry*, *op. cit.*, pp. VII–XI.

55. R. N. Rogers and E. D. Morris, *Anal. Chem.*, **38**, 410 (1966).

56. R. N. Rogers and E. D. Morris, *Anal. Chem.*, **38**, 412 (1966).

57. R. N. Rogers and L. C. Smith, *Anal. Chem.*, **39**, 1024 (1967).

58. R. Schmidt, *Kunstoffe*, **56**(12), 837 (1966).

59. C. Sykes, *Proc. Roy. Soc. (London)*, **A148**, 422 (1935).

60. *Thermal Analysis Newsletter*, No. 4, p. 14, Perkin-Elmer Corp., Norwalk, Conn.

61. *Thermal Analysis Newsletter*, No. 5, pp. 4, 6, Perkin-Elmer Corp., Norwalk, Conn.

62. N. T. Wakelyn and P. R. Young, *J. Appl. Polymer Sci.*, **10**, 1421 (1966).

63. E. S. Watson, M. J. O'Neill, J. Justin, and N. Brenner, *Anal. Chem.*, **36**, 1233 (1964).

64. F. H. Winslow, M. Y. Hellman, W. Matreyek, and R. Salovey, *J. Polymer Sci.*, **B5**, 89 (1967).

65. B. Wunderlich, *J. Phys. Chem.*, **69**, 2078 (1965).

66. B. Wunderlich and C. M. Cormier. *J. Phys. Chem.* **70**. 1844 (1966).

67. B. Wunderlich and C. M. Cormier, *J. Polymer Sci.*, Part A-2, **5**, 987 (1967).

CHAPTER 2

Pyrolysis–Gas Chromatographic Techniques for Polymer Identification*

G. M. BRAUER

NATIONAL BUREAU OF STANDARDS
WASHINGTON, D. C.

2-1 INTRODUCTION

Thermal decomposition is perhaps the oldest characterization technique still used by the chemist. From the days of the alchemist to the present time, the testing of a material in a flame was often the first step to quickly identify a substance. C. G. Williams in 1860 isolated the basic isoprene unit by pyrolyzing natural rubber. Since that time various investigations employing thermal decomposition techniques have demonstrated that pyrolytic fragmentation and identification of the fragments can serve as an effective means of determining the nature and structure of polymers.

---

*Contribution of the National Bureau of Standards, not subject to copyright.

Pyrolysis can be applied immediately to almost any type of sample as received. The thermal decomposition is quick and easy to perform and the products of the decomposition provide a good guide to the identity of the polymer. Pyrolysis can take place by two types of degradation processes that may occur separately or in combination: (1) random scission involving rupture that occurs at random points along the chain leading to fragments that are generally large compared to the original monomer unit, and (2) chain depolymerization; that is, the reversal of the chain polymerization process, in which monomer units are released successively by "unzipping" from a chain end. Complete analysis of the degradation mechanism would involve determination of degradation products, molecular weights, rates of volatilization versus time and conversion, initial molecular weight and molecular weight distribution, dilution of the polymer in a relatively inert substance, and rates and activation energies of the degradation processes; all of this entails, of course, a large effort. It is possible, however, to differentiate between the two depolymerization processes in some cases by observing the molecular weight of the residue as a function of the extent of the reaction. The molecular weight drops rapidly as random degradation proceeds, but may remain constant in chain depolymerization as whole polymer molecules are converted to volatile monomeric products that escape from the residual sample. Examination of the degradation products also differentiates between the two processes: chain depolymerization often produces quantitative yields of the monomeric building block (methyl methacrylate, α-methylstyrene); the ultimate product of random degradation is likely to be a disperse mixture of fragments of widely varying molecular weight. Thus, pyrolysis of polyethylene in a vacuum yields a spectrum of hydrocarbons varying in molecular weight from 16 (CH_4) to 1000. Intermediate between those two extremes are polymers that yield, on heating, a mixture of monomers and chain fragments of varying sizes. Other polymers like poly(vinyl chloride) or poly(methyl acrylate) pyrolyze to fragments not related in structure to the original polymeric building blocks, along with fragments that are parts of the chains.

The depolymerization kinetics and products of the degradation of polymers for a variety of polymers have been studied by Madorsky(1), Grassie(2), Jellinek(3), and Wall and co-workers(4). These investigators found that the types and relative amounts of the pyrolysis products are functions of the molecular structure and the kind and frequency of side groups. Thus the thermal stability and degradation products can be related to the strengths of the C—C bonds in the polymer chain, i.e., secondary > tertiary > quaternary.

In recent years, pyrolytic methods in conjunction with instrumental procedures have gained increased attention. The popularity, especially of gas chromatographic techniques, is attested by over 250 papers dealing with this subject(5–11b) that have appeared in the literature since Davison et al.(12) first suggested this approach in 1954. An extensive review of pyrolysis–gas chromatographic techniques has been given by Levy(13).

2-2 QUALITATIVE IDENTIFICATION

Improvements in gas chromatographic techniques such as temperature programing of columns, high resolution of components, and high sensitivity detection of effluents, which are important for the successful combination with pyrolysis, have been developed. One of the prerequisites for pyrolysis–gas chromatography to gain as widespread use in identification of organic compounds as infrared or mass spectrometry is the ability to yield data for interlaboratory comparison. The mechanisms of pyrolytic reactions are rarely predictable and the quantitative composition of the pyrolyzate may exhibit excessive sensitivity to variations of the pyrolysis conditions bound to occur in different laboratories. The nature and relative amounts of pyrolysis products often vary widely with the type of pyrolysis unit used as well as with the experimental conditions such as column packings and column temperatures employed. Development of standardized procedures has been slow. For this reason, little universal value can be attributed to a large fraction of the pyrolysis–gas chromatographic data presently available in the literature. To improve interlaboratory comparison, future studies should focus attention on those design features of pyrolysis units that control the course of the pyrolysis process and provide the most desirable conditions for maximum interlaboratory reproducibility and correlation between the structure of the pyrolyzed material and the composition of the products. Uniform methods of expressing results would also be helpful for interlaboratory comparison of results.

The absence of functional groups of sufficient reactivity, the low solubility and chemical inertness, especially of thermosetting or cross-linked polymers, and the complexity of many polymeric systems favor the use of pyrolytic methods for the analysis of polymers. Compared to mass spectrometric(*14–17*), infrared(*18–23*), and ultraviolet(*24*) techniques, identification of degradation products by gas chromatography has the following advantages: (1) pyrolysis products can be rapidly separated; (2) separation can be easily recorded automatically; (3) only a few milligrams of sample are required; (4) products can often be identified by their retention times or the effluents can be further characterized; (5) the chromatogram of the pyrolysis products (pyrogram) yields a detailed "fingerprint" that is useful for identification; (6) the pyrolysis unit can be incorporated into a chromatograph, a relatively inexpensive instrument. The ideal technique should give reproducible degradation patterns so that variations in relative peak areas of the pyrolysis fragment should not exceed more than $\pm 2\%$ within a laboratory or $\pm 5\%$ between laboratories(*25*). Such precision may be required for the quantitative analysis of some polymer mixtures and for the determination of copolymers.

Pyrolysis units can be classified in three groups according to their mode of operation: (1) pulse mode units, (2) continuous mode units, and (3) units that can be operated using both the pulse and continuous modes. In pyrolysis, as carried out in pyrolysis–gas chromatography (PGC), the primary rupture of bonds is frequently followed by a complex series of competitive reactions between the radicals and the fragments formed. The course of these reactions is largely dependent on the particular experimental parameters used, such as sample weight, pressure, nature and linear velocity of the carrier gas, shape and dimensions of the pyrolysis unit, temperature profile of the unit, and temperature–time characteristics of the sample(*26*) which in turn are a function of the rate of heating and the density, heat capacity, and thermal conductivity of the polymer under investigation.

Secondary or undesirable side reactions are minimized by keeping the weight of a representative sample to a minimum, preferably using micro- or submicrogram quantities. The pyrolysis unit should be designed so that primary pyrolysis products can escape rapidly from the high temperature zone. The primary pyrolysis products formed in the vicinity of the surface of the source of heat in the pulse model rapidly enter the low temperature zone and are frozen. Thus, the probability of secondary reactions and recombinations drops sharply to zero. Primary pyrolysis products formed on the surface of the sample in a continuous mode unit expand (after the endothermic depolymerization reaction) into higher temperature zones where the probability of secondary reactions rapidly increases. This effect, however, is reduced when the products become more diluted in the carrier gas. Relative effects of pressure and flow on the quantitative reproducibility of the pyrograms are negligible when microgram quantities of material are pyrolyzed for 1 sec with a filament type unit(26). For qualitative analysis, samples of 1 mg or larger are commonly used and the heat transfer controls the pyrolysis. High heat transfer coefficients can rarely be obtained, especially where the pyrolyzed sample has gathered into a droplet that is suspended in the coiled filament(27). In this case, pyrolysis of the sample is completed long after the filament has reached equilibrium temperature. However, the sample temperature remains much lower because of the small heat transfer coefficients. To achieve good reproducibility, samples of the same size placed at the same location on the filament should be used, and the heating rate and equilibrium temperature should be carefully controlled.

Farre-Rius and Guiochon(27) noted that for small samples (less than 1 μg) the difference between sample and filament temperature is small. At the equilibrium temperature of the filament, the half-decomposition time of many polymers is several orders of magnitude smaller than the time needed to reach this equilibrium temperature (usually 30 msec to 3 sec). Thus, the polymer decomposition is controlled by the heating rate of the filament and by heat transfer to the sample, not by the equilibrium temperature of the filament.

A current-temperature calibration is required for the filament. This can be obtained by observing microscopically the melting of very thin layers of substances of known melting points that have been deposited from solution on the filament. Lehrle(11b) recommends the following standards in the 100° to 1000°C temperature range: acetanilide 115°C, adipic acid 151°C, 2,4-dinitrophenylhydrazine 197°C, lithium nitrate 253°C, fluorescein 320°C, potassium dichromate 398°C, silver chloride 455°C, lead chloride 501°C, potassium iodate 560°C, strontium bromide 643°C, potassium bromide 730°C, sodium chloride 801°C, potassium carbonate 891°C, and barium chloride 962°C. At higher temperatures optical pyrometers may be used. Different parts of the filament may be calibrated and the temperature gradients along its length may be determined. Filaments should be calibrated *in situ*, for specified wall temperature and diameter of the pyrolysis unit.

A method for measuring temperature rise times (TRT) of very fast TRTs based on monitoring the emission of light with a photomultiplier has been described by Levy and Fanter(27a). Because the photomultiplier has a very fast response, it proved to be the most suitable system for measurement of temperature rise times of pulse pyrolysis units. The response of the photomultiplier is sufficiently fast (1.4 nsec) to follow the rise time of any pyrolyzer, and the voltage output is compatible with oscilloscopes. A system equipped with a regular photomultiplier tube is applicable only when the equilibrium temperature is higher than the temperature at which light emission begins (about 550°C). Photomultiplier tubes sensitive in the infrared would extend the application of the technique to lower temperatures.

For qualitative identification, pulse mode units in which ideally thermal energy is supplied to the solid sample as a "pulse" giving rise to temperature–time profiles similar in shape to a half square wave (that is, a constant and reproducible pyrolysis temperature is reached nearly instantaneously) are most commonly used.

A thin film of sample is usually coated onto a Nichrome or platinum spiral(28) or nickel ribbon(29) or is placed in a small boat or dish (25,30) so that the weight of the residue remaining after heating can be determined (Fig. 2-1). Although the filament may catalyze the degradation, Jones and Moyles(31) showed that with 20–30-μg samples the pyrograms obtained with Nichrome, platinum, or gold-plated platinum filaments are identical. The power supply to the filament is generally controlled by a variable transformer and timed by a stopwatch, but exact measurement of the filament temperature is difficult. More elaborate automatic time and voltage controls or filament systems featuring feedback temperature control have been suggested(11b,32, 33,33a). If desired, the pyrolyzer temperature can also be manually programed to obtain more rapid equilibrium and to remove the pyrolysis products from the heated zone immediately after they are formed

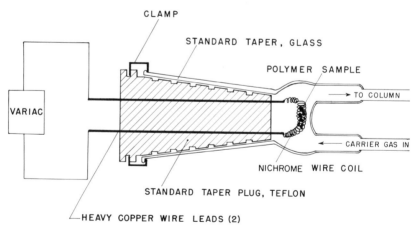

CLAMP

STANDARD TAPER, GLASS

POLYMER SAMPLE

VARIAC

TO COLUMN

CARRIER GAS IN

NICHROME WIRE COIL

STANDARD TAPER PLUG, TEFLON

HEAVY COPPER WIRE LEADS (2)

Figure 2-1. Hot wire pyrolyzers.

(a) Nichrome wire coil. Reprinted by courtesy of *Analytical Chemistry*(28, p. 454).

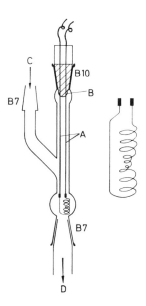

(b) Spiral filament. A: tungsten leads; B: plug; B7 and B10 tapered joints; C: carrier gas entry; D: chromatographic column. Reprinted by courtesy of the *Journal of Gas Chromatography* (77, p. 90).

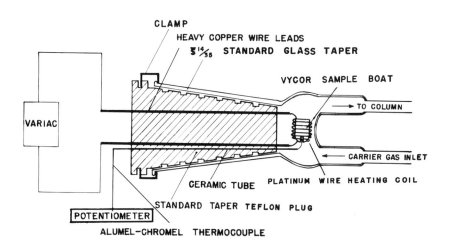

(c) Vycor boat unit. Reprinted by courtesy of *Analytical Chemistry* (30, p. 673).

47

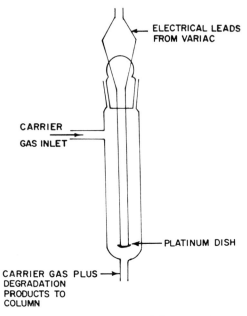

(d) Platinum dish unit. Reprinted by courtesy of the *Journal of Gas Chromatography*
(*25*, p. 78).

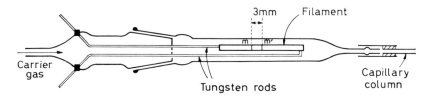

(e) Ribbon filament degradation unit. The sample is deposited from a solution evenly
spread between the engraved marks mm'. Reprinted by courtesy of *Polymer*(*128*,
p. 524).

(*34,35*). Pyrolysis units based on high frequency induction heating
(*36,37,37a*) radiation(*38*), dielectric discharge(*32*) and arc(*39,40*) also
operate on the pulse principle and frequently provide pyrolysis conditions similar to those existing in filament units. A very useful induction
unit employs a small ferromagnetic wire that is coated with sample.
The wire is pushed by means of a magnet into the pyrolysis capillary
that is surrounded by an induction coil. The coil will heat an iron wire
of 0.6-mm diam to the Curie temperature in 2×10^{-3} sec, whereupon

the relative magnetic permeability of the wire suddenly drops to a value close to unity and very little power is adsorbed from the field. The initial heating takes place on the skin of the filament and is then transferred to the bulk of the filament. The total volume of the pyrolysis zone is less than 0.5 μl. Heating time can be controlled from 0.06 to several seconds. The pyrolysis temperature can be varied by choosing a ferromagnetic conductor with a suitable Curie point temperature. Such Curie point pyrolyzers are now commercially available(37a). Excellent pyrograms were obtained with 0.02- to 0.8-μg samples using capillary columns.

Advantages of this pyrolysis unit include the use of microgram samples (especially important in forensic investigations), the rapid establishment of a precise and reproducible pyrolysis temperature that is essentially dependent on the composition of the ferromagnetic conductor and rapid heating with a constant temperature-time profile (40a). Even the commercial Curie-point filament instruments have a heat-up period of the order of 0.2 sec or less(11b). Thus the technique is well suited to the study of fast degradation rates, e.g., reaction times less than 5 sec. However, the remote possibility of catalytic side reactions due to the heating element should not be overlooked. Only one instance of this occurrence has been reported: the pyrolysis of poly (ethylene glycols) is markedly influenced by the presence of iron oxide (rust)(33a). A disadvantage of this technique is that a given sample can be subjected only to the Curie temperature and not to a temperature sequence.

For quantitative studies of the mechanism and the kinetics of polymer degradation where accurate analysis of the volatile and nonvolatile reaction products obtained at a certain accurately controlled temperature and under closely controlled conditions is required, it is often preferable to employ continuous mode preheated tube furnaces (to be discussed later) than to refine the design of the filament-type pyrolyzer.

For a simple systematic scheme of polymer identification, the pyrolysis technique should be rapid, simple to perform, and suitable for direct application to polymer-containing samples of any form. Despite the fact that the filament-type pyrolyzer does not allow optimum control of degradation conditions, the pyrograms are reproducible and entirely satisfactory for identification purposes when polymers of known composition are available for comparison.

Pyrolysis temperatures kept between 500° and 800°C for 1 to 20 sec are usually recommended. This is a temperature range particularly useful for qualitative information in which large characteristic fragments are preserved intact to a large extent, yet enough breakdown products are produced to permit their characterization. At temperatures above 1000°C, the pyrograms will be less suitable for identification, since secondary reactions become predominant, leading to increasing amounts of simple molecules such as H_2, CO, CO_2, C_2H_2, C_2H_4, CH_4, C_6H_6, or H_2O that give less characteristic patterns than those observed for monomers or primary degradation products. Although pyrograms containing from 30 to 50 peaks (for polyolefins) have been reported(40), and an even larger number of peaks should be expected for other polyolefins, the relative retention times and peak height ratios of three to five major peaks are usually sufficient for identification. Thus a single set of column operating conditions that will give characteristic pyrograms for degradation products of all types of polymers is desirable.

Systematic identification of plastics was attempted by Nelson et al. (41) by pyrolyzing 0.2–0.5-mg samples for 10 sec at 650°–750°C in an argon gas chromatograph using a 4-ft column of 5% silicone oil on Chromosorb W. Similar plastics were distinguished from pyrograms obtained at two different temperatures.

Groten(42) has described many applications of pyrolysis–gas chromatography to polymer characterization. The pyrolysis of the sample was conducted by heating of a platinum coil to 950°C for 26 sec, and a $\frac{1}{4}$ in. by 12 ft column containing 20% Carbowax on Diatoport P was used. Identifications were based mainly upon the moderately volatile products. For the 150 different polymers investigated, the individual members of a group generally gave pyrograms that allowed unambiguous identification of the original polymer. Where the standard conditions resulted in ambiguous pyrograms, only slight variations in pyrolysis times and/or temperatures were necessary to establish an identity. Cox and Ellis(43) employ a furnace-microreactor kept at 700°C to pyrolyze 0.1-mg samples. The relative retention time of the peak is expressed as the ratio of the retention time of the respective peak to that of the reference peak which is arbitrarily selected as the peak of the last product eluted during a 15-min period after pyrolysis. Pyrograms may thus be related to those obtained on other instruments by measuring retention times of the reference peaks with respect to the retention time for n-butane or benzene. For rapid identification, the retention times are plotted as the percentage fractions of the retention time for the reference peak with the positions of the distinctive peaks represented by rectangles of width equal to twice the standard deviation in the relative retention times, averaged over at least five determinations. Retention data for some polymers are given in Fig. 2-2.

Resins derived from coal tar can be characterized by PGC mainly from their cyclopentadiene, styrene, and indene content(*44*). Pyrolytic techniques for the systematic identification of elastomers are described by Voigt(*45,46*). Feuerberg and Weigel(*47*), Hulot and Lebel(*48*), Label(*49*), Fiorenza and Bonomi(*50*), and Cole et al.(*51*). Although the experimental conditions vary considerably, all methods yield pyrograms that will distinguish rapidly among all common elastomers either in the pure state or in admixture with others. On vulcanization the number and relative retention times of the peaks is not altered, but changes in the peak height ratios may occur. Simultaneous flame ionization and electron capture detection are very useful in the identification and determination of polymers in compounded cured rubber stocks employing a two-channel recorder(*51*). For qualitative studies temperature programing was employed, but for quantitative work isothermal conditions were preferred. Most polymers could be identified by flame ionization detection, but with polymers containing halogens, nitrogen, sulfur, or oxygen, selective dual-channel detection simplified the identification. The presence of different vulcanizing agents may also be detected from the pyrograms(*45*). Fillers probably hold the decomposition products more tenaciously; this may explain why the proportion of light fractions (ethylene, propylene) in the pyrolyzate is higher in the case of filled rubber than in the case of crude rubber.

Pyrolysis–gas chromatography of specimens of paint films is an effective method of identifying the organic matrix in the paint and

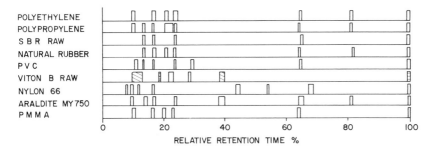

Figure 2-2. Chart of relative retention time data for some polymers. Negative peaks are indicated by cross-hatching. Only peaks that have well defined relative retention times have been included. Carrier gas: argon. Column: 20 g silicone oil MS 550 per 100 g 80 to 100 mesh Celite. Detector: Lovelock ionization detector. Reprinted by courtesy of *Analytical Chemistry* (*43*, p. 95).

for quality control(*52–55*). Hoover(*54*) and Bober(*55*) described techniques for injecting liquid paints or lacquers into a pyrolysis unit and analyzing the solvent and pyrolyzed resin in a single run. A special injection block, equipped with a cylindrical sieve, can be used for sampling liquid–solid samples(*55*). The solid components are retained in the sieve without clogging the injection port, which is connected with the column via a three-way valve.

Pyrograms can be used for the qualitative determination of resin components in adhesives(*56a,b*), characterization of anion and cation ion exchange resins(*56c*), identification of polymers in paper(*56d*), and qualitative analysis of phenol and cresol-formaldehyde resins(*56e*).

Fisher and Neerman(*56*) described the identification of brake lining constituents, especially resin binders, by PGC.

Identification of synthetic fibers and fiber blends is generally possible from the chromatograms, but all cellulose and protein fibers give very similar pyrograms(*57,57a*). Proteins give reproducible pyrograms related to their amino acid content(*58–60*). Pyrolysis is conducted at a relatively low temperature (300°C) and the amines are stabilized at 110°C prior to chromatography on 15% Quadrol (tetrakis-2-hydroxy-propyl ethylenediamine) or silanized Chromosorb P(*58*). The pyrogram from egg and serum albumin exhibited significant differences, which should be expected since the cystine content of the latter is about four times greater than that of egg albumin. Every amino acid-containing substance tested by this technique gave a unique pyrogram. Kanomata and Mashiko(*59*) studied all the amino acids by a similar procedure and compared the casein and egg albumin pyrograms. Reasonably reproducible pyrograms with 6–7% standard deviations expressed as coefficients of variation of the peak areas were obtained by Stack(*60*) for reference proteins pyrolyzed through a Carbowax 1500 column programed from 30° to 150°C. Adequate differentiation of albumin and α- and γ-globulin was achieved, but collagen and gelatin gave very similar pyrograms. In a tooth sample, moderate differences were observed between peak areas of the pyrograms of mature enamel and those of "chalky" enamel from lesions of dental caries in which the surface of the enamel was intact. Comparison of areas of major peaks of developing dentin and enamel showed considerable variation.

Using higher pyrolysis temperatures, Merritt and Robertson(*61*) analyzed a group of 17 amino acids and 10 peptides by a combined PGC-mass spectrometer system that provides for decomposition of the sample, separation of degradation products, and qualitative identification of these products by means of a single integrated operation. The chromatographic column was programed from $-180°$ to $+125°C$ since the pyrolysis products varied widely in boiling point. The separated components were eluted into the ion source of a time-of-flight mass spectrometer, operating with a spectrum scan rate of 10,000 spectra per sec. This allowed viewing the spectrum on an oscilloscope screen or displaying a strip chart recording of the spectrum in 5 sec. The authors believe that the identification of a unique pyrolysis product for each amino acid as obtained in this study suggests that improvements in this technique may make it possible to obtain sequence information of the amino acids present in proteins.

PGC has also been applied to life detection and chemotaxonomy (*62*). The pyrograms obtained after controlled pyrolysis and chromatography of microorganisms grown under similar conditions showed similarity and distinguishing differences. The major peaks involved the protein constituents and are likely to be most informative for describing the major relationships among microorganisms. Four peaks that arose from the pyrolysis of the proteins are indicated as useful biological markers; two of these peaks are useful as internal reference peaks to which other peaks are related in time. Different chemical compositions were noted for microorganisms grown in different media; these differences were demonstrated in the pyrograms as well as in the percentage of nitrogen and carbon present. It is likely that PGC may prove useful in characterizing such high molecular weight substances as enzymes, nucleic acids, and antibodies.

Direct pyrolysis of water samples containing organic matter such as starch or gelatin, when combined with gas chromatographic separation of the produced fragments, can be used for qualitative and quantitative characterization of aqueous solutions (*63*). A horizontally mounted sample injector is connected through a Swagelok reducer to the pyrolysis tube. The pyrolytic unit consists of a combustion furnace and a 60-in. long by $\frac{3}{16}$ in. Monel pyrolysis tube filled with granular nickel which is retained by a small plug of quartz wool at each end. A check valve is connected to the carrier gas inlet of the pyrolysis tube to prevent pressure surges in the steam generator which is the source of carrier gas. The carrier gas line and the portion of the pyrolysis tube outside the furnace are maintained at 125°C with heating tapes to prevent steam condensation. A gas chromatograph with hydrogen flame ionization detector is used for separation and measurement of the pyrolytic fragments. The pyrolysis tube is kept at 700°C, and the $\frac{3}{16}$ in. column filled with 20% Carbowax 20 M on 60–80 mesh Chromosorb W(AW-DMCS) is kept at 120°C. The instrument is operated under standard conditions for at least 24 hr before analysis of the aqueous solutions is attempted. The sample sizes are from 0.1 to 0.25 ml.

After calibration with standard solutions, the peaks can be used for quantitative determination in a manner similar to conventional techniques used in spectroscopic analysis. For complex mixtures or mixtures of closely related compounds, the concentrations of the organic components can be calculated with the help of mathematical models which relate all PGC peaks to the concentration of each component. With the application of least squares technique in matrix form, it is possible to interpret very complex pyrograms.

Zulaica and Guiochon(64) pyrolyzed polymers at 625°C and were able to identify heavy ester plasticizers using silicon gum SE 30 or poly(neopentylglycol adipate) on etched glass beads. These authors recommend using retention indices suggested by Wehrli and Kovats (65) in identifying the plasticizers.

Pyrograms can detect and identify small amounts of copolymeric constituents or crosslinking agents. The limits of identification of one polymer in another depend entirely on their identities, that is, on their respective fragmentation pattern on pyrolysis, but sensitivity is highest if, for at least one component, the depolymerization proceeds through an "unzipping" mechanism. This is the case with polymers containing an α-alkyl recurring unit, such as poly(methyl methacrylate) or poly-α-methylstyrene or those such as polytetrafluoroethylene in which a high yield of monomer is produced. Thus, 0.2% of copolymeric constituents in poly(methyl methacrylate) can be detected with a thermal conductivity detector, but qualitative identification from the pyrograms becomes difficult(28). Similarly, the detection of 0.1 weight per cent of butyl rubber in polybutadiene is readily obtainable.

Noffz and Pfab(66) investigated copolymers of vinyl acetate with n-butyl acrylate and with di-n-butylfumarate-di-n-butyl maleinate which could not be distinguished by IR or elementary analysis. For both systems, they could identify the mono-, di-, and trimeric fragments by comparison of retention times and mass spectrometric analysis. The presence of dibutyl succinate and the dibutyl esters of ethylene dicarbonic acid and of vinylethylene dicarbonic acid in the pyrolyzate of the vinyl acetate-di-n-butylfumarate-di-n-butyl maleate copolymer established the presence of the maleic and fumaric ester in the polymer.

With more sensitive detectors, such as electron-capture detectors, the limit of identification, especially for compounds containing halogens, nitrogen, and sulfur, can undoubtedly by considerably increased.

The original condensation polymer can often be reconstructed from the fragments obtained on pyrolysis, especially if the polymer contains phenyl groups, as can be seen from the pyrogram of a phenol-formaldehyde shown in Fig. 2-3 (67).

The pyrogram of a copolymer depends on the sequence–length distribution. Pyrograms will differentiate between random copolymers and block polymers or polymer mixtures (28,32,46,68,68a,69), which generally cannot be distinguished by IR techniques. The presence of a foreign monomer may interrupt chain transfer processes involved in the degradation. Similar products result but their quantities as determined from peak heights or peak height ratios are different. Even for closely related polyolefins, the pyrograms will distinguish between poly(ethylene-propylene) block and random copolymers of the same composition (46).

Figure 2-4 shows pyrograms of polypropylenes of varying tacticity (70). The reason for the different pyrolysis products of the polypropylenes of varying stereoregularity is the steric arrangements of the methyl groups. Mass spectrometry indicates that peak pairs which differ for polymers of different tacticity have the same molecular weight and mass spectrometric decomposition pattern (70). Thus, diastereomeric olefins formed on pyrolysis are separated by the chromatographic column. For hydrocarbons with less than 11 carbon atoms, no diastereoisomers can be detected in the pyrogram; for compounds with 11 to 13 carbon atoms, a pair of diastereoisomers can be observed. These results agree with those expected from theoretical considerations. Pyrolytic products containing 14 or more carbon atoms show changes in peak height according to tacticity; however, a definitive assignment of diastereoisomeric pairs is only possible for C_{15} isomers. From these characteristic peaks it is possible to determine the degree of tacticity of the polymer.

The combination of hydrogenation and PGC as developed by Kolb and Kaiser (71) permits the identification of unsaturated substances formed during the pyrolysis. In this method, the unsaturated compounds are saturated by hydrogen in a continuous process immediately after breakdown, and separated consecutively on the gas chromatographic column. The basic advantage of this technique is that one can obtain the respective saturated breakdown products that characterize the C—C bonds in the original polymer, independently of the number of double bonds formed during the thermal breakdown. Furthermore, by elimination of the unsaturated components, the number of peaks is reduced and the chromatogram becomes less complex. Identification

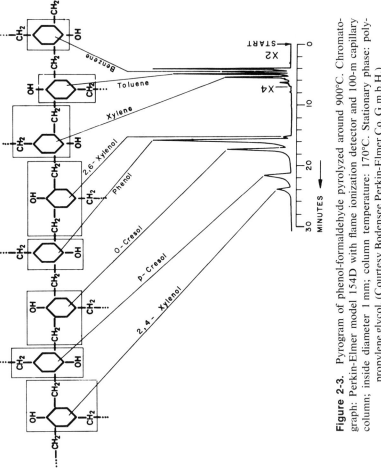

Figure 2-3. Pyrogram of phenol-formaldehyde pyrolyzed around 900°C. Chromatograph: Perkin-Elmer model 154D with flame ionization detector and 100-m capillary column; inside diameter 1 mm; column temperature: 170°C. Stationary phase: polypropylene glycol. (Courtesy Bodensee Perkin-Elmer Co. G.m.b.H.)

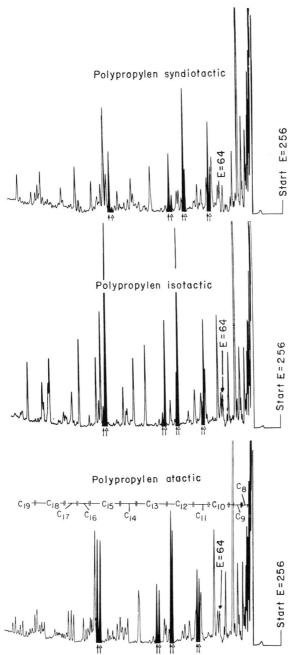

Figure 2-4. Pyrograms of polypropylenes of varying stereoregularity, using high frequency pyrolyzer. Macrocapillary column; 100 m length. Reprinted by courtesy of the *Fresinius' Zeitschrift für Analytische Chemie* (*70*, pp. 134, 135).

58   G. M. BRAUER

of individual peaks is also facilitated because many more saturated than unsaturated hydrocarbons are available for calibration. These authors pyrolyzed polyethylene at 1000°C for 10 sec. A packed column containing 15 wt% of OS-138 poly(phenyl ether) on Celite 545 was programed linearly from 50° up to 240°C at a rate of 5°C/min; hydrogen was used as carrier gas. The first peak of the repeated groups of triplet peaks of the pyrogram was identified as the normal paraffin (Fig. 2-5). More complete resolution of the initial (highly volatile) products shown in Fig. 2-5 can be accomplished by cryogenic temperature programing(29,72) as shown in Fig. 2-6.

Since the olefins are the result of pyrolysis, it is evident that the double bond can be located only on the end of each breakdown product. Thus, one can assume that the second and third peaks in each original

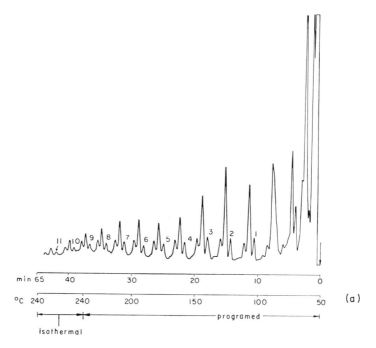

Figure 2-5. Pyrolysis of polyethylene:
(a) pyrogram of polyethylene (peaks 1–11 correspond to the C_9–C_{19} normal paraffins);
(b) pyrolysis of polyethylene with subsequent hydrogenation of the pyrolysis products (peaks 1–11 correspond to the C_7–C_{17} normal paraffins). Column: 2 m × 3 mm i.d. containing 15% OS-138 poly(phenyl ether) on Celite 545; column temperature: programed as given; carrier gas: hydrogen, 25 ml/min. Reprinted by courtesy of the *Journal of Gas Chromatography(71*, pp. 233, 234).

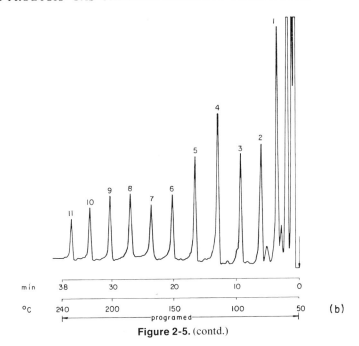

Figure 2-5. (contd.)

triplet correspond to the respective α- and α,ω-olefins. The addition of α-olefins to the original sample establishes that the second peak in each triplet corresponds to the linear α-olefin identical to that of the respective n-paraffin in the same triplet(73). Further identification is accomplished by oxidation of the unsaturated effluents with $KMnO_4$, reacting the resulting acids with diazomethane and analyzing the methyl ester formed by gas chromatography. This procedure established the presence of α, ω-olefins in the original pyrolysis products.

Cieplinski et al.(74) have investigated extensively the thermal degradation products of polyolefins. Samples were pyrolyzed in a reaction chamber as described by Ettre and Varadi(75) and the volatile reaction products were passed through a linearly programed temperature, open tubular column coated with Apiezon L. As expected, this column had a much higher resolving power than the packed column; as a result, not only were the triplet peaks separated better, but also a large number of small peaks located between the triplets could be observed that were undetected on the packed column. On pyrolysis at 690°C a large number of triplet peaks was obtained, but with this column the last peak in each group was identified as the normal paraffin. The peaks are evenly spaced up to C_{22}, where the temperature

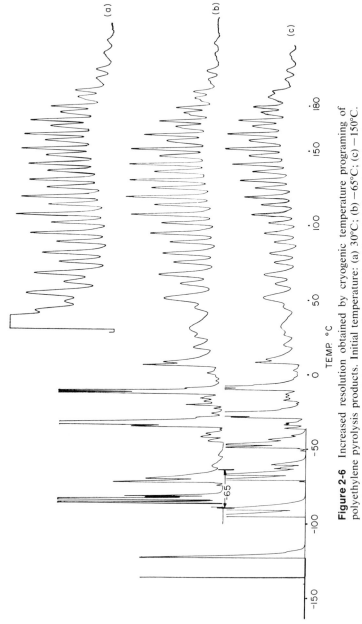

Figure 2-6 Increased resolution obtained by cryogenic temperature programing of polyethylene pyrolysis products. Initial temperature: (a) 30°C; (b) −65°C; (c) −150°C. Pyrolysis temperature: 800°C for 15 sec. Column: 8 ft × ¼ in. 10% diethylene glycol succinate. Reprinted by courtesy of the *Journal of Gas Chromatography* (29, p. 231).

programing ended. From here on the consecutive homolog peaks start to emerge in the usual logarithmic scale of an isothermal run. Comparison of pyrograms of high- and low-density polyethylenes indicates significant differences for peaks above C_{21}, with the relative amounts of the two major peaks being reversed (Fig. 2-7). Thus, for the low-density polyethylene the last peak corresponding to the *n*-paraffin is

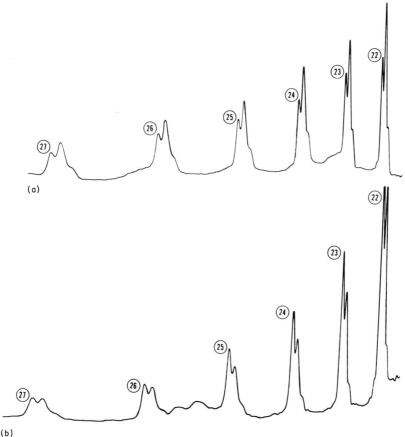

Figure 2-7. Pyrograms of polyethylene: (a) polyethylene (Ziegler process), density $d = 0.960 \text{ g/cm}^3$; (b) polyethylene (high pressure process) $d = 0.918 \text{ g/cm}^3$; 50–70 mg samples pyrolyzed at 690°C. Column, 150 ft × 0.01 in. i.d. (open tubular) coated with Apiezon L liquid phase; column temperature, 250°C; carrier gas, helium. Inlet pressure, 30 psig. Perkin-Elmer model 226 chromatograph with a 5-mV, 1-sec full-scale potentiometer recorder. The peak numbers indicate the carbon numbers of the corresponding normal paraffins. Reprinted by courtesy of the *Fresinius' Zeitschrift für Analytische Chemie* (74, p. 365).

always larger, whereas for Ziegler-type polyethylene the first peak predominates. The low density polymer yields more branched isomers and low molecular weight hydrocarbons (n-C_3 to n-C_5) than the high density one(75a). The mass distribution of straight chain and branched scission products also differs. Low density polyethylenes show maximum peaks at n-C_{18} to n-C_{19} and Ziegler polyethylene at n-C_{22} to n-C_{23} and n-C_{30} to n-C_{32}.

For polymethylene pyrolyzed at 640°C the triplets are better separated. Apparently due to the low molecular weight of the polymer, the yield of hydrocarbons above C_{17} is very small. On plotting the adjusted retention time versus carbon number or boiling point for the various peaks of each group, a linear relationship is found indicating that each peak in a particular group is representative of a member of a particular homologous series. Comparison of pyrograms of polyethylene and polymethylene gives a larger number of minor peaks for the former, most of which are identified as linear hydrocarbons. This correlates with the assumption that these small peaks are the result of breakdown at the branched positions in the original macromolecule.

The effect of chain branching may be studied by pyrolyzing polymers having known structures(37a). Ethylene–propylene copolymers yield more methane on pyrolysis than an ethylene homopolymer with a similar degree of unsaturation. The ethylene–butene copolymer pyrogram differs from that of polyethylene in having a greatly increased ethane peak. Only a small increase in n-butane due to side chain scission is found in the ethylene-hexene-1 copolymer. However, there is a large increase in butene-1 possibly caused by the intramolecular hydrogen transfer from the side chain to the point of scission.

Van Schooten and Evenhuis(76), in their studies of the degradation of α-olefins, hydrogenated the pyrolysis products on a platinum-on-alumina catalyst (0.75 wt% Pt on Al_2O_3, 30–50 mesh) at 200°C before the products entered the GLC column. All olefins, but also benzene and substituted benzenes, are completely hydrogenated to the corresponding alkanes or cycloalkanes by this procedure. From the pyrograms the authors drew the following conclusions regarding degradation mechanisms of α-olefins, that should be very useful for the identification of unknown polyolefins: (1) the depolymerization reaction increases with branching, but is relatively insensitive to the size of the branches, (2) the depolymerization reaction predominates over hydrogen transfer reactions in the absence of tertiary hydrogen atoms, (3) with increasing size of the branches an increasing number of alkyl side groups split off, (4) intramolecular hydrogen transfer is an important reaction in the pyrolysis of all saturated polyolefins and takes place predominantly, although not exclusively, with the hydrogen of the fifth carbon atom. For the polyolefins studied by this technique, the largest total yield of pyrolysis products was found for polypropylene (23%) and was more than fourfold that for polyethylene.

Many polymers can be characterized from their pyrograms at a particular temperature. Furthermore, changes in the pyrogram with changes in the temperature of pyrolysis can be utilized as a further parameter for characterization of complex polymers.

Figure 2-8 shows the pyrograms of polystyrene degraded at 1025°, 825°, and 425°C (*30*). Similarly the pyrograms of polymethylene are greatly dependent on the pyrolysis temperature (Fig. 2-9)(*74*). When the pyrolysis is conducted at 620°C (instead of 640°C), the large composite peak for the low molecular weight hydrocarbons disappears and the number of isomeric degradation products is reduced. The n-$C_{14}H_{30}$ is the major component, whereas on pyrolysis at 640°C the n-dodecane gives the largest peak. On pyrolysis at 690°C the composite peak corresponding to the light hydrocarbons becomes dominant and overlaps the C_8–C_9 peaks. The height of the C_{10}–C_{13} peaks decreases, especially that representing the C_{13} hydrocarbons. The pyrogram of isotactic polypropylene on the other hand, differs greatly from that of polymethylene with a large increase in the yield of light hydrocarbon isomers that are formed on scission at the more reactive tertiary carbon atoms. Another characteristic feature of this pyrogram is the presence in large concentrations of certain hydrocarbons, whereas others with an intermediate number of carbon atoms are nearly completely absent.

Pyrograms of various high density polyethylenes show no distinguishing characteristics at 770°C, whereas at 480°C significant differences are apparent(*37a*). At lower temperatures the yield of pyrolyzates is very small. Low density polyethylenes show small differences in their pyrograms at 770°C and more significant differences at 480°C, but these differences were not as marked as those observed between high density polymers. Pyrograms enable a positive identification of high from low density polyethylenes at 480° and 770°C. Again, the effect is most marked at 480°C. Thus, the correct choice of pyrolysis temperature is of major importance in the identification of polymers having similar properties. Therefore, a preliminary set of experiments should be conducted to determine the optimum conditions for the characterization of the specific polymer system.

Samples can be pyrolyzed at a series of temperatures, and the changes

in degradation behavior—as evidenced by the (1) "appearance temperatures" of various peaks, and (2) relative abundance of products as
a function of temperature—are noted. Changes of the most characteristic breakdown products versus temperature can also be plotted. For
homopolymers the temperatures at which degradation products are
first obtained may be more distinctive than the retention times of the
products. The temperature dependence of degradation rates often
allows the distinction of random copolymers from block copolymers
and mixtures of homopolymers. Generally, there is a very close simi-

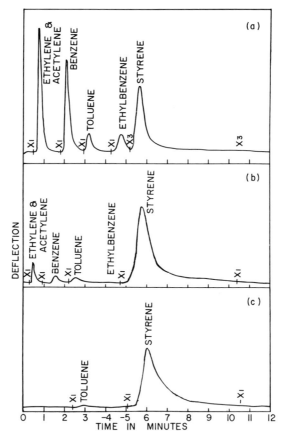

Figure 2-8. Pyrograms of polystyrene at various pyrolysis temperatures: (a) 425°C;
(b) 825°C; (c) 1025°C. Column, Apiezon L; column temperature, 140°C; flow rate, 60 ml/
min. Attenuation scale indicated by numbers in figure. Reprinted by courtesy of *Analytical Chemistry* (*30*, p. 674).

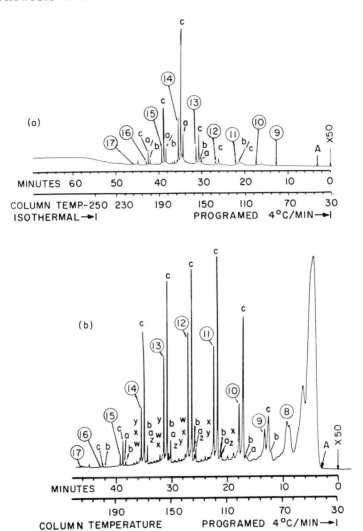

Figure 2-9. Pyrograms of polymethylenes at various pyrolysis temperatures: (a) 620°C; (b) 640°C; (c) 690°C. Column and instrumentation as in Fig. 2-7. Reprinted by courtesy of *Fresenius' Zeitschrift für Analytische Chemie* (74, pp. 366, 368).

larity between mixtures of homopolymers and block copolymers, and their pyrograms will differ only in extremely favorable cases. The pyrograms in Fig. 2-10 were obtained for a single specimen for a series of successive degradations in fixed periods of time at standardized in-

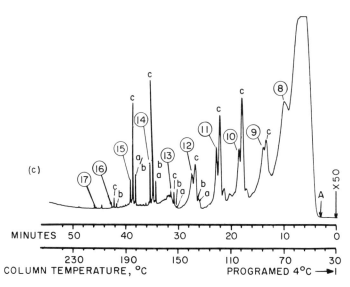

(c)

MINUTES   50   40   30   20   10   0

230   190   150   110   70   30
COLUMN TEMPERATURE, °C   PROGRAMED 4°C ➞

Figure 2-9. (contd.)

creasing temperatures (77). Each short horizontal line represents a pyrogram. The sample is heated to 150°C for 10 sec and the pyrogram is recorded. The temperature is then raised repeatedly in steps of 100°C. The residue after the previous heating is the remaining sample. These temperature-series pyrograms provide a very useful way of characterizing polymers since not only the product retention times, but also the variations of yield of products with temperature, are used as characterization parameters. Comparison of pyrogram series also makes it possible to estimate relative thermal stabilities of polymers; such assessments are more informative and more rapid than conventional weight-loss studies.

Gas chromatographic analysis of the degradation products over a wide range of temperatures also yields valuable information about the decomposition mode, the relative importance of various pyrolytic reactions, and the relative thermal stability of polymers. Thus, poly-(methyl methacrylate), poly(ethyl methacrylate), polystyrene, and polytetrafluoroethylene are examples where the degradation produces only monomer by an unzipping mechanism; poly(methyl acrylate) yields small additional peaks (methanol, ethanol, and methyl methacrylate), which indicates additional complicating side reactions. Pyrograms of poly(vinyl chloride) and poly(vinyl acetate) give hydrochloric

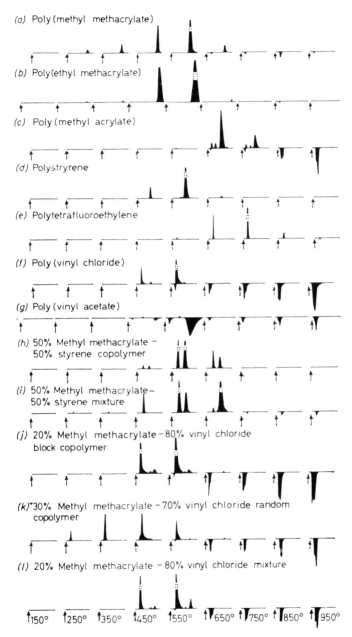

(a) Poly (methyl methacrylate)

(b) Poly (ethyl methacrylate)

(c) Poly (methyl acrylate)

(d) Polystryrene

(e) Polytetrafluoroethylene

(f) Poly (vinyl chloride)

(g) Poly (vinyl acetate)

(h) 50% Methyl methacrylate – 50% styrene copolymer

(i) 50% Methyl methacrylate – 50% styrene mixture

(j) 20% Methyl methacrylate – 80% vinyl chloride block copolymer

(k) 30% Methyl methacrylate – 70% vinyl chloride random copolymer

(l) 20% Methyl methacrylate – 80% vinyl chloride mixture

150°   250°   350°   450°   550°   650°   750°   850°   950°

Figure 2-10. Temperature-series pyrograms. Each short horizontal line represents a chromatogram obtained on repeated heating in steps of 100°C. Detector, katharometer; carrier gas, nitrogen. Reprinted by courtesy of the *Journal of Gas Chromatography* (*69, 77*, p. 92).

67

acid and acetic acid, respectively. These products arise from the elimination of the side groups, leaving the backbone of the polyacetylene as a stable residue which decomposes only at a much higher temperature to produce principally acetylene. On the other hand, random copolymers of methyl methacrylate and vinyl chloride lead to a marked reduction in thermal stability with elimination of hydrochloric acid starting already at 250°C.

Eggertsen and Stross(78) described a hot-filament thermal analysis technique for the determination of the thermal stability and of the trace-volatile contents of polymers. The apparatus, which is a versatile pyrolysis gas chromatography unit, was converted to an analog of the thermobalance by programed heating of the glass-coated platinum filament and by substitution of a short column packed with glass wool for the separating column so that the total volatiles were monitored by the flame ionization detector. Of course, the column can be filled with suitable packing materials when it is desirable to separate and identify products at any stage of the thermal decomposition. As the sample was heated to 600°C the volatile products were monitored by the detector, a dual recorder was used to chart both temperature and volatiles yield. Polymer stabilities were generally compared by determining from the charts the temperatures required to attain decomposition rates corresponding to 0.1, 1, and 5% of the total measured peak area per minute. The temperatures at these rates of volatile evolution were designated $T_{0.1}$, T_1, and T_5, respectively. In a few tests, a sufficiently high detector sensitivity was used to show decomposition at 0.01%/min and thus permit a determination of $T_{0.01}$. An example is shown in Fig. 2-11 for a 0.02-mg sample of powdered polystyrene. Thermal stabilities were compared also on the basis of temperatures at which certain percentages of the total peak area had appeared. Thermal stability measurements of several polymers were generally consistent with results by conventional thermogravimetric analysis. Advantages of the method are its high sensitivity for the detection of low decomposition rates (0.01%/min could be readily observed with less than 1 mg of sample), the speed of temperature adjustment, and a small sample requirement.

The same procedure allowed also the rapid estimation of monomers or other trace volatiles responsive to the detector by heating of the filament to a temperature just below the decomposition point of the polymer. Two heating techniques were used for removing volatiles in conjunction with their analysis by a suitable column: (1) heating for short periods or "pulses" so that the vapors are driven off sharply into the column and good resolution of the components is obtained, and (2)

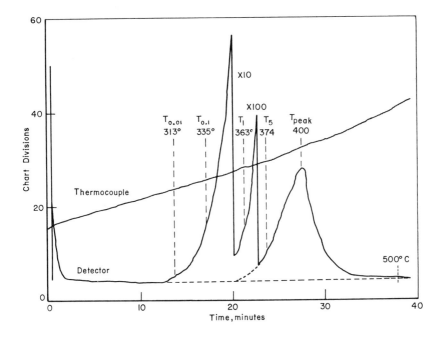

Figure 2-11. Thermal decomposition of polystyrene (sample weight, 0.2 mg; heating rate, 6°C/min). Reprinted by courtesy of the *Journal of Applied Polymer Sciences* (*78*, p. 1174).

continuous heating which insures complete recovery of the volatiles, but gives poor resolution. The lower detection limit of this technique was estimated at about 10 ppm which corresponds to 0.01 μg in the 1-mg sample.

Other characteristics useful for identifying polymers may be obtained from pyrograms on controlled pyrolysis occurring in (1) an oxidizing or reducing atmosphere, (2) the presence of depolymerization catalysts, (3) the presence of nonvolatile acids or bases, (4) the presence of hydrolytic agents, or (5) the presence of ionizing radiations from various sources (radioactive substances, lasers, high-intensity, UV emitters).

Gas chromatographic analysis of polymers after oxidative degradation has been briefly explored (*79*). The polymer was packed in the precolumn with a suitable support. The precolumn was thermostated at 203°C and 1 ml of oxygen was injected. The oxidation products entered the chromatographic column as a plug and gave typical chromatograms.

The same support must be used to obtain reproducible chromatograms. The procedure could be applied to rank the relative severity of oxidative degradation and to observe the effect of various additives, such as catalysts or antioxidants. Perry(80) has suggested pyrolysis of polymers containing labeled monomers and initiators tagged with radioactive tracers, and studying the fragments separated by gas chromatography. A pair of detectors, one being a radio-assaying detector such as a flow-proportional counter, used in parallel would give valuable information of the polymer structure and mechanism of polymerization.

Laser-induced polymer decompositions have not been studied in detail. Giles et al.(81) decomposed a carbon-filled phenolic resin within a mass spectrometer. The products produced by the intense power never exceeded mass number 100. Laser input from 5×10^5 to 8×10^8 W gave the same decomposition products, which differ considerably from those obtained in thermal decomposition. Recently a pyrolysis apparatus using a pulsed ruby laser has been described(81a). Comparison of the chromatograms obtained with this laser apparatus for black polyethylene and polyethylene DYLT and rubber and neoprene gave simpler chormatograms and allowed greater distinction than did the pyrograms obtained on degradation with a filament or tube furnace type heater. It would be of interest to investigate the mechanism of laser-induced degradation of a variety of polymers using vapor phase chromatography and other instrumental methods for characterizing products. The high energy conditions causing this decomposition are the nearest analogy to a plasma. Thus, such studies may be useful in determining ablative properties of polymeric materials.

Mercury-sensitized decomposition by means of high intensity UV radiation appears promising(82). Advantages of this technique include the relative ease with which reproducible results may be obtained and the simplicity of the apparatus. Although most of the work in this field has been with gas and liquid samples, preliminary degradation of polymeric solid materials has also proved successful.

Peak identification of the pyrolyzates is often a major problem. Especially in mechanistic studies, where a knowledge of the identity of the pyrolysis products is essential, the chromatographic fractions must be further analyzed. The products eluted from the chromatograph can be condensed and identified from their IR(56a,85b) and mass spectra (61,85b). Many chemical identification methods have been used in conjunction with gas chromatographic analysis(82a). The principal method involves reactive columns, such as columns for the selective removal of components, catalytic hydrogenation, dehydration, desulfurization, and reagent precolumns. Carbon–hydrogen–nitrogen analysis may also be employed. Vapors eluted from a column may be passed through reactors after gas chromatographic separations. Titrimetric and coulometric detection to identify gas chromatographic effluents are also feasible.

Merritt and Walsh(83) employ a stream splitter, attached to the exit tube from the thermal conductivity cell, that allows the effluent to bubble through a vial containing an appropriate classification reagent. Results of group classification tests, when used in conjunction with retention volume data from the corresponding pyrograms, often give positive identification of the components of a mixture. Casu and Cavallotti(84) describe a simple device that reveals the presence of functional groups in effluents by spots which develop with qualitative reagents on a horizontally advancing strip just beneath the exit tube. The rate of advancement of the strip is the same as is shown on the recorder chart. By incorporation of a stream splitter, it should be possible to analyze a number of functional groups in a single operation. Combining PGC and thin-layer chromatography (TLC) also is feasible by incorporating a GC column into a setup similar to that described by Rogers(85) or Kaiser(85a). This procedure involves programing a thin-layer chromatographic plate across the exit part of a pyrolysis cell as a function of the temperature of the sample. The plate can then be developed to separate the collected components, and specific reagent sprays can be employed to detect the zones of interest. The capabilities of TLC nicely complement those of gas chromatography and mass spectrometry. Thus, permanent gases that can be analyzed by GLC or mass spectrometry cannot be handled by TLC; however, high molecular weight polar compounds that may be difficult to analyze by other methods can be separated and identified by TLC.

Precolumns are sometimes desirable for retaining heavy ends of pyrolyzates and serve to protect the analytical column from contamination. Coupled with backflushing they decrease analysis time and prolong column life.

Removing certain classes of compounds selectively from the original pyrolysis mixture (such as the removal of unsaturated hydrocarbons by passing them through solutions of $Hg(ClO_4)_2$ or H_2SO_4, or the use of molecular sieves to separate branched from unbranched compounds), with the corresponding disappearance of peaks from the pyrograms, has been suggested(*86, 87*). Catalytic alteration of the chemical compounds by means of a reaction chamber in front of the column(*88, 89*) (such as hydrogenation over a heated catalyst, which saturates multiple bonds and replaces halogen, oxygen, sulfur, and nitrogen atoms so that the resulting products are mainly the parent hydrocarbon and/or the next lower homolog) is also possible.

Yasuda(*90*) outlines a procedure for the identification and characterization of polymers by pyrolytic hydrogenation gas chromatography using a slightly modified microhydrogenation unit. A 30% tricresyl phosphate column is first used to group the products into light aliphatic and aromatic products. Reasonably good retention measurements for aromatic products are obtained for this column. If the light aliphatic products need separation, a 25% hexadecane column coated on 40–60 mesh acid-washed C-22 firebrick is recommended. With complex pyrograms such as those obtained from elastomers, a third sample is pyrolyzed with the hydrogenation unit attached. The hydrogenated products are chromatographed on the hexadecane column. By comparing the relative retention times of the pyrolysis products with those of authentic samples, the products can be identified. In Fig. 2-12 the pyrograms of natural rubber using a tricresyl phosphate (TCP) and hexadecane (HD) column and after microhydrogenation using an HD column, are shown. From 60 to 150 μg samples are generally used, but it is possible to identify 5×10^{-8} g of polymeric material.

Dimbat and Eggertsen(*91*) describe a similar pyrolysis-GC instrument. They could determine ethylene–propylene copolymer coated on paper in concentrations down to 0.001 wt% which corresponds to only 0.2 μg of polymer. When such small samples are analyzed, it is important to elute the components of interest from the column in the shortest possible time to avoid their spreading in the column and thus maximizing the peak-to-noise ratio. Very short $\frac{1}{8}$ in. columns that will reduce lateral diffusion are therefore preferable. The low flow rates used in these columns make it important that the detector as well as the sample injector have small volumes. It has been shown that with no additional complexity to the standard technique, it is possible to employ exceedingly small samples down to the picogram level with the aim of approaching the hypothetical concept of a "polymer monolayer"(*92*). Samples of 1 μg or less may produce simpler fragmentation patterns than do samples of greater weight, perhaps because of the elimination of secondary reactions occurring during migration of primary degradation fragments through a hot polymer mass. Thermal depolymerizations conducted on the micro-

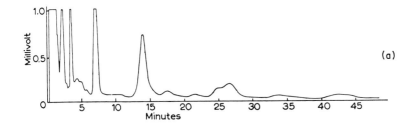

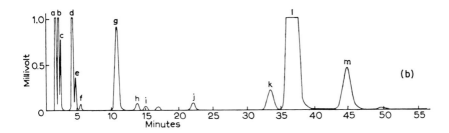

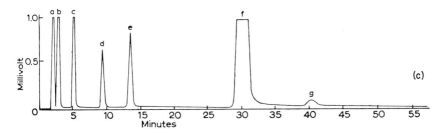

Figure 2-12. Pyrogram of natural rubber. Pyrolysis temperature, 950°C (max) in 10 sec heating. (a) From tricresyl phosphate column on 40–60 mesh acid-washed C-22 firebrick. Column temp., 100°C; sample weight, 0.10 mg. (b) From hexadecane column on 40–60 mesh acid-washed C-22 firebrick. Column temp., 27°C; sample weight, 0.13 mg. Identification of pyrolysis products: a = ethylene or acetylene; b = methane; c = ethane; d = propylene; e = propyne; f = propane; g = isobutylene, 1-butene or 1,3-butadiene; h = *trans*-2-butene; i = *cis*-2-butene; j = 3-methyl-1-butene; k = 2-methyl-1-butene; l = 2-methyl-1,3-butadiene; m = 2-methyl-2-butene. (c) Microhydrogenation of pyrolysis products. Chromatographic and pyrolysis condition same as for (b) pyrogram. Catalyst, 9 ft × ¼ in. aluminum tubing packed with 20% platinum coated on 60–80 mesh acid-washed Chromosorb W, hydrogenation temp., 225°C, sample size, 0.10 mg. Identification of hydrogenated products: a = methane; b = ethane; c = propane; d = isobutane; e = *n*-butane; f = 2-methyl-butane; g = *n*-pentane. Reprinted by courtesy of the *Journal of Gas Chromatography* (*90*, p. 79).

73

scale often do not give quantitative yields of monomer; surprisingly, at the submicro level a similar situation is encountered.

For most pyrolytic work the hydrogen flame ionization detector (FID) is now the detector of choice because of its greater sensitivity as compared to the thermal conductivity detectors (TCD). The response of the FID is dependent on many factors that must be carefully controlled, if good repeatability is to be obtained(93). The packed columns with a TCD give simpler pyrograms while open tubular columns combined with a FID show more characteristic pyrograms. The FID does not respond to certain compounds, such as water and the oxides of carbon. When these components are to be determined, another detector, such as the TCD should be employed and the sample size should be increased to 0.1 mg. However, some polymer pyrolyzates such as cellulose esters contain much water, which makes detection with a TCD impossible. Electron capture detectors in combination with a microcoulometer are most useful for analyzing pyrolyzates containing nitrogen, sulfur, or halide-containing compounds.

Franck and Wünscher(93a) analyzed the total gaseous reaction products with a TCD and the organic products with a FID. Helium and nitrogen were the carrier gases. Nitrogen served as a molecular weight standard; gases of molecular weight above or below 28 produced, respectively, negative or positive responses of the TCD.

Even greater sensitivity can be obtained with a thermionic ionization gauge in combination with a mass analyzer which can detect quantities as low as 10^{-11} g of low molecular weight or thermally unstable compounds(94). Use of a mass spectrometer as a detector and analyzer for column effluents has also been suggested(61, 95–98a). Since with this procedure thermal fragmentations can be easily performed in the 0.01- to 0.001-μg range, it is the method of choice for the identification of components that are poorly resolved on chromatographic columns.

Amy et al.(98) have described the advantages of analyzing individual trapped fractions in lieu of the analysis of gas chromatographic effluents directly entering the ion source of a mass spectrometer. They also discussed the shortcomings of the various trapping techniques to collect individual fractions for subsequent mass spectrometric analysis. A recent study(99) suggests trapping of fractions by a small capillary tube packed with 20 mg of activated coconut charcoal 70–100 mesh, and plugged with glass wool to collect the effluent fractions.

Parsons(100) investigated the Gow-Mac density detector for molecular weight determination of certain volatile pyrolysis products from polymers as an aid in identification of these substances. By using several carrier gases and in particular a carrier gas of higher and lower molecular weight than the unknown substance, the molecular weight of the unknown may be bracketed with good accuracy. The positive and negative peaks obtained (depending on whether the unknown substance has a higher or lower molecular weight than the carrier gas) often serve to classify a complex mixture in a molecular weight range. This qualitative information is very useful with columns where the retention times of polar substances are not related to the order of molecular weight or boiling point. The author demonstrated the application of this technique to molecular weight determinations on two peaks present in the pyrolysis products of polyethylene glycol adipate and polypropylene glycol adipate.

2-3 QUANTITATIVE ESTIMATION OF COPOLYMER COMPOSITION

Quantitative data for copolymer compositions can be obtained from (1) peak heights or areas of pyrolyzates of samples of known weight, or (2) peak height or area ratios for peaks that are characteristic for each component. Both methods involve direct comparison with calibration curves obtained from polymers of known composition. Polymer decomposition is sensitive to minor changes in pyrolysis conditions. Hence, quantitative analysis requires more stringent control than is necessary for strictly qualitative identification. Such factors as total sample size, state of subdivision, mode of packing, and attainment of equilibrium temperature often affect the yield of a particular product. Preliminary experiments with homopolymers allow the selection of a suitable pyrolysis temperature. Copolymer compositions are then estimated by referring to the appropriate calibrations for the components present.

Every effort must be made to avoid condensation on the walls of the column. This requires location of the pyrolyzer within the heated zone of the gas chromatographic column.

Figure 2-13 gives pyrograms of typical SBR-polybutadiene vulcanizates and a calibration curve relating peak height ratio to weight per cent styrene(42). Esposito(101) has demonstrated the applicability of the internal standardization technique used with pyrolytic gas chromatography for the quantitative analysis of methacrylate, styrene, and styrenated alkyd resins in various coating systems. Pyrolysis of methyl methacrylate-ethylene dimethacrylate copolymer gives only

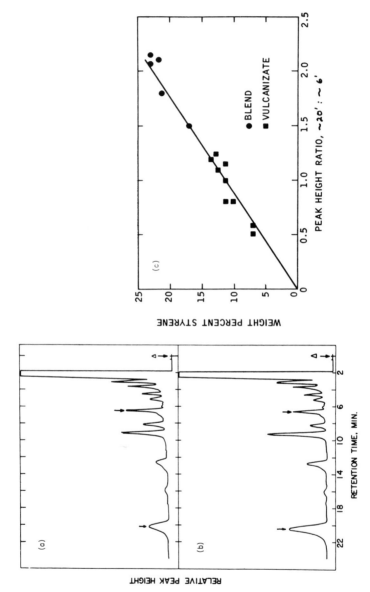

Figure 2-13. Pyrograms of typical SBR-polybutadiene vulcanizates for (a) low styrene content and (b) high styrene content (arrows indicate peaks used for quantitative styrene analysis), and (c) calibration curve for styrene content of SBR-PBD blends and vulcanizates. Reprinted by courtesy of *Analytical Chemistry* (42, p. 1210).

one major peak (methyl methacrylate) using a hot-filament detector. The composition of methyl methacrylate-ethylene dimethacrylate copolymer can, however, be determined by pyrolyzing a weighed sample and using the ratio of sample weight to area of the methyl methacrylate peak for obtaining a standard analysis curve (Fig. 2-14) *(28)*. Under favorable conditions and with careful control of the pyrolysis column and detector variables, constituents can be determined within ± 0.5%. Table 2-1 lists some of the copolymers that have been successfully analyzed by this technique. Cole et al. *(51)*, by using simultaneous flame ionization and electron capture (dual channel) chromatography, were able to quantitatively determine the polymer composition in compounded cured rubber stocks such as the following blends: natural rubber in NR/cis(polybutadiene)-4, neoprene in CR/NBR (nitrile-butadiene), butyl in IIR (isobutylene-isoprene)/CR, Hypalon (CSM) in Hypalon/CR, acrylonitrile in NBR, and NBR in SBR/NBR (styrene-butadiene). The presence of carbon black and other compounding agents did not alter the characteristics of the pyrolyzate. This may well be in part because of the relatively low

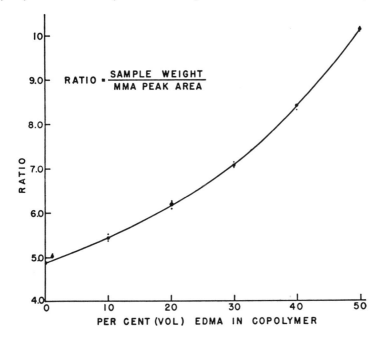

Figure 2-14. Standard curve for analysis of a methyl methacrylate-ethylene dimethacrylate copolymer. Reprinted by courtesy of *Analytical Chemistry (28*, p. 456).

TABLE 2-1

Some Copolymer Compositions Quantitatively Analyzed by PGC

Copolymer system	Ref.
Ethyl acrylate–styrene	*68a*
Methyl methacrylate–ethyl acrylate	*68a,102,103*
Methyl methacrylate–n-butyl acrylate	*102*
Methyl methacrylate–ethyl methacrylate	*28,77,102*
Methyl methacrylate–butyl acrylate	*68a*
Methyl methacrylate–n-propyl methacrylate	*102*
Methyl methacrylate–n-butyl methacrylate	*102*
Methyl methacrylate–ethylene dimethacrylate	*28*
Methyl methacrylate–styrene	*32,77,92,103a*
Butyl methacrylate–hexyl methacrylate	*104*
Vinyl chloride–vinyl acetate	*32,77*
Vinyl acetate copolymer	*105*
Vinyl chloride–methyl methacrylate	*77*
Vinyl acetate–butyl acrylate	*106*
Vinyl acetate–butyl maleate	*106*
Vinyl acetate–2-ethylhexyl acrylate	*106*
Vinyl acetate–2-ethylhexyl maleate	*106*
Vinylidene chloride–methyl methacrylate	*107a*
Linear and branched polyethylene	*107*
Ethylene–vinyl acetate	*108*
Ethylene–ethyl acrylate	*108*
Ethylene–propylene	*69,108a*
Ethylene–propylene. coated on paper	*91*
Ethylene–propylene. block and random copolymer	*46,42*
Ethylene–butene	*69,109*
Ethylene–isobutylene	*109a*
Ethylene–methyl acrylate. block and random copolymers	*68*
Ethylene–methyl methacrylate. block and random copolymers	*68*
Ethylene–styrene (graft)	*110*
Ethylene–propylene–dicyclopentadiene terpolymer	*69,111*
Propylene–butene-1	*69*
Propylene–styrene (graft)	*112*
Dacron–wool	*57a*
Dacron–cotton	*57a*
Elastomers	*42,51,113,114–114b*
SBR–polybutadiene	*42*
SBR–chloroprene	*114d*
Phenol, 3-methylphenol, and 3,5-dimethylphenol–formaldehyde	*115*
Resin content in thermosetting composites	*116a*
Resin additives in polychloroprene adhesives	*56a*
Ethylene oxide–propylene oxide	*109*
Polyaryl polyisocyanate in urethane foam	*85b*
Cellulose esters	*42,114c*
Cellulose ethers	*114c*
Hydroxyethyl group in hydroxyethyl starch	*116*
Plasticizer in polymer	*64*

concentration of most of the compounding ingredients, and also because their pyrolysis products are of relatively high molecular weight. Similar results were obtained for NR/SBR, NR/BR (butadiene), and SBR/BR systems(*113*). The reliability of the analytical data were within 2–3%, which appears better than the $\leq$ 6% claimed for the analysis of similar copolymers by pyrolysis and subsequent analysis of the products by IR spectroscopy(*117*). For the analysis of propylene in both raw and vulcanized ethylene-propylene (EPM) copolymers, pyrolysis at 450°C, followed by measurement of the strong absorption bands at 909 and 889 cm^{-1} that vary in intensity according to propylene concentration, seems to be comparable to chromatographic methods(*118*). However, thin-film IR techniques are sensitive to the degree of alteration and to the presence of polyethylene and polypropylene crystallinity as well as to composition.

Essentially all of the present-day automotive tires are made with elastomers of the following kind: natural rubber, styrene-butadiene, and *cis*-1,4-polybutadiene rubber in various compositions. For this NR/SBR/BR terpolymer, the pyrolysis–IR technique of MacKillop (*119*) appears to be the method of choice for the rapid routine analysis of these three elastomers in vulcanized rubber compounds.

Lehrle and Robb(*77*) estimated the composition of various copolymers within ±2% (Table 2-2). Even higher accuracies were obtained by Jones and Reynolds(*92*) for styrene–methyl methacrylate and styrene–ethyl acrylate copolymers.

TABLE   2-2

Percentage of Vinyl Chloride in Vinyl Chloride–Vinyl
Acetate Copolymers[a]

By chlorine estimation (mean of 2 results)	By IR analysis (±1%)	By degradation (±2%)
60.8 ± 0.6	54.7	55.8
69.4 ± 0.1	64.4	65.2
74.1 ± 0.3	72.3	72.2
69.1 ± 0.9	66.7	67.8
81.8 ± 4.4	84.8	83.9
87.9 ± 1.0	89.0	87.7

[a]Reprinted(*77*, p. 90) by courtesy of Preston Technical Abstracts Co.

Two copolymers of the same over-all composition may differ widely in the way the two types of monomer units are distributed in the polymer molecule. The pyrogram of a copolymer depends on the sequence-length distribution. The differences in the pyrograms of block and random copolymers allow estimation of the comonomer distribution. For ethylene–propylene copolymers, this is illustrated in Fig. 2-15(69). The two extremes of a 1:1 ethylene–propylene copolymer are the completely alternating copolymer and the copolymer in which the molecule consists of one long block of ethylene units and one long block of propylene units. The former type of ethylene–propylene copolymer is structurally identical with a completely hydrogenated rubber, whereas the latter type will in many respects behave like an intimate mixture of the two homopolymers. In the third idealized copolymer, the monomer sequence–length distribution corresponds to a random insertion of the two monomers. In Fig. 2-15 the main peaks of the pyrogram containing about 50 mole% ethylene are compared with those of the pyrograms of hydrogenated natural rubber and a 1:1 molar mixture of polyethylene and polypropylene. The copolymer with nearly random monomer distribution gives a pyrogram with peak heights intermediate between the two extremes. Pyrograms for the

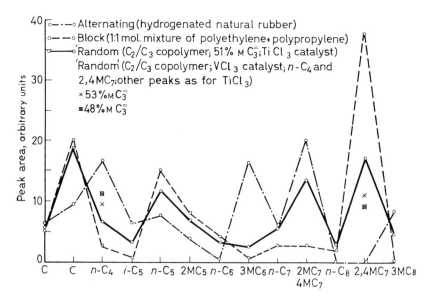

Figure 2-15.   Pyrograms of ethylene-propylene copolymer   Reprinted by courtesy of *Polymer*(69, p. 562).

copolymer prepared with a γ-TiCl$_3$-containing catalyst differ from those prepared with a VCl$_3$-containing catalyst only in the n-butane (n-C$_4$) and 2,4-dimethylheptane (2,4-MC$_7$) peaks. On plotting the ratios of heights of the 2,4-MC$_7$ to n-C$_4$ peaks versus composition, differences in the degree of alteration between these copolymers show up very clearly.

Ethylene–propylene copolymers prepared with VOR$_3$ catalysts contain methylene sequences of two units, thus indicating a tail-to-tail coupling of two propylene units and/or the presence of one ethylene unit between two head-to-head propylene units(*120,121*). The characteristic peaks for methylene sequences of two units are the 2,5-dimethylhexane (2,5-MC$_6$), the 3-methyl-heptane (3-MC$_7$), and the 4-methyloctane (4-MC$_8$) peaks. Indeed, copolymers synthesized with VOCl$_3$ catalyst give pyrograms with markedly higher 2,5-MC$_6$, 3-MC$_7$, and 2- and 4-MC$_8$ peaks (indicative of the presence of three methylene units) than those of any of the copolymers prepared with other catalyst systems. This result is a good illustration of the potentialities of PGC in the elucidation of polymer structure.

Etyylene–propylene copolymers of identical overall composition, 23 and 24 mole% propylene, respectively, differed in the amount of isoalkanes in the C$_5$ to C$_{15}$ region(*75a*). The sample with 4% crystallinity, as determined by X-ray diffraction measurements, yielded more branched chain fragments than the one with a more pronounced block structure and 30% crystallinity. Nearly amorphous samples with less than 1% crystallinity can be distinguished from their pyrograms. X-ray patterns of these copolymers exhibited nearly vanishing crystalline 110-reflexes. A significant change in the shift in the position of the maximum of the amorphous halo occurred. This seems to be consistent with differences in the "amorphous" blockiness of the copolymers. Further results suggest that for a wide range of ethylene–propylene compositions synthesized under kinetically controlled conditions, the distribution of the straight chain fragments is almost identical with the actual sequence length distribution of the ethylene units, as calculated by kinetic theory. Best fit has been observed in samples with relatively short sequences of the comonomeric units. Satisfactory correlation between theoretical and experimental values of the propylene sequence length distribution has been found in samples with nearly equimolar composition.

Random copolymers of ethylene with methyl acrylate or methyl methacrylate yield on pyrolysis a lower ratio of methanol/methyl acrylate or methyl methacrylate, respectively, than do block polymers of the same composition (Fig. 2-16)(*68*). DTA measurements give a first-order transition for block polymers only, and by measuring the area under the transition an indication of the minimum chain length between acrylate units can be obtained.

The styrene content of a copolymer of styrene grafted onto polyethylene can be determined to within 10% by pyrolyzing the sample at 750°C and analyzing the products on a column of polyoxyethylene glycol supported on Kieselguhr(*110*). The determination of the composition of grafted polypropene and of polypropene–polystyrene mixtures has also been reported(*112*).

The sequence concentration of triads in molecular chains of vinylidene chloride–vinyl chloride copolymers over a wide range of copolymer compositions can be determined by PGC(*119a*). Using a furnace-type pyrolyzer with a sample holder with very small heat capacity, pyrograms of 0.1- to 0.3-mg samples of the polymers and the copolymer at 430°C were obtained. The main degradation product of poly(vinyl chloride) was benzene, while poly(vinylidene chloride) yielded monomer and 1,3,5-trichlorobenzene. Copolymers with a high vinylidene chloride content yielded large amounts of *m*-dichlorobenzene besides vinylidene chloride and trichlorobenzene while those

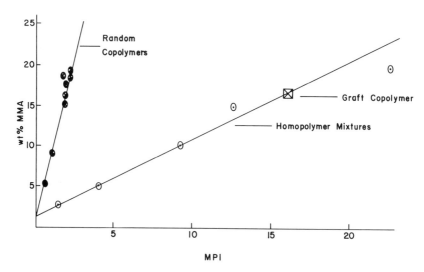

Figure 2-16. Relationship of major pyrolyzate index (MPI) to methyl methacrylate (MMA) content for ethylene–methyl methacrylate copolymers. MPI = area MMA peak/ (area C_8 peak/1-mole fraction MMA in resin). Reprinted by courtesy of *Analytical Chemistry*(*68*, p. 1836).

with a high vinyl chloride content yielded monochlorobenzene in addition to benzene, vinylidene chloride, and 1,3,5-trichlorobenzene. The relative yield of each component was calculated from the peak area on the pyrograms, making molecular sensitivity corrections for the flame ionization detector, and was used to calculate the triad contrations. The experimentally determined concentrations of triads agreed with those calculated from the copolymerization theory. Similarly, the distributions of chlorinated polyethylenes with various chlorine to carbon ratios were studied(*119b*). The experimental results, in which the concept of random terpolymerization between C_2H_4, vinyl chloride, and 1,2-dichloroethylene was adopted, were in fairly good agreement with those obtained by IR spectroscopy.

Only recently, detailed studies using PGC to gain insight into polymer microstructure have been conducted. Deur-Siftar(*107*) describes a procedure for the characterization of polyethylenes of high and low density with various degrees of branching and of crystallinity. Using a specially developed pyrolyzer(*122*), he analyzed the most volatile fractions because of the characteristic changes in their composition that take place with changes in structure of the polyolefin. These characteristic differences in the amount of unsaturated compounds are much more distinctive at moderate degradation temperatures than at high pyrolysis temperatures. Since the amount of butadiene and butenes obtained at a pyrolysis temperature of 500° to 600°C depends strongly on the presence of linear and branched polyethylene chains, two indices were devised from peak height ratios of the related compounds:

BI = peak height ratio of butadiene to butene isomers;
BI¹ = peak height ratio of [propylene + pentene isomers] to butene isomers

To obtain the composition of blends, the BI index is determined for the blend and each constituent separately. The percentage of the constituent can then be estimated to better than 2%, using the equation

$$\% \text{ of low density component} = \frac{BI_s - BI_H}{BI_L - BI_H} \cdot 100$$

where BI_s, BI_H, and BI_L are the respective indices for the sample under investigation and the high and low density polyethylenes, respectively.

There is a linear relationship between the density of branched polyethylenes and the BI′ indices.

An empirical relationship,

$$\% \text{ crystallinity} = \frac{BI'}{3.5} \cdot 100$$

allowed the determination of the crystallinity of the samples. Comparison of the values obtained by this procedure showed agreement within 5% with the broad-line NMR values for high density polyethylenes and within 0.5% of those obtained by normal density data for low density polyethylenes. (Table 2-3).

However, fractionated polyethylenes in the range of 23,000 to 1,050,000 gave identical pyrolysis products. Similarly, polystyrenes of different molecular weight gave the same pyrograms when pyrolyzed at the same temperature (*123*).

Perry (*25*) observed that the pyrolyzate of polybutadiene containing a high percentage of 1,2 links, has a higher ethylene-to-butadiene ratio (is richer in branched olefin fragments) than the polymer containing mainly 1,4-butadiene (Table 2-4). This difference should make it possible to develop a quantitative determination for these components in polybutadiene. Such a procedure could be valuable for the structural determinations of microquantities that cannot be analyzed by the established spectroscopic methods.

Using 0.05 mg samples and a pyrolysis temperature of 550°C, Vacherot (*124*) observed that 1,4-*cis*- and 1.4-*trans*-polyisoprenes yield a ratio of dipentene/isoprene of about 0.3. The 3,4-polyisoprene

TABLE 2-3

Comparison of the Degree of Crystallinity Found by PGC, NMR, and Density Data[a]

	Crystallinity degree determined by		
Sample	PGC %	NMR %	Density %
Hostalen	84.5	89.4	—[b]
Marlex	83.0	87.0	—
Okiten F-12	52.6	—	52.5
Alkathene XHB-48	51.9	—	51.5
Okiten WNC-18	48.4	—	48.5
Polythene G-03	49.1	—	49.1

[a]Reprinted (*107*, p. 76) by courtesy of Preston Technical Abstracts Co.
[b]Data not available.

TABLE 2-4

Pyrolysis Products of Polybutadienes Containing Varying Percentages of 1,2-Links[a]

% 1,2 links	Ratio ethylene/butadiene
18	3.3
32	4.0
63	5.3
79	7.0

[a]Reprinted(25, p. 79) by courtesy of Preston Technical Abstracts Co.

yields another degradation product, presumably a *cis*-hydrocarbon. Plotting the ratio of the peak area of the unidentified peak to that of dipentene versus percentage of 3,4- and 1,4-isoprene in the polymer as determined by NMR, yields a linear relationship that can be used to estimate the amount of 1,4- and 3,4-additions in this type of synthetic polyisoprene.

Jernejcik and Premru(125) found differences in the pyrograms of natural and synthetic polyisoprenes pyrolyzed at 550°–750°C. From the pyrograms it appeared that more components of higher volatility are obtained from synthetic isoprene than from natural rubber. The authors suggested that these results could be used for investigating structural differences between unvulcanized natural and synthetic polyisoprene rubbers. However, differences in the pyrograms of vulcanized natural rubber and synthetic rubber were small. Thus the procedure is not suitable for the study of vulcanized samples.

Quantitative structural characteristics of phenol–formaldehyde polycondensates can also be obtained from PGC. These polycondensates are three-dimensional reticulate macromolecules. Most of the bridges between the aromatic rings are CH_2 groups that are bonded in *o* or *p* positions with respect to the phenolic group. Some ether bridges can also be present if the resins are not highly cross-linked. The presence in the pyrolysis products of *m*-cresol or of polymethylphenols; having a methyl group in the 3 or 5 position indicates that such phenols were present in the original synthesis mixture because there are few CH_2 bridges in the *m* position in the phenol-formaldehyde resins. Thus, during pyrolysis, additional methyl groups can occur only in the *o* and/ or *p* positions. Indeed, Martinez and Guiochon(115) found that there exists a quantitative relationship between the concentration of phenol,

3-methylphenol, and 3,5-xylenol in the pyrolysis products of a resin and in the mixtures used to prepare this resin (Table 2-5). Similarly, Wiley and coworkers(*126,127*) correlated structure and pyrolytic degradation kinetics of copolymers of styrene or methyl methacrylate with pure *m*- and *p*-divinylbenzene. These investigators showed that the products derived from the meta-disubstituted structural unit in the meta cross-linked copolymers appear more rapidly than do those from the para-disubstituted units in the para-copolymer structures. Furthermore, the relative rates of appearance of the disubstituted fragments are related to the distribution of the divinyl derived units in the network.

Use of the volatile products of polymer pyrolysis as a calibrating mixture for gas chromatographic columns has been suggested(*127a*).

TABLE 2-5

Relationship Between Composition of Phenolic Components Used in Their Synthesis and Composition of Their Pyrolysis Products[a]

Raw material, mole %			Pyrolysis products, mole %		
Phenol	3-Methyl-phenol	3,5-Dimethyl-phenol	Phenol	3-Methyl-phenol	3,5-Dimethyl-phenol
100	—[b]	—	100	Trace	—
—	100	—	4.7	93.8	1.8
—	—	100	3.6	4.6	91.8
33.3	33.3	33.3	32.4	34.4	33.2
50.0	33.3	16.7	48.4	34.4	17.2
33.3	16.7	50.0	29.6	21.1	49.3
16.7	50.0	33.3	16.9	47.0	36.1

[a]Reprinted(*115*, p. 150) by courtesy of Preston Technical, Abstracts Co.
[b]Data not available.

2-4   ANALYSIS OF PYROLYSIS PRODUCTS

Gas chromatography offers a rapid means of analysis of volatile pyrolyzates and study of the mechanism and kinetics of degradation which until a few years ago were often done by more time-consuming separations or by mass spectrometry. Similar to other pyrolytic techniques, results are dependent on the experimental conditions employed. Since in the flash pyrolysis the degradative reactions do not proceed to equilibrium, their extent depends not only on the pyrolysis temperature, but is also influenced by such factors as rate of flow of carrier gas, geometry of the reaction chamber, sample size and sample mounting, and rate of cooling of the products. An ideal reactor should have a large heating area in relation to the sample. The temperature should rise as rapidly as possible to the required temperature and then cool as quickly as possible at the end of the degradation period in order to define closely the duration of the degradation. The need for small sample size and high level of temperature control (including a consideration not only of temperature rise time but also the fall time after switching off power to the filament, wire, or furnace) should be emphasized. For kinetic studies the measured rates of decomposition must be independent of the thickness of the sample, otherwise it cannot be assumed that the specific pyrolysis rate is being measured. For small samples where film thickness of the order of 200 Å may be required, about 10^{-8} g of the sample can be deposited on the filament with a pipette of 10^{-4} ml capacity and sample concentrations of 5×10^{-4} g/ml. Any solvent that has not evaporated is removed by heating the sample to 50° to 70°C, and the filament is replaced in the degradation unit. The possibility of using valving to prevent egress to the column of pyrolysis products formed on the cooling pyrolyzer has been suggested(*33a*). At the low sample levels, losses of pyrolysis products on walls become a severe problem. However, more sophisticated pyrolyzers, either of the Curie-point type or featuring feedback temperature control and improved flow control, should alleviate many shortcomings of the present generation of instruments.

For many determinations the flash pyrolyzers described above are quite satisfactory. Many of the variables associated with filament-type heaters in studying the kinetics of polymer decomposition have been discussed by Barlow et al.(*128*). As can be seen from Fig. 2-17, the rate of decomposition is dependent on sample thickness down to a film thickness of about 200–400 Å (*77,128*). Using a capillary column and an argon triode or flame ionization detector, the degradation of samples as small as 10^{-8} g can be studied, since better than 10^{-10} g of the product can be detected. Poor reproducibility of the measurements, arising from the method of mounting the sample and time and temperature errors resulting mainly from the temperature-time profile of the filament, have been overcome by depositing the sample within a limited region of a Nichrome ribbon filament and supplying an initial current boost. Unless complicating factors are present, the evolution of volatiles from a bulk-pyrolyzed polymer follows a first-order rate equation. Thus, a plot of $-\ln(1-x)$ versus time (where x = fractional conversion of original sample) will be linear over the range for which first-order

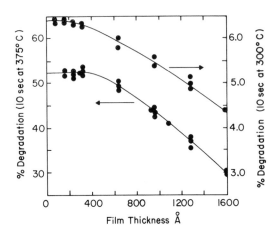

Figure 2-17. The rate of the thermal degradation is ultimately independent of film thickness when the latter is sufficiently small. Polymer, poly(methyl methacrylate). Reprinted by courtesy of the *Journal of Gas Chromatography* (77, p. 94).

conditions apply. A first-order plot for the pyrolysis of fractionated poly(methyl methacrylate), $M_n = 580{,}000$ at 370°C, is shown in Fig. 2-18 (*128*). The graph is linear up to 30% conversion and the observed specific rate k_{obs} can be calculated from this initial gradient. There is a positive intercept of 2.0 ± 0.3 sec on the time axis which corresponds to the sum of the filament-boosting time (1 sec) and the time required for the sample itself to attain the temperature of the filament. A single point determination of conversion at, e.g., 10 sec would provide an erroneously low value of k_{obs} (broken line Fig. 2-18) when inserted into the integrated rate equation.

For closest control of degradation conditions and accurate measurement of temperature, the sample can be pyrolyzed in a vacuum or a closely controlled atmosphere using the apparatus of Madorsky and Straus (*128a*), Sonntag (*128b*), Cramers and Keulemans (*129*), Farre-Rius and Guiochon (*130*), or Garn and Anthony (*131*), that are particularly suited to study the kinetics and thermodynamic aspects of the pyrolysis of volatile organic substances. This is also recommended at temperatures below 350°C where degradation is usually slow and the pyrograms will show tailing. The volatile fractions are collected and should be chromatographed immediately to avoid possible changes in their composition. For example, the pyrolysis products of poly-(methyl methacrylate), degraded at 500° or 800°C in a vacuum, polymerized within 10–12 days to a white solid (*8*). Products degraded

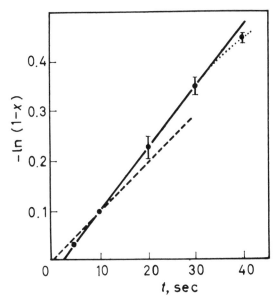

Figure 2-18. First-order plot for the pyrolysis of a poly(methyl methacrylate) fraction (number average molecular weight $\bar{M}_n$ = 580,000) at 370°C. The broken line through the origin illustrates the erroneous specific rate obtained for a single point (10 sec) determination (i.e., zero-error neglected). Reprinted by courtesy of *Polymer*(*128*, p. 534).

at 1200°C did not solidify, probably because of the low monomer content in the reaction mixture. Farre-Rius and Guiochon(*130*), in their studies of the kinetics of polyesters, condensed the high boiling waxy products in a stainless steel coil maintained at 150°C and located at the exit of the pyrolysis tube. These products were recovered after each experiment and weighed. The carrier gas was then passed through two other copper tube traps: an empty tube immersed in a dry-ice bath and a second trap, filled with molecular sieve, immersed in liquid nitrogen. This trap caught the light products that still had a significant vapor pressure at −75°C. Once each hour the contents of the traps were injected rapidly into the chromatograph by heating the traps to 300°C within 20 seconds. A commutation system placed the traps into the circuit of either a chromatograph equipped with a flame ionization detector and a temperature programer, or a second chromatograph with a catherometer detector and a silica gel column. The instrument operated at room temperature and permitted the analysis of the gaseous products that were released from the last trap. This trapping system allowed a quantitative recovery of all volatile products.

A great number of tubular reactors that are incorporated into the chromatograph have been described in the literature (*75,122,131–133*). A commercial version of the pyrolyzer designed by Ettre and Varadi has become commercially available (Fig. 2-19). It utilizes a quartz pyrolysis chamber in an electric furnace. Quartz boats containing the samples can be manipulated by magnets and iron bars into the hot zone. The carrier gas sweeps the products rapidly out of the chamber to reduce the possibility of secondary reactions. An easily constructed pyrolyzer (Fig. 2-20) is based on a similar design (*133*). A $\frac{3}{8}$ in. o.d. quartz tube is surrounded by a small tube furnace. The tube tapers to $\frac{1}{4}$ in as it leaves the furnace. The inlet end of the tube is connected by means of a Swagelok union and flexible polyethylene tubing to the outlet port of the gas sample valve. The exit end of the quartz tube is fitted with an adapter which can be fastened directly to the sample inlet port of the gas chromatograph. The temperature of the furnace is controlled by a 2-amp variable transformer. A thermocouple, inserted between the furnace wall and the quartz inner tube, indicates the pyrolysis temperature within ±10°C. This external thermocouple is calibrated against a second thermocouple located in the same position that the sample boat would occupy. The calibration is made with the pyrolyzer demounted and the carrier gas flowing through the tube.

Figure 2-19. Commercial pyrolysis accessory for gas chromatographs. (Courtesy Perkin-Elmer Co.)

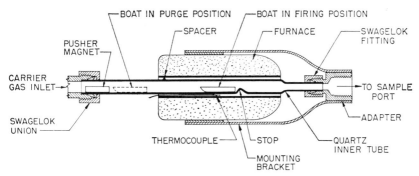

Figure 2-20. A simple furnace-pyrolyzer. Reprinted by courtesy of the *Journal of Gas Chromatography* (*133*, p. 397).

Cramers and Keulemans (*129*) used a tubular reactor especially designed for quantitative studies of thermodynamic aspects of the pyrolysis of volatile organic substances. The reactor (Fig. 2-21) is a metal tube of 1 m length and 1 mm i.d. It is coiled around a silver core and surrounded by a silver jacket. The carrier gas is preheated to the reaction temperature. The reactor has a considerable thermal capacity, thus almost isothermal conditions can be achieved for the endothermic degradation reactions. The reactor dimensions assure that the time for heating and cooling of the reactants is small compared to the reaction time; thus, a negligible spread in residence time of the sample molecules is obtained.

The unit of Prosser et al. (*132*) allows preheating of the inert gas to the pyrolysis temperature and was especially designed to determine the effect of additives such as metals or metallic oxides on pyrolysis reactions and products. The effect of additives on the temperature distribution throughout the sample is minimized by preheating the inert gas to the pyrolysis temperature. In the design of Garn and Anthony (*131*) the sample holder is connected to the sample loop of the gas chromatograph by a long narrow diffusion path. This arrangement causes the decomposition to take place in an atmosphere of its own decomposition product gases, while only a negligible amount is retained within the sample holder and the diffusion path. The decomposition product gases are repetitively sampled into the gas chromatograph by means of a solenoid-operated sampling valve controlled by an adjustable timer. This timer also controls the integration of the chromatographic peaks through a set of time delays.

A knowledge of the degradation mechanism of the polymer under investigation makes it possible to select suitable stationary phases and optimum conditions for the chromatographic separation of the reaction

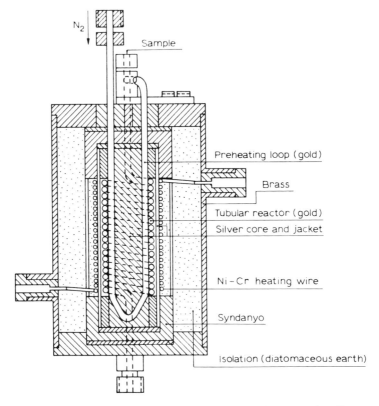

Figure 2-21.   Top view of microreactor for gas phase pyrolyses. Reprinted by courtesy
of the *Journal of Gas Chromatography* (*129*, p. 59).

products. If monomeric products are preponderant, columns that give
favorable elution times for the monomer and also detect dimers, tri-
mers, and low molecular weight homologs should be chosen. If random
degradation occurs, two or more columns of widely varying polarity
should be used. This allows better separation of products which can be
identified by their retention indices. If the products vary widely in
molecular weight and volatility, programed temperature columns are
preferred.

Gas chromatographic procedures have been used to analyze
pyrolysis products and to study degradation mechanisms of many
macromolecules. Some of the polymers studied are listed in Table
2-6. Similar methods should find increasing applications in studies
of the kinetics of polymer degradation over wide ranges of tem-

peratures, and in determining degradative mechanisms of complex molecules. Such measurements are especially useful if they are complemented by other thermal methods of analysis such as thermogravimetric analysis (TGA)(*133a–133c,149*) or differential thermal analysis (DTA)(*68,133c*). If necessary, unknown products can be identified by IR or mass spectrometric analysis(*85b,98a,133c,133d*).

Chiu(*149*) described a combined TG-GC technique which follows the weight changes of a sample as it is heated under controlled conditions, collects the volatiles in a sample trap at various stages as indicated on the TG curve, and then analyzes them intermittently by GC. The technique features precise control of temperature and atmosphere and the use of minimum thermal energy to perform pyrolysis, therefore reducing the production of secondary products and providing simple and reproducible GC scans. This approach is similar to the oven-pyrolysis GC method, except that the extent of pyrolysis is now guided and measured quantitatively by the TG curve. Impurities in the sample, such as solvents, additives, monomers, etc., can be separated prior to pyrolysis of the main species and analyzed by GC. Interaction among impurities and main decomposition products can be minimized and the amount of impurities can be determined from the TG scan.

The coupled TG-GC is a powerful tool for studying polymer blends and copolymers. As shown in the TG scans in Fig. 2-22, poly(α-methylstyrene) is much less stable than polystyrene. A physical mixture of approximately one-to-one ratio, prepared by solution casting techniques, shows an initial weight loss of 2% caused by the volatilization of residual solvent benzene, which can be easily collected and identified by GC. The second weight loss step is a measure of the amount of poly(α-methylstyrene), and the third step, a measure of polystyrene.

The products from the various weight loss steps are analyzed by GC, and their pyrograms are shown as bar graphs in Fig. 2-22 to compare with those of model substances. Pyrolysis of the total mixture shows all the components in a more complex chromatogram. On the other hand, a stepwise analysis provides both qualitative and quantitative determination of each component in the sample.

Differentiation of styrene-methyl methacrylate homopolymer blend and copolymer is based on the comparison of the products which are obtained during the first and last 10–20% of the pyrolysis. A blend of polystyrene and poly(methyl methacrylate) produces predominantly methyl methacrylate (MMA) in the initial stage of decomposition and predominantly styrene in the final stage. On the other hand, a styrene-methyl methacrylate copolymer produces both MMA

TABLE 2-6

Analysis of Polymer Degradation Products by PGC

Polymer	Ref.
Polymethylene	*74,133e*
Polyethylene	*37a,46,134*
Polypropylene	*46,70,134*
Polybutene	*46,134a*
Polyisobutylene	*134c*
Poly-4-methylpentene-1	*46*
Polybutadiene	*134*
Polyisoprene	*134*
Polystyrene	*30,70,77,134,134b*
Poly(ethyl acetate)	*66*
Poly(acrylic acid)	*93a*
Poly(methyl methacrylate)	*30,128,134d*
Poly(*n*-butyl methacrylate)	*30*
Polyacrylonitrile	*77*
Poly(vinyl acetate)	*70*
Poly(vinyl propionate)	*70*
Poly(vinyl alcohol)	*70,75*
Poly(vinyl chloride)	*70,135,133c,135a*
Poly(methyl methacrylate)–poly(vinyl chloride)	*11b*
Poly(vinylidene chloride)	*70*
Polytetrafluoroethylene	*133d,135b*
Copolymer of vinyl chloride–vinylidene chloride	*70*
Copolymers of vinyl acetate with methacrylic, acrylic, and maleic esters	*136*
Polyesters	*130,137,138*
Polycarbonate	*138a,139*
Polyamide	*139a*
Polyamides based on *m*- and *p*-phenelenediamines and iso- and terephthalic acids	*140*
Polyurethane	*85b,139a*
Phenol–formaldehyde	*115,141*
3-Methylphenol–formaldehyde	*115*
3,5-Dimethylphenol–formaldehyde	*115*
Styrene–*m*- and *p*-divinylbenzene copolymer	*127*
Poly-2,2'-(*m*-phenelene)-5,5'-bibenzimidazole	*142*
Cellulose	*98a,143,144,145*
Cellulose triacetate	*143*
Nitrocellulose	*75*
Cellobiose	*144*
Starch	*145b*
Amylomaize starch	*145c*
Paper	*146*
Beechwood	*145a*
Furfuryl resins	*147*
Binder resins in brake linings	*56*
Pitch resins	*148*
Silicone	*133b*

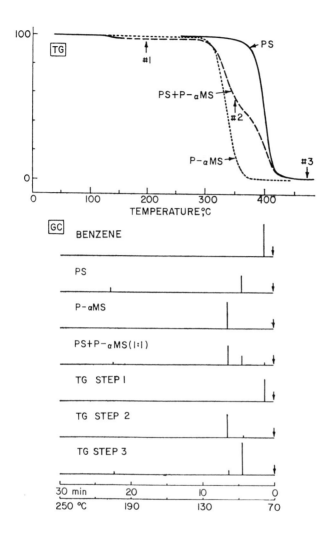

Figure 2-22. TG-GC of polystyrene (PS), poly(α-methylstyrene) (P-αMS), and their blend. TG conditions: sample size, 2 mg; He flow, 160 ml/min; heating rate, 5°C/min. GC conditions: 6 ft × ⅛ in. stainless steel column, containing Chromosorb W(acid-washed, 80–100 mesh) coated with 10% silicone rubber UC W-98. Column temperature programed from 70° to 250°C at 6°C/min. Carrier gas, helium; inlet pressure, 100 psig; flow rate, 30 ml/min. Injection port temperature, 200°C; detector block temperature 250°C. Dual flame hydrogen detector. Reprinted by courtesy of *Analytical Chemistry* (*149*, p. 1518).

95

and styrene monomers as the main products in both the initial and the final stages of decomposition. Furthermore, the production of a relatively large amount of styrene dimer in the case of a homopolymer or a blend, and of only a small amount in a random copolymer, strongly suggests the possibility of using such a technique for studying block and graft copolymers.

Figure 2-23 shows the TG and GC scans for pyrolysis of a low density polyethylene, a poly(vinyl acetate) homopolymer, and an ethylene-vinyl acetate copolymer containing 30 wt% of vinyl acetate. These GC scans were obtained by programing the column from 40° to 240°C. The TG scan shows a two step weight loss. Step 1 liberates mainly acetic acid with a retention time of 3.2 min for either poly(vinyl acetate) or ethylene-vinyl acetate copolymer. Step 2 involves the breakdown of the ethylene segments, producing a pyramidal pyrogram with a series of evenly spaced doublet peaks believed to be homolog unsaturated and saturated normal hydrocarbons. By introducing comonomer units such as vinyl acetate, the ethylene segments are interrupted and the ratio of the homolog peaks is altered. The higher the vinyl acetate content, the larger is the alteration of the regular pattern. Poly(vinyl acetate) homopolymer represents the extreme of such an alteration. By careful analysis of the pyrogram and proper identification of the individual peaks, valuable information can be obtained of the sequence distribution of the copolymer chain.

The degradation products of polycarbonates can be determined by the retention data for pure substances and by spectroscopic analysis(*138a*). The number of end groups per unit weight of poly (4.4′-isopropylidenediphenyl carbonate) is inversely proportional to the molecular weight. Since the molecular weight and percent yield of *p-tert.* butylphenol obtained on degradation is constant, the molecular weight of the polycarbonate can be estimated from the relative yield of the phenol.

The analysis of effluent gases from heated wire and programed pyrolysis of polymers has been reviewed by Kenyon(*150*) and Groten (*151*).

2-5 THERMAL STABILITY

Studies of thermal stability are important in evaluating polymers and in guiding research to new plastics for use as ablative materials, in applications of plastics in a hot environment, or for use as additives in

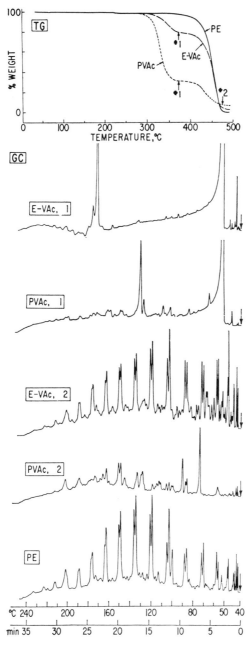

Figure 2-23. TG-GC of polyethylene (PE), poly(vinyl acetate) (PVAc) and, an ethylene-vinyl acetate copolymer (E-VAc). TG and GC conditions same as in Fig. 2-22. Reprinted by courtesy of *Analytical Chemistry* (*149*, p. 1519).

97

such materials as aviation lubricants. Furthermore, such studies allow the determination of the effect of previous history of the sample such as irradiation or the presence of crosslinking agents, stabilizers, additives, or fillers in composite materials. Considerable data exist in the literature concerning the thermal stabilities of various polymers. Methods for determining the rates of pyrolytic decomposition utilize three general techniques: (1) measurement of the weight loss of the sample as a function of temperature (TGA), (2) differential thermal analysis (DTA), and (3) measurement of the amount of volatiles produced. In the last method, the volatiles may be bled into an evacuated system and evaluated by pressure measurements, or the volatiles may be observed in a carrier gas stream with a thermal conductivity detector as described by Rogers et al.(*152*). Ayres and Bens(*153*), Vassalo (*154*), and Eggertsen and Stross(*78*) (the technique used by the last investigators had been described under Section 2-2 on qualitative techniques). Since the filament pyrolyzer can be heated to 1000°C, the method can be used advantageously to test polymers of very high thermal stability. The sensitivity of the method makes it attractive for studying pyrolytic decomposition at low rates. Thus, the first traces of decomposition products are registered immediately, in contrast to TGA methods which require a long time before significant weight changes are observed. In order to observe volatiles that do not respond to the flame ionization detector, another detector, such as a thermal conductivity detector, is necessary. In the case of water, the highly sensitive flame ionization detector can be usefully applied if the water is passed through a calcium carbide column to produce acetylene.

Perry(*25*) describes a technique in which the volatile products in a Perkin-Elmer Differential Scanning Calorimeter (DSC) are swept via a four-way gas sampling valve, either directly and continuously into a hydrogen flame ionization detector or intermittently through a suitable GC column into the detector. This system has the following advantages over TGA; (1) it has much higher sensitivity, making it possible to use smaller samples—this is advantageous for the elimination of temperature gradients; (2) the DSC makes it possible to use a wide range of temperature programing while the atmosphere can be varied as required; (3) simultaneous DTA observations can be made on the heated sample; (4) pyrolysis products can be separated and identified, if necessary.

Ross(*155*) has used PGC to study the degradation of ablative plastics. The technique locates the degradation front and gives quantitative results for the per cent phenolic resin versus the distance normal to the back face of the material. The specimen is carefully machined so as to remove successive 0.020 in. cuts starting with the charred face. Each cut is then analyzed for per cent volatiles by weighing 0.5 mg samples on a platinum ribbon before and after pyrolysis which is conducted at 1000°C for 15 sec in a nitrogen atmosphere. The per cent phenolic resin in each cut is determined by passing the pyrolysis products through a gas chromatograph and using previously prepared calibration curves. The curve of per cent phenolic resin versus distance to the back face of the material shows the zones of charring, partial degradation, and virgin material. Comparison of several curves indicates that the slope of the curve at the inflection point is a function of the heat flux experienced by the material during reentry heating.

Hirsch and Lilyquist(*156*) determined the thermal stability of volatile model compounds related to thermostable polymers by PGC. The weighed sample was volatilized in the pyrolysis zone of a Perkin-Elmer pyrolyzer and the pyrolyzate vapors, together with the unpyrolyzed samples, were swept by means of helium into a temperature-programed gas chromatograph. Comparison of the peak area of the starting material remaining unpyrolyzed at a given temperature, with the peak area of an unpyrolyzed reference sample heated to only 550°C to volatilize but not to decompose the sample, provided the data necessary to obtain a measure of the relative thermostability of the compound in question. In this way, the temperature resistance (per cent decomposition) in the gas phase in an inert medium of 18 model compounds related to thermostable polymer structures was determined at two standard temperatures, 750° and 870°C.

2-6 SUMMARY

The combination of pyrolysis and gas chromatography has become a powerful, almost routine, technique for empirically evaluating polymeric substances by comparison of "fingerprint" fragmentation patterns with those obtained from polymers of known composition. The combination of these methods furnishes a powerful tool in the rapid qualitative characterization of the gross structure of macromolecules, the detection of traces of monomers or volatile impurities, the study of the thermal stability of polymers, and the identification of their pyrolysis products. The shape of the pyrograms is dependent on the structural characteristics, such as the degree of branching or cross-linking, stereoregularity, crystallinity, monomer sequence, and length distribution in block and graft copolymers. Thus, pyrolysis-gas chromatography opens up new avenues in studying the ultimate arrangement of monomeric units within the polymer chain. Analysis of pyrolyzates by gas chromatography is usually preferable to infrared analysis because the former technique is more sensitive, gives more detailed "fingerprint" type information, and can be more readily carried out directly in series with the pyrolysis step.

To obtain reproducible quantitative results, operating conditions must be rigorously controlled. However, an increasing number of methods for the quantitative analysis of random copolymeric systems or copolymer mixtures have been described. The combination of pyrolysis and gas chromatography provides a rapid analysis of the reaction products and hence permits detailed studies of the kinetics of polymer degradation. Since the construction of pyrolysis units is a relatively simple task, many workers have designed their own units. Under carefully controlled conditions, reproducible results may be obtained on a given apparatus. However, data obtained in one laboratory are generally difficult to reproduce quantitatively in another, and this greatly hampers direct comparison and possible compilation of pyrolysis–gas chromatographic data for interlaboratory use.

REFERENCES

1. S. L. Madorsky, *Thermal Degradation of Organic Polymers*, Wiley-Interscience, New York, 1964.
2. N. Grassie, *Chemistry of High Polymer Degradation Processes*, Wiley-Interscience, New York, 1956.
3. H. H. G. Jellinek, *Degradation of Vinyl Polymers*, Academic Press, New York, 1955.
4. L. A. Wall, *SPE J.*, **16**, 810, 1031 (1960).
5. R. W. McKinney, *J. Gas Chromatog.*, **2**, 432 (1964).
6. A. V. Signeur, *Guide to Gas Chromatography Literature*, Plenum Press, New York, 1964.
7. Gas Chromatography Abstracting Service, Preston Technical Abstracts Co., Evanston, Ill.
8. G. M. Brauer, *J. Polymer Sci.*, Part C, **8**, 3 (1965).
9. W. W. Wenlandt, *Thermal Methods of Analysis*, Interscience, New York, 1964.
10. R. Audebert, *Ann. Chim.* (Paris), **3**, 49 (1968).
11. M. Dressler and N. Krejci, *Chem. Listy*, **61**, 1455, 1571 (1967).
11a. S. G. Perry. *Advan. Chromatogr.*, **7**, 221 (1968).
11b. R. S. Lehrle, *Lab. Pract.*, **17**, 696 (1968).
12. W. H. T. Davison, S. Slaney and A. L. Wragg, *Chem. Ind. (London)*, **1954**, 1356.
13. R. L. Levy, *Chromatog. Rev.*, **8**, 48 (1966).
14. L. A. Wall, in *Analytical Chemistry of Polymers* (G. M. Kline, ed.), Vol. II, pp. 249–268, Wiley-Interscience, New York, 1962.
15. G. P. Happ and D. P. Maier, *Anal. Chem.*, **36**, 1678 (1964).
16. S. D. Bruck, *J. Polymer Sci.*, Part A-1, **5**, 2458 (1967).

17. A. V. Amelin, T. M. Muinov, O. F. Pozdnyakov, and V. R. Regel, *Mekh. Polim.*, **1**, 80 (1967).

18. Sadtler Research Laboratories, *Infrared Spectra of Commercial Products, Pyrolyzates*, Philadelphia, Pa.

19. M. Tryon, and E. Horowitz, in *Analytical Chemistry of Polymers* (G. M. Kline, ed.), Vol. II, p. 317, Wiley-Interscience, New York, 1962.

20. M. S. Brash and T. S. Light, *Appl. Spectry.*, **19**, 114 (1965).

21. G. Lindley, *Lab. Pract.*, **14**, 826 (1965).

22. T. Sugita and I. Mitsuko, *Bull. Chem. Soc. Japan*, **38**, 1620 (1965).

23. P. J. Hearst, *J. Paint Technol.*, **39**, (506), 119 (1967).

24. G. J. Rozentals, *Anal. Chem.*, **38**, 334 (1966).

25. S. G. Perry, *J. Gas Chromatog.*, **5**, 76 (1967).

26. R. L. Levy, *J. Gas Chromatog.*, **5**, 107 (1967).

27. F. Farre-Rius and G. Guiochon, *Anal. Chem.*, **40**, 998 (1968).

27a. R. L. Levy and D. L. Fanter, *Anal. Chem.*, **41**, 1465 (1969).

28. J. Strassburger. G. M. Brauer. M. Tryon. and A. F. Forziati. *Anal. Chem.*. **32**. 454 (1960).

29. W. M. Barbour, *J. Gas Chromatog.*, **3**, 228 (1965).

30. F. A. Lehmann and G. M. Brauer, *Anal. Chem.*, **33**, 673 (1961).

31. C. E. R. Jones and A. F. Moyles, *Nature*, **191**, 663 (1961).

32. A. R. Barlow, S. Lehrle, and J. C. Robb, *Polymer*, **2**, 27 (1961).

33. J. A. Cogliano, *Rev. Sci. Instr.*, **34**, 439 (1963).

33a. S. G. Perry, *J. Chromatogr. Sci.*, **7**, 193 (1969).

34. J. Voigt and W. G. Fischer, *Chemiker Ztg.*, **88**, 919 (1964).

35. W. E. Harris and H. W. Habgood, *Programmed Temperature Gas Chromatography*, John Wiley, New York, 1966.

36. W. Simon, P. Krinsler, J. A. Voellmin, and H. Steiner, *J. Gas Chromatog.*, **5**, 53 (1967).

37. H. Simon and H. Giacobbo, *Angew. Chem.*, *(Int. Ed.)* **4**, 938 (1965).

37a. F. W. Willmott, *J. Chromatogr. Sci.*, **7**, 101 (1969).

38. S. B. Martin, *J. Chromatog.*, **2**, 272 (1959).

39. T. Johns and R. A. Morris, in *Development in Applied Spectroscopy* (E. N. Davis, ed.), Vol. 4, pp. 361–368, Plenum Press, New York, 1965.

40. J. C. Sternberg and R. L. Little, *Anal. Chem.*, **38**, 321 (1966).

40a. G. W. Fischer, *G-I-T. Fachz. Lab.*, **13**, 13 (1969).

41. D. F. Nelson, J. L. Yee and P. L. Kirk, *Mikrochem. J.*, **6**, 225 (1962).

42. B. Groten, *Anal. Chem.*, **36**, 1206 (1964).

43. B. C. Cox and B. Ellis, *Anal. Chem.*, **36**, 90 (1964).

44. F. Sonntag, *Brennstoff-Chem.*, **47**, 263 (1966).

45. J. Voigt, *Kunststoffe*, **51**, 18, 314 (1961).

46. J. Voigt, *Kunststoffe*, **54**, 2 (1964).

47. H. Feuerberg and H. Weigel, *Kautschuk Gummi*, **15** WT 276 (1962).

48. H. Hulot and P. Lebel, *Rubber Chem. Technol.*, **37**, 297 (1964).

49. P. Lebel, *Rubber Plastics Age*, **46**, 677 (1965).

50. A. Fiorenza and G. Bonomi, *Rubber Chem. Technol.*, **37**, 741 (1964).

51. H. M. Cole, D. L. Petterson, V. A. Sljaka, and D. S. Smith, *Rubber Chem Technol.*, **39**, 259 (1966).

52. P. L. Kirk, *J. Forensic Sci. Soc.*, **5**, 102 (1965).

53. J. S. Kelly, *J. Paint Technol.*, **38**, 302 (1966).

54. W. S. Hoover, Jr., *Paint Varnish Prod.*, **54** (9), 61 (1964).
55. H. Bober, *Fette, Seifen, Anstrichmittel*, **67**, 920 (1965).
56. G. E. Fisher and J. C. Neerman, *Ind. Eng. Chem. Prod. Res. Devel.*, **5**, 289 (1966).
56a. W. Fischer and H. Meuser, *Adhaesion*, **11**, 145 (1967).
56b. W. Fischer, G. Leukroth, and H. Meuser, *Adhaesion*, **1969**, 140.
56c. A. Carpov and E. Hagen, *Plaste Kaut.*, **15**, 358 (1968).
56d. M. Chêne, O. Martin-Martin-Borret, A. Bollon, and A. Perret, *Papeterie*, **88**, 1587 (1966) (in French).
56e. M. Tsuge, T. Tanaka, and S. Tanaka, *Bunseki Kagaku*, **18**, 47 (1969) (in Japanese); cited in *Chem. Abstr.*, **70**, 97454 (1969).
57. H. Hasse and J. Rau, *Melliand Textilber.*, **47**, 434 (1966).
57a. V. Gokcen and D. M. Cates. *Appl. Polymer Symposia*, **2**, 15 (1966).
58. L. N. Winter and P. W. Albro, *J. Gas Chromatog.*, **2**, 1 (1964).
59. K. Kanomata and Y. Mashiko, *Nippon Kagaku Zasshi*, **87**, 57 (1966) (in Japanese); cited in *Chem. Abstr.*, **65**, 12542 (1966).
60. M. V. Stack, *J. Gas Chromatog.*, **5**, 22 (1967).
61. C. Merritt, Jr., and D. H. Robertson, *J. Gas Chromatog.*, **5**, 96 (1967).
62. V. Oyama and G. C. Carle, *J. Gas Chromatog.*, **5**, 151 (1967).
63. I. Lysyj and K. H. Nelson, *Anal. Chem.*, **40**, 1365 (1968).
64. J. Zulaica and G. Guiochon, *Anal. Chem.*, **35**, 1724 (1963).
65. A. Wehrli and E. Kovats, *Helv. Chim. Acta*, **42**, 2709 (1959).
66. D. Noffz and W. Pfab, *Fresenius' Z. Anal. Chem.*, **228**, 188 (1967).
67. Bulletin, *Accessary for Gas Chromatography*, GC202, Bodensee Perkin-Elmer and Co., G.m.b.H., Überlingen, Germany, 1964.
68. K. J. Bombaugh, C. E. Cook, and B. H. Clampitt, *Anal. Chem.*, **35**, 1834 (1963).
68a. H. McCormick. *J. Chromatogr.*, **40**, 1 (1969).
69. J. Van Schooten and K. Evenhuis, *Polymer*, **6**, 561 (1965).
70. D. Noffz, W. Benz, and W. Pfab, *Fresenius' Z. Anal. Chem.*, **235**, 121 (1968) .
71. B. Kolb and K. H. Kaiser, *J. Gas Chromatog.*, **2**, 233 (1964).
72. C. Merritt, Jr., and J. T. Walsh, *Anal. Chem.*, **35**, 110 (1963).
73. E. W. Cieplinski, L. S. Ettre, B. Kolb, and G. Kemner, *Fresenius' Z. Anal. Chem.*, **209**, 302 (1965).
74. E. W. Cieplinski, L. S. Ettre, B. Kolb, and G. Kemner, *Fresenius' Z. Anal. Chem.*, **205**, 357 (1964).
75. K. Ettre and P. Varadi, *Anal. Chem.*, **35**, 69 (1963).
75a. L. Michajlov, P. Zugenmaier, and H. J. Cantow. *Polymer*, **9**, 325 (1968).
76. J. Van Schooten and J. K. Evenhuis, *Polymer*, **6**, 342 (1965).
77. R. S. Lehrle and J. C. Robb, *J. Gas Chromatog.*, **5**, 89 (1967).
78. F. T. Eggertsen and F. H. Stross, *J. Appl. Polymer Sci.*, **10**, 1171 (1966).
79. R. G. Scholz, J. Bednarczyk, and T. Yamauchi. *Anal. Chem.*, **38**, 331 (1966).
80. S. G. Perry, *J. Gas Chromatog.*, **2**, 54 (1964).
81. W. H. Giles, W. Brandkamp, L. Farace, and J. Bergvist, *Am. Chem. Soc., Div. Polymer Chem.*, Preprints, **8** (1), 522 (1967).
81a. O. F. Folmer and L. V. Azarrago, *J. Chromatog. Sci.*, **7**, 665 (1969).
82. R. S. Juvet, R. L. Tanner, and J. C. Y. Tsao, *J. Gas Chromatog.*, **5**, 15, 1967.
82a. A. B. Littlewood, *Chromatographia*, **1**, 133 (1968).
83. C. Merritt, Jr. and J. T. Walsh, *Anal. Chem.*, **34**, 903 (1962).
84. B. Casu and L. Cavallotti. *Anal. Chem.*, **34**, 1514 (1962).
85. R. N. Rogers, *Anal. Chem.*, **39**, 730 (1967).

85a. R. Kaiser. *Chem. Brit.*. **5**. 54 (1969).

85b. T. Takeuchi, S. Tsuge, and T. Okumoto, *J. Gas Chromatog.*, **6**, 542 (1968).

86. J. E. Hoff and E. D. Feit, *Anal. Chem.*, **36**, 1002 (1964).

87. R. Bassette and C. H. Whitnah, *Anal. Chem.*, **32**, 1098 (1960).

88. M. Beroza, *Anal. Chem.*, **34**, 1801 (1962).

89. M. Beroza and R. Sarmiento, *Anal. Chem.*, **36**, 1744 (1964).

90. S. K. Yasuda, *J. Chromatog.*, **27**, 72 (1967).

91. M. Dimbat and F. T. Eggertsen. *Microchem. J.*. **9**. 500 (1965).

92. C. E. R. Jones and G. E. J. Reynolds, *J. Gas Chromatog.*, **5**, 25 (1967).

93. J. C. Sternberg, W. S. Gallaway, and D. T. L. Jones, in *Gas Chromatography* (N. Brenner, ed.), Academic Press, New York, 1962.

93a. A. Franck and K. Wünscher, *Chemiker Ztg.*, **91**, 7 (1967).

94. P. Varadi and K. Ettre, *Anal. Chem.*, **35**, 410 (1963).

95. J. A. Voellmin, P. Kriemler, I. Omura, J. Seibl, and W. Simon, *Microchem. J.*, **11**, 73 (1966).

96. J. A. Voellmin, I. Omura, J. Seibl, K. Grob, and W. Simon, *Helv. Chim. Acta*, **49**, 1768 (1966).

97. R. Ryhage, *Anal. Chem.*, **36**, 759 (1964).

98. J. W. Amy, E. M. Chait, W. E. Baitinger, and F. W. McLafferty, *Anal. Chem.*, **37**, 1265 (1965).

98a. A. E. Lipska and F. A. Wodley, *J. Appl. Polymer Sci.*, **13**, 851 (1969).

99. J. N. Damico, N. P. Wong, and J. A. Spon, *Anal. Chem.*, **39**, 1045 (1967).

100. J. S. Parsons, *Anal. Chem.*, **36**, 1849 (1964).

101. G. G. Esposito, *Anal. Chem.*, **36**, 2183 (1964).

102. R. L. Gatrell and T. J. Mao, *Anal. Chem.*, **37**, 1294 (1965).

103. C. W. Stanley and W. R. Peterson, *SPE Trans.*, **2**, 298 (1962).

103a. F. Spagnola, *J. Gas Chromatog.*, **6**, 609 (1968).

104. J. E. Guillet, W. C. Wooten, and R. L. Combs, *J. Appl. Polymer Sci.*, **3**, 61 (1960).

105. J. G. Cobler and E. P. Samsel, *SPE Trans.*, **2**, 145 (1962).

106. J. C. Daniel and J. M. Michel, *J. Gas Chromatog.*, **5**, 437 (1967).

107. D. Deur-Siftar, *J. Gas Chromatog.*, **5**, 72 (1967).

107a. T. Takeuchi, T. Okumoto, and S. Shin, *Bunseki Kagaku*, **18**, 614 (1969) (in Japanese); cited in *Chem. Abstr.*, **71**, 50713 (1969).

108. E. M. Barrall, II, R. S. Porter, and J. F. Johnson, *Anal. Chem.*, **35**, 73 (1963).

108a. V. M. Androsova. N. Sendov. and M. Shabaeva. *Ind. Lab.*. (USSR). **34**. 795 (1968).

109. E. W. Neumann and H. C. Nadeau, *Anal. Chem.*, **35**, 1454 (1963).

109a. E. Hagen and G. Hazkoto, *Plaste Kaut.*, **16**, 21 (1969).

110. K. Jobst and L. Wuckel, *Plaste Kautschuk*, **12**, 150 (1965).

111. R. Hank, *Kautschuk Gummi*, **18**, 295 (1965).

112. O. Kysel and V. Durdovic, *Chem. Zvesti*, **19**, 570 (1965) (in Slovakian); cited in *Chem. Abstr.*, **63**, 14982 (1965).

113. T. Yoshimoto and H. Arasawa, *Nippon Gomu Kyokaishi*, **38**, 278 (1965) (in Japanese); cited in *Chem. Abstr.*, **63**, 13531 (1965).

114. J. Dolinar, M. Jernejcic, and L. Premru, *J. Chromatog.*, **34**, 89 (1968).

114a. S. Mashimo. K. Hoshikawa. N. Okubo. T. Watanabe. and J. Wasaburo. *Nippon. Gomu Kyokaishi*, **41**, 499 (1968).

114b. V. R. Alishoev. V. G. Berezkin. Z. P. Markovich. E. I. Talalaev. L. V. Sitnikov. and A. I. Malyshev. *Ind. Lab.* (USSR). **34**. 1427 (1968).

114c. W. D. King and D. J. Stanonis, *Tappi*, **52**, 465 (1969).
114d. Y. Umezawa, Y. Hasebe, Y. Hirai, and T. Furuse, *Nippon Gomu Kyokaishi*, **39**, 497 (1966).
115. J. Martinez and G. Guiochon, *J. Gas Chromatog.*, **5**, 146 (1967).
116. H. R. Tai, R. M. Powers, and T. F. Protzman, *Anal. Chem.*, **36**, 108 (1964).
116a. D. J. O'Neil, *Anal. Lett.*, **1**, 499 (1968).
117. T. Takeuchi and K. Murase, *Kogyo Kagaku Zasshi*, **68**, 2505 (1965) (in Japanese); cited in *Chem. Abstr.*, **65**, 7415 (1966).
118. J. E. Brown, M. Tryon, and J. Mandel, *Anal. Chem.*, **35**, 2172 (1963).
119. D. A. MacKillop, *Anal. Chem.*, **40**, 607 (1968).
119a. T. Shin, T. Okumoto, and T. Takeuchi, *Makromol. Chem.*, **123**, 123 (1969).
119b. T. Shin, T. Okumoto, and T. Takeuchi, *Macromolecules*, **2**, 200 (1969).
120. J. Van Schooten, E. W. Duck, and R. Berkenbosch, *Polymer*, **2**, 357 (1961).
121. J. Van Schooten and S. Mostert, *Polymer*, **4**, 135 (1963).
122. D. Deur-Siftar, T. Bistricki, and T. Tandi, *J. Chromatog.*, **24**, 404 (1966).
123. T. A. Turner and S. L. Eisler, *AD 644 648,* Clearinghouse Fed. Sci. and Tech. Information, U.S. Dept. Commerce, Springfield, Va.
124. M. Vacherot, *J. Gas Chromatog.*, **5**, 155 (1967).
125. M. Jernejcic and L. Premru, *Rubber Chem. Technol.*, **41**, 411 (1968).
126. R. H. Wiley, G. DeVenuto, and F. E. Martin, *J. Macromol. Chem.*, **1**, 137 (1966).
127. R. H. Wiley and F. E. Martin, *J. Macromol. Sci., (Chem.),* **A1**, 635 (1967).
127a. V. G. Berezkin, I. B. Nemirovskaya, and B. M. Kovarskaya, *Ind. Lab.* (USSR), **35**, 175 (1969).
128. A. Barlow, R. S. Lehrle, J. C. Robb, and D. Sunderland, *Polymer*, **8**, 523 (1967).
128a. S. L. Madorsky and S. Straus, Soc. Chem. Ind., Plastics and Polymer Group, Monograph 13, *High Temperature Resistance and Thermal Degradation of Polymers,* p. 60, Society of the Chemical Industry, London, 1961.
128b. F. Sonntag, *Kolloid-Z. Z. Polym.*, **224**, 69 (1968).
129. C. A. M. G. Cramers and A. I. M. Keulemans, *J. Gas Chromatog.*, **5**, 58 (1967).
130. F. Farre-Rius and G. Guiochon, *J. Gas Chromatog.*, **5**, 457 (1967).
131. P. D. Garn and G. D. Anthony, *Anal. Chem.*, **39**, 1445 (1967).
132. R. A. Prosser, J. T. Stapler, and W. E. C. Yelland, *Anal. Chem.*, **39**, 694 (1967).
133. C. B. Honaker and A. D. Horton, *J. Gas Chromatog.*, **3**, 396 (1965).
133a. G. Blandenet, *Chromatographia*, **5**, 184 (1969).
133b. B. Lengyel, *Kem. Kozlem*, **30**, 271 (1968); cited in *Chem. Abstr.*, **70**, 58371 (1969).
133c. E. A. Boettner, G. Ball, and B. Weiss, *J. Appl. Polymer Sci.*, **13**, 377 (1969).
133d. R. D. Collins, P. Fiveash, and L. Holland, *Vacuum*, **19**, 113 (1969).
133e. Y. Tsuchiya and K. Sumi, *J. Polymer Sci. Pt. B*, **6**, 357 (1968).
134. J. Zulaica and G. Guiochon, *Bull. Soc. Chim. France*, **1966**, 1351.
134a. E. M. Barrall, R. S. Porter, and J. F. Johnson, *J. Chromatog.*, **11**, 177 (1963).
134b. S. Tsuge, T. Okumoto, and T. Takeuchi, *J. Chromatogr. Sci.*, **7**, 250 (1969).
134c. Y. Tsuchiya and K. Sumi, *J. Polymer Sci., Pt. A-1*, **7**, 813 (1969).
134d. G. Bagby, R. S. Lehrle, and J. C. Robb, *Polymer*, **9**, 284 (1968).
135. W. C. Geddes, *European Polymer J.*, **3**, 267 (1967).
135a. Y. Tsuchiya and K. Sumi, *J. Appl. Chem.*, **17**, 364 (1967).
135b. W. Coleman, L. Scheel, and C. Gorski, *Am. Indust. Hyg. Assoc. J.*, **29**, 54 (1968).
136. J. C. Daniel and J. M. Michel, *J. Gas Chromatog.*, **5**, 437 (1967).

137. C. Belinski, IAA Accession No. A66-11678 (in French); cited in *Chem. Abstr.*, **64**, 17787 (1966).
138. C. C. Luce, E. F. Humphrey, L. V. Guild, H. H. Norrish, J. Coull, and W. W. Castor, *Anal. Chem.*, **36**, 482 (1964).
138a. S. Tsuge. T. Okumoto. Y. Sugimuro. and T. Takeuchi. *J. Chromatogr. Sci..* **7**. 253 (1969).
139. A. Davis and J. H. Golden, *J. Gas Chromatog.*, **5**, 81 (1967).
139a. E. Hagen, *Plaste Kaut.*, **15**, 711 (1968).
140. E. P. Krasnov et al.. *Vysokomolekul Soedin.* **8**. 380 (1966) (in Russian); cited in *Chem. Abstr.*, **64**, 19810 (1966).
141. C. Landault and G. Guiochon, *Anal. Chem.*, **39**, 713 (1967).
142. G. P. Shulman and E. Lochte, *J. Macromol. Sci. (Chem.)*, **A1**, 413 (1967).
143. J. Kammermaier. *Kolloid-Z.* **209**. 20 (1966).
144. K. Kato, *Agr. Biol. Chem. (Tokyo)*, **31**, 657 (1967) (in English); cited in *Chem. Abstr.*, **67**, 101 150 (1967).
145. K. Kato and H. Komorita, *Agr. Biol. Chem.*, **32**, 21 (1968).
145a. V. Reiser. M. Kosik. V. Durdovic. and R. Domansky. *Holzforsch. Holzverwert.*, **20**, 148 (1968) (in German); cited in *Chem. Abstr.*, **71**, 23084 (1969).
145b. D. J. Bryce and C. T. Greenwood. *Appl. Polymer Symp..* **2**. 149 (1966).
145c. D. J. Bryce and C. T. Greenwood. *Appl. Polymer Symp..* **2**. 159 (1966).
146. S. Glassner and A. R. Pierce, III, *Anal. Chem.*, **37**, 525 (1965).
147. S. H. O'Neill, R. E. Putscher, A. Dynako, and C. Boquist, *J. Gas Chromatog.*, **1**, 28 (1963).
148. C. Karr, Jr., J. R. Comberiati, and W. C. Warner, *Anal. Chem.*, **35**, 1442 (1963).
149. J. Chiu, *Anal. Chem.*, **40**, 1516 (1968).
150. A. S. Kenyon, *Tech. Methods Polym. Eval.*, **1**, 217 (1966).
151. B. Groten in *Gas Effluent Analysis* (W. Lodding. ed.). pp. 101–142. Marcel Dekker. New York, 1967.
152. R. N. Rogers, S. K. Yasuda, and J. Zinn, *Anal. Chem.*, **32**, 672 (1960).
153. W. M. Ayres and E. M. Bens, *Anal. Chem.*, **33**, 569 (1961).
154. D. A. Vassalo, *Anal. Chem.*, **33**, 1823 (1961).
155. R. M. Ross, *J. Macromol. Sci. (Chem.)*, **3**, 675 (1969).
156. S. H. Hirsch and M. R. Lilyquist, *J. Appl. Polymer Sci.*, **11**, 305 (1967).

CHAPTER 3

Stress–Strain Temperature Relations in High Polymers

J. A. SAUER

DEPARTMENT OF MECHANICS AND MATERIALS SCIENCE
RUTGERS — THE STATE UNIVERSITY
NEW BRUNSWICK, NEW JERSEY

A. E. WOODWARD

DEPARTMENT OF CHEMISTRY
THE CITY COLLEGE OF THE CITY UNIVERSITY OF NEW YORK
NEW YORK, NEW YORK

3-1 INTRODUCTION

The mechanical properties of high polymers, i.e., their response to various types of external stress or strain conditions, result from both their unique macromolecular nature and their particular chemical and physical structure. The basic units from which a solid polymer is formed are not individual atoms or ions but are giant molecules. These molecules consist of linear or branched chains of atoms in which the atoms themselves are joined together by strong primary valence bonds while the molecular chains, except where direct cross-links exist, are held together by much weaker secondary bonds such as Van der Waal forces or hydrogen bond forces.

Most polymer solids of the thermoplastic type contain chain molecules having a fairly wide molecular weight distribution. The average molecular weight is generally well above 5000, and may extend into the millions. As a result, many of these thermoplastic materials have the ability to be drawn or spun into films or fibres of high strength per unit weight. In polymer solids of the thermosetting type, the chains are highly cross-linked into a three-dimensional network and the entire solid is essentially one large molecule.

In polymers, as in low-molecular-weight organic glasses and crystals, the possibility of rotation about single chemical bonds exists. Depending on the temperature and the composition, there may be considerable molecular flexibility even in the solid state as a result of microbrownian motion of the various segmental units. At the same time, their high average molecular weight causes polymers to have an unusually high viscosity, compared to organic liquids, in the temperature range above their major softening or melting temperature. Partly as the result of a broad molecular weight distribution and partly as a result of the many different forms of motion that can occur, the transition zone separating the rigid solid state from the viscous liquid state tends to be broad. Furthermore, if the average molecular weight is sufficiently high, the polymer, even though not chemically cross-linked, will convert, upon passing through the so-called glass transition, to a flexible rubbery elastic solid rather than to a viscous liquid.

One interesting aspect of high polymers is that, even when they have the necessary chain regularity to form ordered structures, they do not become completely crystalline in the solid state as do many of the simpler organic substances. Even single crystals of highly stereoregular polymers grown from dilute solution with great care do not attain the theoretical density expected on the basis of their unit cell dimensions. All the so-called crystalline polymers, such as polyethylene, nylon, teflon, etc., are thus only partly crystalline, and the amount and kinds of disordered or defect material present are important factors that affect both the stress–strain response and the over-all mechanical behavior.

A feature of the polymeric materials is that their mechanical behavior is markedly affected by temperature. All noncross-linked polymers, whether amorphous or partly crystalline, tend to change their mechanical stiffness, or rigidity, by several orders of magnitude upon passing through one or more temperature regions. The temperature location of the major softening region depends upon the intra- and intermolecular forces that are operative for the particular polymer and hence varies greatly with the specific composition. For amorphous polymers, upon passing through this softening region, the modulus falls from a value of the order of 10^{10} dyn/cm^2 in the glassy state to about 10^7 dyn/cm^2 in the rubbery state. For the partly crystalline polymers, there are generally two major softening zones, one in the vicinity of the glass transition temperature, corresponding to onset of main chain motions in the rigid amorphous regions, the other near the melting point, corresponding to loss of cohesion and order in the crystalline regions. The amount of modulus reduction in the vicinity of the glass transition is greatly reduced in the crystalline polymers as compared with amorphous polymers and will depend upon the degree of crystallinity of the sample.

In many polymers, the rigidity of the material varies considerably with temperature even below the temperature region where conversion from the solid to a rubber, or to a viscous liquid, takes place, and several distinct relaxation regions may be present, depending upon the specific structure and composition, the nature and types of side branches, the barriers to segmental reorientation, and the presence of defects or impurities. For example, high density polyethylene exhibits three or more relaxation processes between liquid nitrogen temperatures and the melting temperature, with the elastic modulus being about three times greater in magnitude at 77°K than it is at room temperature. In most polymers, the observed relaxation regions tend to be rather broad, and this is indicative of the presence of a distribution of internal relaxation times in these macromolecular materials.

The manner in which stress–strain parameters, such as the tensile, shear, or bulk modulus, vary with temperature and with time is essential fundamental information that must be known or determined before intelligent use and application of plastics is possible. It is desirable, therefore, for polymers of known composition and structure to have experimental measurements of moduli over the widest possible temperature and frequency ranges. This, however, is difficult to do experimentally and hence empirical procedures have been devised to extend our knowledge of the temperature (or frequency) dependence, especially for amorphous polymers, by use of some form of a time–temperature equivalence principle. Whether obtained under transient or dynamic conditions, data on mechanical stress–strain parameters, together with data from the use of other physical tools, such as nuclear magnetic resonance (NMR) studies and dielectric studies, provide a basis for determination of relaxation or retardation spectra, and for interpretation of relaxation mechanisms in terms of specific compositional and structural features.

It is not the intention of this article to review in detail the numerous investigations that have been and are being made of stress–strain relations in polymers. Rather our purpose is the following: to outline the various types of stress–strain relations that may be applicable to polymers, depending upon environmental conditions; to describe the experimental arrangements, both static and dynamic, that are used to investigate mechanical properties; to indicate the temperature and time dependence of various stress–strain parameters; to tabulate modulus values at various selected temperatures; to compare experimental values with theoretical values and to relate these values with specific compositional features and with values for other common types of materials; to delineate and give examples of many of the important external factors such as test temperature, strain rate, and frequency, and of internal factors such as tacticity, cross-linking, crystallization, etc., that affect modulus–temperature behavior; and finally to attempt to correlate information gained from study of modulus–temperature behavior with information gained from study of other types of physical measurements.

In Section 3-2 of this paper various types of stress–strain relations are presented. These include those applicable to elastic solids, to linear viscoelastic solids, and to rubberlike solids. Also discussed in this section are some of the various theoretical treatments which have been developed to allow calculation of values of stress–strain parameters from consideration of composition and molecular structure of the polymer and of assumed intramolecular and intermolecular potentials.

In Section 3-3 a brief description is given of the various experimental techniques that have been developed for measurement of tensile, shear, and bulk moduli and for investigation of creep behavior, stress relaxation behavior, and response to dynamic loading. Also given in this section are tables of comparative values of moduli of different polymers for several selected temperatures. In addition, the effects of varying test conditions, such as alterations of strain rate, frequency, and test temperature, are described and illustrated.

A number of factors that affect the modulus–temperature relationship are discussed in Section 3-4. These factors include chemical composition and structure, morphology, crystallinity, degree of crosslinking, amount of plasticizer, amount of filler, water content, molecular weight and molecular weight distribution. Also in this section the various relaxation regions are identified and the significance of these in terms of molecular motion and of polymer structure is discussed.

In Section 3-5 information obtained from study of the temperature dependence of polymer rigidity is compared and contrasted with that obtained from measurement of other physical properties. Correlations and discrepancies between measured stress–strain parameters and other physical measurements are presented for polymers of widely different chemical composition.

Finally, Section 3-6 summarizes current knowledge in general terms, outlines some of the areas where our understanding of the experimentally observed phenomena is still incomplete, and suggests some problems and areas where additional experimental and theoretical studies would be welcome.

3-2 STRESS–STRAIN RELATIONS

A. Elastic Solids

1. GENERAL RELATIONSHIPS

The state of stress at a point in a stressed elastic solid can be described in terms of a stress tensor $(1,2)$.

$$(\sigma) = \begin{pmatrix} \sigma_{xx} & \tau_{xy} & \tau_{xz} \\ \tau_{yx} & \sigma_{yy} & \tau_{yz} \\ \tau_{zx} & \tau_{zy} & \sigma_{zz} \end{pmatrix} \tag{3-1}$$

whose elements are the stress components, referred to a Cartesian coordinate system, acting on the faces of an infinitesimal element placed at that point (Fig. 3-1).† Although there are nine such components, consideration of the equilibrium of an infinitesimal element shows that $\tau_{xy} = \tau_{yx}$, $\tau_{xz} = \tau_{zx}$, and $\tau_{yz} = \tau_{zy}$.‡ For convenience, we designate the six independent components by the notation $S_i (i = 1, 2, \ldots 6)$. The S_i values in terms of the normal and shear stress components are as shown in Fig. 3-1.

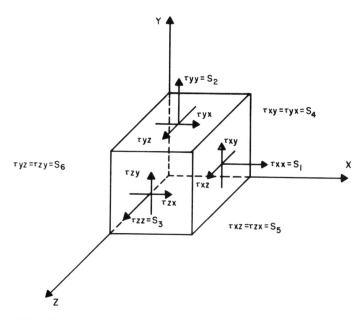

Figure 3-1. Shear and normal stress components acting on an infinitesimal element. Only stresses on visible faces shown.

The strain can likewise be defined in terms of a symmetrical strain tensor(*1*)

$$(\epsilon) = \begin{pmatrix} \epsilon_{xx} & \frac{1}{2}\gamma_{xy} & \frac{1}{2}\gamma_{xz} \\ \frac{1}{2}\gamma_{xy} & \epsilon_{yy} & \frac{1}{2}\gamma_{yz} \\ \frac{1}{2}\gamma_{xz} & \frac{1}{2}\gamma_{yz} & \epsilon_{zz} \end{pmatrix} \tag{3-2}$$

where the ϵ's along the principal diagonal are the normal strains and the γ's are the usual engineering shear strains. For simplicity, we designate

---

†To accord with much of the engineering literature, we use the symbol σ to represent normal stresses and the symbol τ to represent component shear stresses.

‡Provided no internal torques or coupled stresses are present, as from magnetic forces.

the six independent strains as e_j $(j = 1, 2, \ldots, 6)$ with the first three subscripts used for the normal strains ϵ_{xx}, ϵ_{yy}, and ϵ_{zz} and the last three for the engineering shear strains (or twice the corresponding off-diagonal components) γ_{xy}, γ_{xz}, and γ_{yz}.

For the ideal elastic solid which obeys Hooke's law, the six independent stress components (S_i) are assumed to be linearly related to each of the six independent strain components (e_j). Thus in the generalized Hooke's law formulation, the stress–strain relations actually involve 36 proportionality constants, or coefficients, C_{ij}, which are measures of material rigidity but which are usually called simply elastic constants or elastic moduli. Actually these coefficients are not really constants, as they depend both on temperature and on measurement frequency. For most materials, including polymers, they generally increase with decreasing temperature or with increasing rate of loading. In terms of these coefficients, the generalized stress–strain relations — valid for small strains — can be expressed by the simple tensor relation

$$S_i = C_{ij} e_j \qquad (i, j = 1, 2, \ldots, 6) \tag{3-3}$$

where summation over the dummy index j on the right-hand side is implied. The 36 possible elastic stiffness constants C_{ij} of Eq. (3-3) reduce to 21 when consideration is given to the relation of the stress and strain components to the strain energy function(2). These considerations require that $C_{ij} = C_{ji}$ and hence the matrix formed by the elastic moduli is a symmetrical one. Thus if no other symmetry conditions are present, as for a triclinic single crystal, 21 elastic constants are required to describe completely its mechanical behavior.

The number of required independent elastic moduli is considerably reduced if some elements of symmetry are present in the given material. For materials possessing one plane of elastic symmetry, eight of these coefficients reduce to zero and the number of independent elastic stiffness parameters reduces to *13*(*1,2*). For orthotropic materials, such as wood or rhombic single crystals, there are three planes of elastic symmetry orthogonal to each other. In this case, the number of independent elastic constants reduces further to nine(*1*). These nine are the three shear moduli C_{44}, C_{55}, and C_{66} relating the shear stresses to the shear strains, three "normal" moduli, C_{11}, C_{22}, and C_{33}, relating the stress components in the x, y, and z directions to the corresponding components of strain, and three other elastic constants, C_{12}, C_{13}, and C_{23}, relating the normal stress in one direction to the normal strains in the two perpendicular directions. Thus for anisotropic bodies having symmetries as indicated, the stress–strain relations become, when expressed in the usual Cartesian axes notation,

$$\begin{aligned}
\sigma_{xx} &= C_{11}\epsilon_{xx} + C_{12}\epsilon_{yy} + C_{13}\epsilon_{zz} \\
\sigma_{yy} &= C_{12}\epsilon_{xx} + C_{22}\epsilon_{yy} + C_{23}\epsilon_{zz} \\
\sigma_{zz} &= C_{13}\epsilon_{xx} + C_{23}\epsilon_{yy} + C_{33}\epsilon_{zz} \\
\sigma_{xy} &= \tau_{xy} = C_{44}\gamma_{xy} \\
\sigma_{xz} &= \tau_{xz} = C_{55}\gamma_{xz} \\
\sigma_{yz} &= \tau_{yz} = C_{66}\gamma_{yz}
\end{aligned} \tag{3-4}$$

For materials with a larger number of symmetry elements, the number of elastic constants can be further reduced. For example, hexagonal single crystals require only five, while cubic crystals require only three (3).

It has not been feasible as yet to evaluate experimentally the various stiffness constants for various polymer crystals, largely because of the unavailability of single crystals of sufficient size. However, with improvements in measuring techniques, and as knowledge of polymer crystallization procedures permits the growth of larger single crystals, studies of the various elastic constants of polymers, as defined by Eqs. (3-3) and (3-4), may become as important a field of investigation as the study of the elastic constants of metals (4).

A further simplification of the stress–strain relations occurs when the material being considered is isotropic, i.e., when its elastic properties are the same in all directions. Although it is doubtful if any bulk polymer meets this condition fully, many molded articles or specimens, especially if carefully annealed, approach this state. Even in crystalline polymers where the individual crystals, or even the larger crystal aggregates such as the spherulites, are themselves anisotropic, the polymer on the whole, in the continuum sense, may frequently be considered as isotropic. This condition will apply only to bulk polymer, however, and not to drawn film or spun filaments, both of which are oriented materials and are therefore highly anisotropic.

For isotropic materials the elastic coefficients C_{ij} must be independent of the choice of coordinate systems. From this it follows that (2)

$$\begin{aligned}
C_{22} &= C_{33} = C_{11} \\
C_{23} &= C_{13} = C_{12} \\
C_{44} &= C_{55} = C_{66} = \tfrac{1}{2}(C_{11} - C_{12})
\end{aligned} \tag{3-5}$$

The stress–strain relations for isotropic materials thus involve only two rigidity parameters and these may be taken as C_{11} and C_{12} or as any two of the three remaining coefficients, C_{11}, C_{12}, and C_{44}.

2. LAMÉ RIGIDITY PARAMETERS – SHEAR MODULUS

The Lamé elastic constants are usually denoted as λ and μ, or as λ and G. The constant λ is the same as C_{12} defined above and the constant G (or μ) is $\frac{1}{2}(C_{11} - C_{12})$, or the same as C_{44} defined above. Hence the physical meaning of G follows directly from the last three equations of Eq. (3-4), when the appropriate substitution is made. These equations now become

$$\tau_{xy} = G\gamma_{xy}$$
$$\tau_{xz} = G\gamma_{xz} \tag{3-6}$$
$$\tau_{yz} = G\gamma_{yz}$$

The Lamé constant G is thus the ordinary shear modulus of elasticity which relates the observed shear strains directly to the applied shear stresses.

The remaining stress–strain relations in terms of the rigidity parameters λ and G can be obtained by use of Eq. (3-5) and by introduction of the concept of volume strain, ϵ_v, defined for small strains as the sum of ϵ_{xx}, ϵ_{yy}, and ϵ_{zz}. On substituting of these conditions into the first three equations of Eq. (3-4), we obtain

$$\sigma_{xx} = C_{11}\epsilon_{xx} + C_{12}(\epsilon_{yy} + \epsilon_{zz}) = C_{12}\epsilon_v + (C_{11} - C_{12})\epsilon_{xx}$$
$$\sigma_{yy} = C_{11}\epsilon_{yy} + C_{12}(\epsilon_{xx} + \epsilon_{zz}) = C_{12}\epsilon_v + (C_{11} - C_{12})\epsilon_{yy} \tag{3-7}$$
$$\sigma_{zz} = C_{11}\epsilon_{zz} + C_{12}(\epsilon_{xx} + \epsilon_{yy}) = C_{12}\epsilon_v + (C_{11} - C_{12})\epsilon_{zz}$$

These equations are now readily expressed in terms of the Lamé parameters, λ and G, viz.,

$$\sigma_{xx} = \lambda\epsilon_v + 2G\epsilon_{xx}$$
$$\sigma_{yy} = \lambda\epsilon_v + 2G\epsilon_{yy} \tag{3-8}$$
$$\sigma_{zz} = \lambda\epsilon_v + 2G\epsilon_{zz}$$

The stress–strain relations for isotropic materials, as expressed by the combined Eqs. (3-6) and (3-8), are frequently written in terms of the single tensor equation

$$\sigma_{ij} = \lambda\epsilon_v\delta_{ij} + 2G\epsilon_{ij} \qquad (i,j = x, y, z) \tag{3-9}$$

where σ_{ij} and ϵ_{ij} are the appropriate components of the stress and strain tensors of Eqs. (3-1) and (3-2), and where the Kroneker δ symbol has the usual meaning:

$$\delta_{ij} = 0, \qquad i \neq j; \qquad \delta_{ij} = 1, \qquad i = j$$

3. BULK MODULUS

The Lamé rigidity constant λ, or C_{12}, does not have a simple physical meaning as does the constant G, but its use simplifies the stress–strain relations. It can readily be expressed in terms of G and other elastic constants, such as the bulk modulus K or Young's modulus E, which do have simple physical meanings. The bulk modulus K, by definition, is the proportionality constant relating an applied hydrostatic pressure $(-p)$ to the change in volume (ΔV) per unit volume, i.e.,

$$-p = K\left(\frac{\Delta V}{V}\right) = K\epsilon_v \tag{3-10}$$

For the case of hydrostatic compression, Eqs. (3-9) become

$$\begin{aligned}
\sigma_{xx} &= -p = \lambda\epsilon_v + 2G\epsilon_{xx} \\
\sigma_{yy} &= -p = \lambda\epsilon_v + 2G\epsilon_{yy} \\
\sigma_{zz} &= -p = \lambda\epsilon_v + 2G\epsilon_{zz}
\end{aligned} \tag{3-11}$$

Upon adding these three equations and solving for $-p$, we find

$$-p = [\lambda + \tfrac{2}{3}G]\epsilon_v \tag{3-12}$$

and hence, by comparison of Eq. (3-12) with Eq. (3-10), we see that the bulk modulus can be written in terms of the Lamé constant and the shear modulus, i.e.,

$$K = \lambda + \tfrac{2}{3}G \tag{3-13}$$

Thus any given elastic material can be characterized by the two Lamé rigidity constants, or by the two moduli K and G, where K, the bulk modulus, is a measure of resistance to volume dilatation and is given by Eq. (3-10) and G, the shear modulus, is a measure of resistance to shear and is given by Eq. (3-6).

4. YOUNG'S MODULUS AND POISSON'S RATIO

Although any two of the three constants already defined, viz., the Lamé constants λ and G and the bulk modulus K, are sufficient to describe completely the elastic behavior of an isotropic material, it is frequently convenient to use two other elastic constants which are readily measurable, viz., Young's modulus, E, and Poisson's ratio, v. Young's modulus is most simply defined in terms of a prismatic body subject to an applied tensile stress considered to be uniform over the plane end surfaces. If we let the z axis of our coordinate system coincide with the axis of the specimen, then the elastic modulus E is defined by the ratio of the stress in the longitudinal direction to the corresponding component of strain, i.e.,

$$E = \frac{\sigma_{zz}}{\epsilon_{zz}} \tag{3-14}$$

To relate Young's modulus to the Lamé parameters, rewrite Eq. (3-9) for the case being considered. We then have

$$
\begin{aligned}
0 &= \lambda \epsilon_v + 2G\epsilon_{xx} = (\lambda + 2G)\epsilon_{xx} + \lambda(\epsilon_{yy} + \epsilon_{zz}) \\
0 &= \lambda \epsilon_v + 2G\epsilon_{yy} = (\lambda + 2G)\epsilon_{yy} + \lambda(\epsilon_{xx} + \epsilon_{zz}) \\
\sigma_{zz} &= \lambda \epsilon_v + 2G\epsilon_{zz} = (\lambda + 2G)\epsilon_{zz} + \lambda(\epsilon_{xx} + \epsilon_{yy})
\end{aligned} \tag{3-15}
$$

Solving for the three normal strains we find

$$\epsilon_{zz} = \frac{(\lambda + G)}{G(3\lambda + 2G)}\sigma_{zz} \tag{3-16}$$

and

$$\epsilon_{xx} = \epsilon_{yy} = -\frac{\lambda}{2G(3\lambda + 2G)}\sigma_{zz} \tag{3-17}$$

On comparing Eqs. (3-16) and (3-14) we see

$$E = \frac{G(3\lambda + 2G)}{\lambda + G} \tag{3-18}$$

Poisson's ratio v is defined as the ratio of the lateral strain to the longitudinal strain. In terms of the coordinate system chosen, we have

$$v = -\frac{\epsilon_{xx}}{\epsilon_{zz}} \tag{3.19}$$

where the minus sign is to take account of the fact that ϵ_{xx} will be negative (contraction) when ϵ_{zz} is positive (expansion). To relate v to the Lamé parameters, substitute into Eq. (3-19) the expressions for the longitudinal and lateral strains from Eqs. (3-16) and (3-17). We obtain

$$v = \frac{\lambda}{2(\lambda + G)} \tag{3-20}$$

A more convenient expression is that relating the more readily measurable quantities v, E, and G. To obtain this, one solves for λ and G from Eqs. (3-18) and (3-20). We then find that the relation between the shear modulus and Young's modulus is given by

$$G = \frac{E}{2(1+v)} \tag{3-21}$$

and the relation between the Lamé parameter λ and E by

$$\lambda = \frac{vE}{(1+v)(1-2v)} \tag{3-22}$$

5. OTHER RELATIONS BETWEEN ELASTIC CONSTANTS

Five different elastic constants have now been defined, although only two are independent. There are thus 10 different combinations that can be taken as basic and the others defined in terms of these (5).

The two constants that are considered to have the greatest physical significance are G (i.e., C_{44}), which measures resistance to shear or change of shape, and K, which measures resistance to volume dilatation. Let us express the other elastic constants in terms of these. Since G is the same as $(C_{11} - C_{12})/2$, we may write, using Eq. (3-13),

$$C_{11} = 2G + C_{12} = 2G + \lambda = 2G + (K - \tfrac{2}{3}G) = K + \tfrac{4}{3}G \qquad (3\text{-}23)$$

Also from (3-13),

$$C_{12} = \lambda = K - \tfrac{2}{3}G \qquad (3\text{-}24)$$

Poisson's ratio in terms of G and K is obtained by substituting Eq. (3-24) into Eq. (3-20). This gives

$$\nu = \frac{(3K - 2G)}{2(3K + G)} \qquad (3\text{-}25)$$

Young's modulus, E, in terms of G and K, is obtained by substitution of (3-13) into (3-18), giving

$$E = \frac{9KG}{3K + G} \qquad (3\text{-}26)$$

However, in the polymer literature the material parameters most often used are not K and G but rather E and G. Only a relatively small number of experimental investigations have been made of the bulk modulus behavior of solid polymers, while considerable information is available concerning the shear modulus or Young's modulus. Hence it is desirable to have expressions for the other elastic constants in terms of E and G. Using the expression already given, one finds

$$\nu = \frac{E - 2G}{2G} \qquad (3\text{-}27)$$

and

$$K = \frac{GE}{3(3G - E)} \qquad (3\text{-}28)$$

Another useful expression is that for the bulk modulus in terms of E and ν. This is

$$K = \frac{E}{3(1 - 2\nu)} \qquad (3\text{-}29)$$

For some polymeric materials such as rubbers, the value of Poisson's ratio is very close to $\frac{1}{2}$. In this case, from Eq. (3-21), the shear modulus is $\frac{1}{3}$ the tensile modulus and K, the bulk modulus, is infinite, i.e., the rubber is essentially incompressible and shows no volume change on loading. For solid polymers below their glass transition, Poisson's ratio usually falls within the range 0.25 to 0.35. For $\nu = 0.3$, the relations among the tensile modulus, the bulk modulus, and the shear modulus become $E = 2.60G$, $E = 1.2K$, and $K = 2.16G$.

It should be noted that the relations of this section are valid only so long as the material is isotropic and the properties are time independent. Actual polymers tend to behave more and more like ideal elastic solids as the temperature is lowered or as the frequency of loading is raised. For an isotropic polymer under such conditions, the stress–strain response of the material requires knowledge of only two elastic constants. For an anisotropic specimen, the number of parameters needed to define the material increases, with the exact number being dependent upon the symmetry conditions that prevail. As already noted, for a simple cubic single crystal the number is three, while for a general anisotropic, triclinic crystal it is 21.

B. Linear Viscoelastic Solids

1. GENERAL BEHAVIOR

At intermediate temperatures, or at intermediate rates of loading — and these conditions are met in a high percentage of polymer applications — it is necessary to take account of the viscoelastic nature of polymeric materials. This aspect of polymer behavior arises because of viscous resistance offered to motion of segmental units and molecular chains by the surrounding medium. The response of polymers to stress is thus a combination of an elastic response due to rapid local readjustments of bond angles and distances and a viscous, or time-dependent, response due to configurational changes, and it is necessary to find material parameters that can be used to describe this complex behavior.

Fortunately, many polymers, at least at small strains, appear to behave as linear viscoelastic materials, i.e., the stress–strain relations are a function of time but not of strain magnitude. Such materials are said to obey the Boltzmann superposition principle(6, 7) and the response of the system to an external stimulus is a result of its entire past stress or strain history. For such linear viscoelastic materials, it is possible to define the mechanical response of a polymer by means of time-dependent tensile or shear moduli $E(t)$ and $G(t)$ or by means of time-dependent tensile and shear compliances $D(t)$ and $J(t)$ and to derive expressions for these in terms of a distribution of relaxation times which is characteristic for each material. Once these functions, or suitably related functions, can be obtained from experiment on a given polymer, it then becomes possible to combine this knowledge with the usual methods and techniques of viscoelasticity and theoretical mechanics to predict mechanical behavior for any given experimental situation.

The desired material characteristics or functions can be obtained from relaxation studies, from creep studies, and from dynamic experiments. To define completely the behavior of a linear viscoelastic material, it is necessary to obtain experimental data over many decades of time and this, of necessity, involves use of several different experimental techniques. Relaxation and creep experiments, for example, can conveniently provide data from about 1 sec to 10^6 sec and dynamic experiments can be used to obtain knowledge of short time dependence in the general range 1 to 10^{-7} sec. It is desirable, and generally necessary, to make measurements over a wide range of temperature, as well as of frequency, so as to cover a sufficiently wide range of material response.

Linear viscoelastic behavior can be described in terms of simple combinations of spring elements, representing elastic response, in which Hooke's law is obeyed, and dashpot elements, representing viscous response in which Newton's law is obeyed, i.e., stress is proportional to rate of change of strain. A linear element and a viscous element in series are said to constitute a Maxwell solid, while a linear element and a viscous element in parallel are said to constitute a Kelvin or a Voigt solid. Each of these models predicts some aspects of observed polymer behavior, but they also lead to some predictions not in accord with the response of actual polymeric materials. The simplest model which leads at least to the salient features of the experimental data consists of three (or four) elements. The three-element model is a spring in series with a Voigt element and the four-element model is a combination of a Voigt element in series with a Maxwell element. Models of this type predict that under a constant stress the material will continue to deform or creep with increasing time, that under strain the stress required to maintain the strain will continue to decrease or relax with time, and that under sinusoidal oscillation at variable frequency the strain will be out of phase with the stress, the modulus will show dispersion, and the mechanical loss or internal friction, as defined in Section 3-2,B,4, will pass through a maximum as a function of frequency (or temperature). Most polymers do exhibit such general behavior, at least to a first approximation, and in appropriate ranges of temperature and frequency. However, the structure of polymers is too complex to be describable in terms of but a single relaxation or retardation time. It is therefore customary to consider generalized models in which a discrete or continuous spectrum of relaxation times is involved in order to represent the behavior of a real polymer system (6).

2. STRESS-RELAXATION BEHAVIOR

Consider first a simple relaxation experiment in which a given material is held at constant deformation, and the tensile stress required to maintain the deformation is then monitored as a function of time. The time-dependent relaxation modulus, $E(t)$, can now be used instead of the static elastic modulus E to characterize the specific material. This relaxation modulus is defined by

$$E(t) = \frac{S(t)}{\epsilon_0} \qquad (3\text{-}30)$$

where $S(t)$ is the observed value of the relaxes stress at time t, and ϵ_0 is the initial value of the strain. Since polymers show stress relaxation to some degree, the rigidity of the material is not constant but decreases with increasing time. For a simple Maxwell model, one would expect the stress relaxation modulus to show an exponential time dependence, i.e.,

$$E(t) = E_0 e^{-t/\tau} \qquad (3\text{-}31)$$

where E_0 is the value of the modulus at time $t = 0$. For a generalized Maxwell model consisting of an array of n discrete units arranged in parallel, the corresponding equation would be given by

$$E(t) = \sum_{i=1}^{n} E_i e^{-t/\tau_i} \qquad (3\text{-}32)$$

where E_i and τ_i are the respective modulus and relaxation time for the ith element. If the actual material approaches at very long times an equilibrium value of the modulus E_∞ that is not zero, allowance can be made for this by including in the generalized Maxwell model one additional spring element without an accompaning dashpot. If such a model is considered, one simply replaces the left-hand side of Eq. (3-32) by $E(t) - E_\infty$.

For a continuous distribution of relaxation times, instead of a discrete set, the relaxation modulus is given by

$$E(t) = \int_0^\infty E(\tau) e^{-t/\tau} \, d\tau \qquad (3\text{-}33)$$

Therefore if $E(t)$ [or $E(t) - E_\infty$] is known from the experimental data, it is, in principle, possible to solve for the distribution function $E(t)$, since $E(t)$ is simply the Laplace transform of $E(\tau)$. It may, however, be difficult to determine $E(\tau)$, as $E(t)$ is usually given by a set of experimental values or a graph and it may not be possible to express this graph in the form of an analytical function whose inverse Laplace transform is known. Another difficulty is that $E(t)$ is usually known only over a finite time scale rather than for the entire time scale from zero to infinity. To surmount these difficulties various approximate procedures have been developed (6) which enable one to determine the distribution function $E(\tau)$ to first or higher-order approximations.

The viscoelastic behavior of a polymer is frequently expressed in terms of a so-called relaxation distribution function $H(\tau)$ [$= \tau E(\tau)$] which arises when a log time scale is used. In this case, we have, instead of Eq. (3-33),

$$E(t) = \int_{-\infty}^{\infty} H(\tau)e^{-t/\tau}d(\ln\tau) \tag{3-34}$$

If the viscoelastic material is subject to shear rather than to tension, all of the above equations are still applicable provided we replace E_i by G_i and $E(\tau)$ by $G(\tau)$. The shear relaxation modulus is related to the tensile relaxation modulus in similar fashion to the relation [Eq. (3-21)] given in the preceding section for the static elastic moduli, viz.,

$$G(\tau) = \frac{E(\tau)}{2(1 + \nu)} \tag{3-35}$$

Similarly, one can write appropriate equations for the bulk relaxation modulus, $K(t)$.

3. CREEP BEHAVIOR

If a constant tensile stress is applied to a viscoelastic material it will continue to deform with increasing time. The behavior of the material can now most conveniently be described in terms of a time-dependent tensile compliance $D(t)$. This creep compliance is defined by

$$D(t) = \frac{\epsilon(t)}{S_0} \tag{3-36}$$

where $\epsilon(t)$ is the measured strain at time t and S_0 is the magnitude of the applied stress.

If the viscoelastic material is represented by a Kelvin unit in series with a Maxwell unit, the tensile compliance will be given by

$$D(t) = D_g + D_0(1 - e^{-t/\tau}) + \frac{t}{\eta} \qquad (3\text{-}37)$$

where D_g is the glassy-state compliance, D_0 the equilibrium or long-time compliance of the Voigt element, τ the retardation time of the Voigt element, and η the limiting steady-state viscosity. The first term thus represents the instantaneous elastic response of the system, the second term represents the delayed elastic response, and the third term represents the continued flow of the material with time. Unfortunately, it is not usually possible to characterize a given polymer by only one relaxation time. A better representation of an actual polymer solid is by a generalized Kelvin model in which a discrete, or a continuous, series of Voigt elements is included along with the series spring and dashpot used to represent the instantaneous response and the limiting flow.

The expression for the time-dependent compliance for a discrete set of τ's is given by

$$D(t) = D_g + \sum_{i=1}^{n} D_i(1 - e^{-t/\tau_i}) + \frac{t}{n} \qquad (3\text{-}38)$$

and for a continuous set by

$$D(t) = D_g + \int_0^\infty D(\tau)(1 - e^{-t/\tau})\,d\tau + \frac{t}{n} \qquad (3\text{-}39)$$

The distribution function $D(\tau)$ can now be used to characterize the time-dependent nature of a given viscoelastic material.

However, as noted earlier for $E(\tau)$, and for the same reasons, it is not easy to obtain the function $D(\tau)$ from the experimental data. Therefore one has the choice of representing the viscoelastic behavior directly in terms of the experimentally measured compliance $D(t)$ or of using approximate analytical procedures to calculate the distribution function $D(\tau)$. Literature data are also frequently given in terms of a retardation function $L(\tau)[= \tau D(\tau)]$, as this is a more convenient function when a log time scale is used. In this case, we have

$$D(t) = D_g + \int_{-\infty}^{\infty} L(\tau)(1 - e^{-t/\tau})\,d(\ln \tau) + \frac{t}{n} \qquad (3\text{-}40)$$

Creep experiments, like relaxation experiments, may also be conveniently carried out under shear conditions rather than tensile conditions. Equivalent equations to those given above apply in this case if one substitutes J_i for D_i and $J(\tau)$ for $D(\tau)$ where the symbol $J(t)$ is used to represent the time-dependent shear creep compliance.

For a completely elastic material the tensile or shear compliance would be simply the inverse of the corresponding tensile or shear modulus. For viscoelastic materials, this simple relation is no longer true, although the moduli and the compliances remain in inverse relation to one another.

A given viscoelastic material can be completely characterized by either its relaxation spectrum $H(\tau)$ or its retardation spectrum $L(\tau)$. If either of these are known over the whole time scale, the other can be calculated and the mechanical response of the material to constant stress, constant strain, alternating stress, or other more complex stress conditions can be predicted(8).

4. BEHAVIOR UNDER SINUSOIDALLY VARYING STRESS

Much of the experimental relaxation data on polymers has been obtained from dynamic experiments in which the response of the system to an alternating stress is observed. In such experiments it is customary(6) to describe material behavior in terms of a complex dynamic modulus $E^*(\omega) = E'(\omega) + iE''(\omega)$, or a complex dynamic compliance $D^*(\omega) = D'(\omega) - iD''(\omega)$. Two quantities are determined experimentally. The first is the in-phase modulus or compliance components $E'(\omega)$ or $D'(\omega)$. The second is usually the out-of-phase components $E''(\omega)$ and $D''(\omega)$, or the tangent of the phase angle δ between stress and strain. This latter, which is a measure of internal friction, is related to the moduli or compliance components as follows:

$$\tan \delta = \frac{E''(\omega)}{E'(\omega)} = \frac{D''(\omega)}{D'(\omega)} \tag{3-41}$$

The viscoelastic material may be considered in terms of a generalized Voigt model, in which case it is more convenient to deal with compliances, or in terms of a generalized Maxwell model, in which case it is simplest to deal with moduli. Consider the generalized Maxwell model having a discrete set of spring-dashpot elements, and hence a discrete set of relaxation terms τ_i. In this model the real and imaginary components of the dynamic complex modulus are (7)

$$E'(\omega) = \sum_i E_i \frac{\omega^2 \tau_i^2}{1 + \omega^2 \tau_i^2} \tag{3-42}$$

$$E''(\omega) = \sum_i E_i \frac{\omega \tau_i}{1 + \omega^2 \tau_i^2}$$

If the relaxation times are closely spaced or assumed to be continuous we may replace the sum by an integral. In this case

$$E'(\omega) = \int_0^\infty E(\tau)\frac{\omega^2\tau^2}{1+\omega^2\tau^2}d\tau$$

$$E''(\omega) = \int_0^\infty E(\tau)\frac{\omega\tau}{1+\omega^2\tau^2}d\tau \tag{3-43}$$

where $E(\tau)$ is the distribution function of relaxation times, and $E(\tau)d\tau$ is the contribution to the respective moduli of those elements whose relaxation times fall between τ and $\tau + d\tau$.

If these equations are written in terms of log time, then $E(\tau)$ should be replaced by the relaxation spectrum $H(\tau)$. Also if one is dealing with alternating shear stress instead of alternating tensile stress, then the following replacements should be made: $G'(\omega)$ for $E'(\omega)$, $G''(\omega)$ for $E''(\omega)$, and $G(\tau)$ for $E(\tau)$.

If dynamic compliances are used instead of moduli, interconversions can be made by noting $D^*(\omega) = 1/E^*(\omega)$. The component compliances are not simple reciprocals of the component moduli, but are given by (6)

$$D'(\omega) = \frac{E'(\omega)}{E'(\omega)^2 + E''(\omega)^2}$$

$$D''(\omega) = \frac{E''(\omega)}{E'(\omega)^2 + E''(\omega)^2} \tag{3-44}$$

Also if we deal with compliances, the retardation spectrum $L(\tau)$ will appear instead of $H(\tau)$.

To determine the relaxation or retardation spectrum, it is helpful to supplement the dynamic method, which gives response at short times, with creep or relaxation data, which measure response at long times. However, by varying temperature as well as frequency and using a time–temperature equivalence principle, an extremely wide range of material response can be obtained by use of the dynamic method alone. Also, because of the difficulties already mentioned in connection with the determination of the functions $E(\tau)$, $D(\tau)$, $H(\tau)$, or $L(\tau)$ from the data, many investigators have simply reported experimental values of the tensile or shear dynamic modulus itself without attempts at determining relaxation spectra. Such data, especially when carried out on carefully prepared specimens, show considerable character and, therefore, analysis of these data enables one to draw pertinent conclusions concerning the relation of various chemical and physical factors to the relaxation behavior and to the occurrence of transition regions. Various examples of material response to relaxation, creep, and dynamic conditions will be given later for polymers of different chemical composition and for polymers subject to different crystallization and annealing conditions.

5. EFFECTS OF TEMPERATURE AND TIME–TEMPERATURE SUPERPOSITION

For viscoelastic materials, it has been observed by many investigators that there is a close relationship between the effects of temperature and the effects of time on material parameters. Leaderman(9) showed many years ago that creep curves taken at different temperatures could be superimposed by a horizontal shift of the log time axis. Tobolsky(7) and co-workers have also shown that stress-relaxation data taken at different temperatures can likewise be superimposed by making an appropriate shift of the time scale. A similar conclusion was reached by Ferry(6) and co-workers relative to dynamic modulus data taken as a function of frequency at various temperatures.

This general phenomenon is known as the time-temperature superposition principle. According to this principle, data on any viscoelastic parameter taken at different temperatures as a function of $\log t$ or $\log \omega$ can be superimposed onto one master curve at some reference temperature by simply introducing a suitable shift factor a_T, which is itself a function of temperature. This implies that the change of temperature simply multiplies all relaxation times by the same factor.

Williams et al. (10) have shown that for a variety of amorphous polymers the shift factor a_T varies with temperature approximately as follows:

$$\log a_T = -\frac{17.44(T - T_g)}{51.6 + T - T_g} \tag{3-45}$$

In this equation the reference temperature is taken as the glass transition temperature. However, any reference temperature T_0 may be used. Also, to obtain superposition, the actual data in the form of stress relaxation moduli $E(t)$ or $G(t)$, or in the form of complex moduli $E'(\omega)$ and $E''(\omega)$ or $G'(\omega)$ and $G''(\omega)$, should be multiplied by the ratio of T_0/T and by the ratio of densities at the respective temperatures, ρ_0/ρ, and then plotted vs. $\log (t/a_T)$ or vs. $\log (a_T\omega)$. The first multiplication is to take account of the fact that for rubberlike materials the modulus varies directly with temperature, and the second multiplication is to take account of the change of density between the actual temperature and the reference temperature due to thermal expansion.

The time–temperature superposition principle is usually applied only to amorphous polymers such as polyisobutylene. However, some attempts have been made to apply it as well to partially crystalline polymers(*11–13*). One problem arising here is that the internal structure of the polymer, i.e., the orientation, the degree of crystallinity, and the size and perfection of the crystalline portions may well be altered by the change in temperature. In this case one would not expect either time–temperature superposition or the Boltzmann superposition theorem to be valid.

For amorphous polymers, however, time–temperature superposition is of considerable interest and usefulness. It enables one to obtain estimates of the distribution functions even when only a limited frequency range is available. Also by varying the temperature, values of $H(\tau)$ or $L(\tau)$ obtained by the different methods can be compared. Although the Eq. (3-45) is a purely phenomenological description of the data, it does have some theoretical justification, and its form can be derived from Doolittle's relation(*14*) between viscosity and available free volume.

6. MOLECULAR THEORY OF VISCOELASTICITY

The phenomenological theory of viscoelastic materials as developed in the preceding subsections is very useful for interrelating different types of experimental measurements, but it gives no insight into the molecular basis for viscoelasticity.

Unfortunately, there is as yet no complete molecular theory which will enable the various viscoelastic parameters to be computed from molecular quantities. However, some notable advances have been made in developing at least a partial molecular basis for understanding viscoelasticity phenomena in certain restricted temperature and frequency regions. For example, the theories as put forth by Rouse(*15*), Bueche (*16*), Zimm(*17*), etc., do make some predictions with regard to the relaxation spectrum $H(\tau)$ and the retardation spectrum $L(\tau)$ that seem to be at least approximately obeyed in intermediate ranges of the time scale.

The Rouse theory, as originally developed, considered the problem of polymer molecules in a dilute solution subject to the action of forces varying sinusoidally with time. The individual molecules were assumed to be completely free to rearrange themselves in random conformation, i.e., completely free rotation about bonds was assumed. Clearly any theory based on these assumptions could not be expected to hold at temperatures below T_g, but it might be useful in describing phenomena in the rubbery region above the glass transition. In fact, the same assumptions, that rotation is free and conformations can change without change in energy, are those made for an ideal rubber.

Both Rouse and Bueche assume, furthermore, that the polymer molecules can be divided into N equal submolecules of arbitrary length and that these submolecules behave like elastic springs (entropy springs) with a spring constant, as in the kinetic theory of rubber elasticity, that is, proportional to absolute temperature. The segment lengths are assumed to be sufficiently large so that the Gaussian distribution function for random chain conformations is realized. This assumption clearly will not be realized for short segment lengths, but it is considered applicable (6) for segments involving 50 or so carbon atoms.

The motion of the individual molecules and segments is also assumed to be opposed by viscous forces arising from movement of the junction points of the various segments relative to the solvent or to the surrounding medium. A monomeric frictional coefficient h_0 or a segmental friction coefficient $f_0 = qh_0$, where q is the number of monomer units in the submolecules, is then introduced. The theory does not account for h_0 or f_0 in terms of any molecular parameters, but considers them as parameters to be determined experimentally or that can be related to the viscosity as measured in steady-state shear flow.

With these assumptions, Rouse attempts to describe the mechanical behavior of this system to applied forces in terms of a normal mode analysis, with each mode making a discrete contribution to the relaxation or retardation spectra. For an applied sinusoidal shear stress, it can be shown (6, 7) that this theory leads to the following expressions for the in-phase and out-of-phase shear modulus.

$$G'(\omega) = nkT \sum_{p=1}^{N} \left(\frac{\omega^2 \tau_p^2}{1 + \omega^2 \tau_p^2} \right) \qquad p = 1, 2, \ldots, N \qquad (3\text{-}46)$$

$$G''(\omega) = nkT \sum_{p=1}^{N} \left(\frac{\omega \tau_p}{1 + \omega^2 \tau_p^2} \right) \qquad p = 1, 2, \ldots, N \qquad (3\text{-}47)$$

where n is the number of molecules per cc, and where the relaxation times, τ_p, associated with the various modes, are proportional to the segmental frictional constant f_0. Since this constant can also be expressed in terms of the difference of the steady-state shear viscosity η and the viscosity of the solvent η_s, one finds for τ_p the following expression:

$$\tau_p = \frac{6(\eta - \eta_s)}{\pi^2 p^2 nkT} \qquad p = 1, 2, \ldots, N \qquad (3\text{-}48)$$

Rouse's theory can be extended to the case of an undiluted polymer. In this case, no solvent viscosity as such enters, but one considers each polymer segment as moving in a medium consisting of the other polymer molecules. The frictional resistance will in this case be much higher and the segmental motions much slower. For this case the above equation becomes

$$\tau_p = \frac{6\eta M}{\pi^2 p^2 \rho R T} \qquad p = 1, 2, \ldots, N \qquad (3\text{-}49)$$

after n is replaced by $(\rho N_0/M)$ where N_0 is Avogadro's number and M the molecular weight. Note that Eq. (3-49) predicts that each relaxation time has the same temperature dependence and hence a change in temperature simply translates viscoelastic parameters along the log t axis. This is in accord with the method of reduced variables and with the time–temperature superposition principle.

The Rouse theory enables one to write expressions for the retardation spectrum $L(\tau)$ and for the relaxation spectrum $H(\tau)$. According to the theory, it is found that log H vs. log t, or the log of the reduced modulus $E_r(t)$ vs. log t, should be a straight line with slope of $-\frac{1}{2}$, and log L vs. log t should be a straight line with slope of $+\frac{1}{2}$.

These predictions are realized quite well for dilute polymer solutions and to some extent for undiluted amorphous polymers. They appear to be applicable in an intermediate range of relaxation times, i.e., in the region above the glass transition, where the modulus has fallen to low values and where the assumptions of free rotation and random configurations are probably valid. Many polymers do show, in accordance with the theory, a wedge-shaped distribution of relaxation times in this intermediate region. The theory is not applicable at or below the glass transition temperature; in fact it would predict that the limiting modulus at very high frequency, or low temperature, should be proportional to T, whereas the modulus of polymers below T_g decreases with increasing temperature. The theory is not applicable also where crystallinity or bulky side branches inhibit free movement of the backbone chain. Difficulties arise also for undiluted polymers if the molecular weight is so high that molecular entanglements affect chain mobility.

It is perhaps of some interest to note that mechanical models can also be devised (*18*) which can rather directly be related to the concepts of these molecular theories. These phenomenological models, however, are not those of the type heretofore discussed, comprising combinations of Maxwell and Voigt elements, but are of a type referred to as "ladder" networks.

Various attempts have been made to overcome some of the difficulties encountered in the Rouse theory and modifications to take account of entanglements for high molecular weight polymers have been considered by Bueche[19]. A more recent theory of Pao[20] based on irreversible statistical mechanics sheds more light on the concept of the monomeric friction constant and shows further that this friction factor itself depends upon frequency.

C. Rubberlike Solids

An ideal rubber is defined as a material in which the internal energy is not a function of the elongation. For such a material, thermodynamic arguments show[7] that the force required to produce a given elongation is a result only of the decrease of entropy which accompanies the deformation. They also show that, for constant elongation, the tensile force to maintain this elongation increases linearly with increase of absolute temperature.

Actual cross-linked elastomers, both natural and synthetic, behave very much like ideal rubbers. They deform elastically under load but they differ from ordinary elastic solids such as glasses, metals, or crystals in that the recoverable elastic deformation may be several hundred per cent rather than a fraction of one per cent. Even noncross-linked polymers may exhibit rubberlike characteristics if their molecular weight is sufficiently high and if the temperature is above that of the glass or melting transition. An observed characteristic of rubberlike materials is that, although they do show complete elastic recovery even after large deformations, Hooke's law does not hold and the stress is a complex function of the elongation. Another observed characteristic is that there is essentially no volume change on extension. This implies that Poisson's ratio for a rubber is very close to 0.5, and that at small strains where Hooke's law holds, the shear modulus is equal to one-third the tensile modulus.

To describe the equilibrium mechanical behavior of a rubber, the so-called theory of rubberlike elasticity has been developed[21,22]. This theory, based on application of statistical mechanics to the behavior of a three-dimensional network of active chains containing freely rotating chain segments, predicts the form of the stress–strain relation as well as its dependence upon temperature. It is customary for a rubberlike material to express the deformation or elongation in terms of the extension ratio α. This ratio is defined as

$$\alpha = \frac{L}{L_0} \tag{3-50}$$

where L is the actual length of the specimen under the applied tensile stress and L_0 is the original unstressed length. The predicted stress–strain relation in terms of the extension ratio α is

$$\sigma = \nu_e kT \left(\alpha - \frac{1}{\alpha^2}\right) \qquad (3\text{-}51)$$

where σ is the tensile stress based on the initial cross-sectional area, ν_e is the number of active chains of the network per unit volume, and k is the usual Boltzmann constant.

As Eq. (3-51) shows, the relation between stress and elongation is not linear and hence the concept of a tensile modulus has meaning only at very small strains. The predicted form of the stress-elongation curve is S-shaped, with the apparent modulus at first decreasing with increasing strain but then rapidly increasing with increasing elongation as high extension ratios are reached. Equation (3-51) is often written in terms of a quantity M_c, defined as the number-average molecular weight of the active chains. In terms of M_c, ν_e is given by

$$\nu_e = \frac{\rho N_0}{M_c} \qquad (3\text{-}52)$$

and hence Eq. (3-51) becomes

$$\sigma = \left(\frac{\rho RT}{M_c}\right)\left(\alpha - \frac{1}{\alpha^2}\right) \qquad (3\text{-}53)$$

where ρ is the density, $R = N_0 k$ is the gas constant, and N_0 is Avogadro's number.

The elastic tensile modulus at small strains can now be written directly in terms of ν_e or M_c and the temperature. Let $L = L_0(1 + \epsilon)$ where ϵ is the usual tensile strain. Then $\alpha = 1 + \epsilon$, and the tensile modulus E at small strains is

$$E = \frac{\sigma}{\epsilon} \cong 3\nu_e kT \qquad (3\text{-}54)$$

or

$$\cong \frac{3\rho RT}{M_c} \qquad (3\text{-}55)$$

Also since at small strains the shear modulus for a rubber is simply one-third the tensile modulus, the above equations can be written

$$G = \frac{\tau}{\gamma} = \nu_e kT = \frac{\rho RT}{M_c} \qquad (3\text{-}56)$$

Thus the theory predicts that the initial tensile or shear modulus should increase linearly with increasing temperature and this prediction is in accord with experiment. Notice also that from the observed slope of the modulus temperature curve one can, by use of Eq. (3-54), (3-55), or (3-56), determine the average molecular weight between effective cross-links or the number of effective chains per unit volume. This method is used extensively for estimating the amount of cross-linking that occurs in a polymer upon irradiation.

For large values of applied deformations, actual rubbers may crystallize. Under these circumstances, Eqs. (3-51) and (3-53) can no longer be expected to apply. For large strains Eq. (3-21), relating the tensile and shear moduli, also no longer holds, since this equation was derived for elastic solids subject to small strains. However, the kinetic theory of rubber elasticity when applied to shear predicts that, for an ideal rubber, the stress–strain relation in shear is a linear one even though this is not true for the stress-strain relation in tension. Hence Eq. (3-56) is applicable for large strains as well as small ones.

The above equations enable one to calculate an expected value of the initial tensile or shear modulus. For a soft vulcanized rubber having a density of 0.923 at room temperature (25°C), and an assumed M_c value of 10,000, we find

and
$$E = 7.43 \times 10^{10} \times .923 \times 10^{-4} = 6.86 \times 10^6 \frac{dyn}{cm^2}$$
$$G = \frac{E}{3} = 2.29 \times 10^6 \frac{dyn}{cm^2} \tag{3-57}$$

These values are the correct order of magnitude values for most elastomers.

Although there is some disagreement on the precise form the correction factor should take, it is necessary to modify Eq. (3-53) to take proper account of the relation between concentration of cross-links and concentration of active chains. Various modified forms have been developed(18,23). One of these is

$$\sigma = \frac{\rho R T}{M_c}\left(1 - \frac{2M_c}{M_n}\right)\left(\alpha - \frac{1}{\alpha^2}\right) \tag{3-58}$$

where M_n is the number-average molecular weight before cross-linking. If this modification is taken into account, the formula for the low-strain elastic modulus becomes

$$E = \frac{3\rho R T}{M_c}\left(1 - \frac{2M_c}{M_n}\right) \tag{3-59}$$

This expression is not valid when $2M_c > M_n$; under these conditions no network has formed and, in addition, this expression gives negative values of E. In many cases M_n is considerably larger than M_c and for high values of this ratio the correction factor in Eqs. (3-58) and (3-59) may be neglected.

D. Theoretical Calculations of Elastic Moduli for Polymer Solids

1. General Considerations

In principle it should be possible to calculate the expected value of the elastic constants for a given crystalline material if the crystal structure and the interatomic potentials are known. Calculations of this type have been made for some nonpolymeric materials and the agreement with experimental data is quite good (4).

Extension of these calculations of elastic moduli to polymers meets with two difficulties. First, polymers are not simple crystals of known crystalline structure. Most polymers have a complex, nonhomogeneous structure that in many cases consists of a combination of fairly well-ordered crystalline units joined together by tie molecules, disordered chains, and/or amorphous regions of varying degrees of order. Second, the correct form of the interatomic or intermolecular potentials to use in the calculations is not known, and hence appropriate force constants must be assumed, frequently from infrared or Raman data on low molecular weight analogs.

Still another difficulty is that in many polymers, as a result of the nature of the chain structure, there is a relatively low energy barrier to torsional motion of chain segments. Hence the local conformation of the polymer molecule and the local interchain cohesion forces may be continually changing as a result of thermal agitation. Even for highly crystalline polymers in which rotational motions in the ordered crystalline regions are considerably hindered, the mechanical response of the polymer to applied loads will be largely determined by the nature and rigidity of the disordered or noncrystalline portion of the polymer. In fact it is not unusual, even in highly drawn polymers, for the over-all specimen modulus to be $\frac{1}{10}$ to $\frac{1}{50}$ times the modulus of the crystalline units as determined by changes in X-ray diffraction spacings with applied stress.

Despite difficulties, various attempts have been and are being made to calculate the expected magnitude of the elastic constants of polymer crystals of different composition. Most of these calculations are based on assumed forms of intra- or intermolecular potentials or on force constants for bond extension and valence angle deformation as estimated from spectroscopic data. Such calculations do differentiate between polymers of different structure but, for other than the extended zigzag conformation, the calculations themselves become quite complex and require the making of various assumptions which are not readily substantiated. To the extent that the crystal structure of the actual polymer in question approaches that of the planar zigzag arrangement, so that bond angle deformation and bond extension are the only forms of deformation present, the agreement between the calculated values and the experimental values is quite reasonable. Many of the theoretical calculations of moduli apply only to the ideal case of extended chains arranged in perfect alignment; only highly oriented crystalline polymers approach this limiting condition. For unoriented bulk polymers, even if measurements are made at liquid helium temperatures or at very high frequencies, the measured modulus values fall one to two decades below the calculated values. For oriented polymers, the specimen modulus is frequently considerably below the modulus of the crystalline elements as determined from changes in X-ray diffraction spacings (24,25).

2. ESTIMATE OF LATTICE MODULUS IN CHAIN DIRECTION

Let us consider a fully extended polymer chain. For polyethylene, for example, the chain conformation would be the usual zigzag one. The distance between alternate carbon atoms is about 2.54 Å and the angle between respective bonds is close to the expected tetrahedral value of 109.5°.

Assuming that when a tensile load is applied to such a chain the bonds remain straight, two types of deformation can occur. The bond lengths can increase and the valence angles can open up. The energy required to produce these types of deformation can be estimated from analysis of IR and Raman spectra. The required energy is considerably smaller for bond angle deformability than for bond extension. For example, an energy only of the order of 1 kcal/mol is necessary to open up the angle between two adjacent valence bonds by about 10°, while an energy of about 10 times this amount is required to extend the bond length about 5% (26).

From the estimated energy values or from the observed vibration frequencies, it is possible to compute an average value of the so-called restoring force, which is generated upon extension of a molecular chain having a particular type of linkage. The calculated modulus value for an array of parallel extended cellulosic chains has been found to fall in the approximate range from 8×10^{11} to 12×10^{11} dyn/cm^2, depending upon the force constants used(27). These calculated values are much higher than observed modulus values for unoriented polymers. However, they are comparable to measured values for some of the natural, highly oriented cellulosic materials. For example, Meyer and Lotmar (27) give the following values for the fiber modulus obtained by longitudinal vibration experiments: native ramie, 5 to 7×10^{11} dyn/cm^2; native hemp, 6 to 8×10^{11} dyn/cm^2 and native flax, 8 to 11×10^{11} dyn/cm^2.

Other investigators such as Lyons(28,29), Treloar(30–32), Asahina and Enomoto(33,34), and Odajima and Maeda(35) have made additional and more refined calculations of the elastic modulus of polymer crystals. These various calculations seldom agree with one another because of differences in assumptions made, slight differences in analytical treatment, and use of different values of force constants, intermolecular potentials, and the interatomic distances. Some of these calculations, such as that of Odajima for a polyethylene crystal, are based on the method of Born and Huang(36). The calculated values of the elastic modulus for various polymer crystals are given in Table 3-1, along with experimental values of what is termed the "lattice" modulus, from observed changes in the X-ray diffraction spacings of fibers and films with applied stress. For the lattice modulus one finds some differences in the values obtained by different experimenters, possibly arising from errors of measurement as well as from differences in sample properties resulting from different past histories.

Inspection of Table 3-1 leads to the following conclusions:

(1) The highest experimental lattice modulus, $\sim 2.5 \times 10^{12}$ dyn/cm^2 occurs for those polymers which do adopt the planar zigzag structure. For such a structure, deformation should occur only by the opening up of bond angles or by the extension of bond lengths. Hence one might expect fairly good agreement between the experimentally observed values and the theoretical, derived ones, and this does seem to be the case. The theoretical values given for PVC (see table) are for syndiotactic PVC which also assumes the planar zigzag structure.

(2) For crystalline polymers in helical conformations with a large number of chain segments per turn of the helix, such as PTFE, the modulus values are still very high ($\sim 1.5 \times 10^{12}$ dyn/cm^2) and the agreement with the theoretically calculated values is good.

(3) For polymers in helical conformation with a small number of chain segments per turn, which therefore have contracted fiber identity

TABLE 3-1

Comparison of Calculated and Measured Lattice Moduli for Various Polymers

		Measured lattice modulus		Calculated lattice modulus	
Material	Plane	Value in 10^{10} dyn/cm²	Ref.	Value in 10^{10} dyn/cm²	Ref.
Polethylene (PE)	(002)	235	(25)	182	(30)
				340	(37)
				290	(38)
				250	(35)
Polyvinylalcohol (PVAl)	(020)	250	(25)	182–340	(30, 37)
Polyvinylchloride (PVC)				160–230	(33)
Polytetrafluoroethylene (PTFE)	(0015)	153	(25)	160	(37)
Cellulose I	(040)	127	(25)	77–121	(27)
				180	(28)
				57	(31)
Polyethyleneterephthalate (PETP)	($\bar{1}$05)	74	(25)	122	(32)
		137	(24)	146	(29)
Polyoxymethylene (POM)	(009)	53	(25)	150–220	(33)
				40–102	(38)
Polypropylene (PP)	(003)	41	(25)	10–49	(33)
				28–33	(38)
Nylon 6 (α form)	(020)	24.5	(25)	157[a]	(29)
				196[a]	(30)
Polystyrene (PS)	($10\bar{2}$)	11.8	(25)		
		9.0	(39)		
Polyethyleneoxide (PEO)	($20\bar{7}$)	9.8	(25)	4.5–4.8	(34)
				7.6–9.0	(25)

[a]Calculations are for nylon 6-6.

periods compared to the extended chain values, rotation about single bonds may also contribute to the deformations produced by applied stress; therefore this must be considered in the theoretical treatment. Hence the lattice-modulus values for materials such as POM, PP, PS, and PEO are expected to be less than for PE. As Table 3-1 shows, the moduli of these helical-type polymers are only about $\frac{1}{4}$ to $\frac{1}{25}$ of the straight chain polymers. For PEO, the 4.8×10^{10} dyn/cm² and 9.0×10^{10} dyn/cm² values were calculated using a Urey-Bradley-type force field but with consideration of only bond angle changes.

In the tests conducted by Sakurada et al.(25), measurements were made of the specimen modulus E_s obtained directly from the slope of the specimen stress–strain curves, as well as the lattice modulus E_l obtained from changes of X-ray spacings. It was found that the over-all specimen modulus varied considerably with the form of the specimen but that the lattice modulus was essentially independent of specimen form or of microcrystalline texture. For example, both a monofilament and a high-tenacity fiber specimen of PE gave the same value of E_l, viz., 235×10^{10} dyn/cm², but the specimen modulus E_s was 2.4×10^{10} dyn/cm² for the monofilament and 14.7×10^{10} dyn/cm² for the high-tenacity fiber. The ratio of specimen to lattice moduli was also found to vary considerably both with type of specimen and material. It varied from a high value of 0.42 for POM monofilament to a low value of 0.01 for a PE monofilament. The results suggest that for polymers with helical conformations like POM and PP, where rotation about bonds can also contribute to deformation under stress, the specimen modulus, which reflects the contribution to the amorphous part of the specimen, is closer in value to the lattice modulus than for the straight chain polymers.

It should also be noted that theoretical estimates of lattice modulus can be obtained from consideration of the Raman shifts of extended chain hydrocarbons. This method has been used by several investigators(40–42). For example, Mizushima and Shimanouchi(41) have shown that the sharp band below 800 cm^{-1} that is present in short chain polymethylenes in the solid state arises from longitudinal accordion-like motion of the extended zigzag carbon backbone. The experimentally observed frequencies of this band for the various n-paraffins tested were found to vary inversely with the number, n, of C atoms or with the chain length, L. These various frequencies could be correlated by use of the simple expression for the fundamental frequency of a continuous elastic rod, viz.,

$$\nu = \frac{m}{2L} \left(\frac{E}{\rho} \right)^{1/2}$$

where m is the order of the vibration, ρ the density, E the elastic modulus, and L the rod length. Mizushima and Shimanouchi(41) calculated E from the experimental value of the fundamental frequency

($m = 1$) and then found that the other predicted frequencies for higher orders were in excellent agreement with experiment. The calculated value of E for accordionlike extension of the zigzag chain was 3.4×10^{12} dyn/cm². This is the same as the value given for PE in Table 3-1 (*37*), where a Urey–Bradley type of force field, taking into account intramolecular force constants as well as intermolecular potentials, was used.

Additional experiments have since been made by Schaufele and Shimanouchi(*42*) on various pure hydrocarbons up to $C_{94}H_{190}$. For this latter material they were able to observe up to 31 overtones. From the empirical relation between the observed frequencies and the ratio (m/n) they were able to calculate an elastic modulus for the fully extended infinite chain. Their value is $E_l = 3.58 \times 10^{12}$ dyn/cm².

3. ESTIMATE OF TRANSVERSE LATTICE MODULUS

Very few calculations have yet been made of the modulus perpendicular to the chain direction of an oriented fiber or crystal. However, there are some data available for polyethylene. The lateral modulus is essentially determined by the intermolecular forces which for the *n*-paraffins, and for polyethylene, are almost entirely of the Van der Waal type.

In the treatment of Enomoto and Asahina(*43*), the intermolecular potentials of methane are used to estimate the intermolecular force constants for polyethylene. The CH_2 group is treated as a unit and the forces are calculated from a Lennard–Jones type of potential function for methane. The force constants corresponding to the three closest distances of approach are taken as 1.8×10^{-2} mdyn/Å for R = 4.12 Å, 1.4×10^{-2} mdyn/Å for R = 4.18 Å, and 0.3×10^{-2} mdyn/Å for R = 4.51 Å. The lateral elastic constants are then calculated using a Urey–Bradley-type force field. The calculated values are:

Along the *a* crystallographic direction, $E_a = 2.09 \times 10^{10}$ dyn/cm².
Along the *b* crystallographic direction, $E_b = 2.11 \times 10^{10}$ dyn/cm².

A somewhat similar calculation, but using slightly different values of the force constants, has been made also by Miyazawa and Kitagawa (*44*), yielding the values $E_a = 5.7 \times 10^{10}$ dyn/cm² and $E_b = 2.1 \times 10^{10}$ dyn/cm². Odajima and Maeda's treatment(*35*) gives values of $E_a = 4.7–5.9 \times 10^{10}$ dyn/cm² and $E_b = 8.3–9.1 \times 10^{10}$ dyn/cm², depending on the set of force constants used.

It is of interest now to compare these calculated values with experimentally observed values. Sakurada et al.[25] have applied known loads to drawn film specimens of different polymers and have measured the shifts in equatorial reflections of the X-ray patterns, taken at room temperature, due to the applied stress. From these shifts they were able to compute values of the transverse moduli, E_t for stresses applied in a perpendicular direction to the direction of draw. Some of their experimental values are given in Table 3-2.

From inspection of this Table 3-2, the following conclusions may be drawn.

(1) All the values of lateral modulus are low compared to the longitudinal values along the fiber axis. As the last column shows, the spread is greatest for the fully extended polymers but is considerably less for the helically coiled polymers for which deformation due to rotation about bond angles is an important response to applied stress.

(2) The experimentally observed values (Y_t) for polyethylene are in approximate agreement with the theoretically deduced values discussed above.

(3) The transverse lattice modulus is two to three times higher for PVAl than for PE. This is clearly a consequence of increased intermolecular cohesion arising from the presence of hydrogen bonds.

(4) The observed values for PP are in approximate agreement with the value 3.95×10^{10} dyn/cm^2 given by Samuels[45] for the intrinsic lateral sonic modulus at 10 kcs.

TABLE 3-2
Experimental Values of Transverse Lattice Modulus of Various Polymers[25]

Material	Lattice Plane	Transverse lattice modulus X-ray $E_t(10^{10}$ dyn/cm^2)	Specimen modulus stress–strain $Y_t(10^{10}$ dyn/cm^2)	Ratio E_t/Y_t	Ratio E_l/E_t
PE, a axis	(200)	3.1	2.0	1.9	75
PE, b axis	(020)	3.8			62
PVAl[a]	(10$\bar{1}$)	8.8	7.1	1.2	28
	(200)	8.7			29
PP	(110)	2.8	2.2	1.3	14
	(040)	3.1			13
POM	(10$\bar{1}$0)	7.8	4.7	1.7	7
PEO	(120)	4.3	0.6	7.3	2.3

[a]Polyvinylalcohol.

(5) The specimen moduli Y_t derived from stress–strain relations are, in general, slightly lower than the transverse lattice moduli. This is in marked contrast to the situation where loads are applied parallel to the fiber axis. In that case, the specimen modulus is only a small fraction of the lattice modulus.

(6) In view of the above, it appears that the modulus of amorphous regions is comparable to that of crystalline regions measured in a direction normal to the fiber axis.

3-3 EXPERIMENTAL METHODS, COMPARATIVE MODULUS VALUES, AND EFFECTS OF TEST ENVIRONMENT

A. Experimental Techniques

It is impossible because of space considerations to cite the many different experimental arrangements that have been developed for determination of the various modulus values. Nor is this necessary, as some of these techniques have now become so accepted and so useful that either the test method is covered by an applicable ASTM specification(46) or instruments of the appropriate type to make the necessary measurements are available commercially. In view of this situation, we will simply describe the general method of measurement used for each type of modulus, give the appropriate equations for determination of the desired stress–strain characteristics for some of the more widely used methods, and cite references to some of the other methods and some of the newer techniques which have been recently developed.

1. STATIC METHODS

a. STRESS–STRAIN PROPERTIES IN TENSION

The most common mechanical property test of all is the so-called simple tension test. Although it is not actually simple in interpretation, as it involves both shear deformation and volume dilatation of the specimen, it is perhaps the most convenient method of assessing the stress–strain characteristics of solid polymers and of determining Young's modulus of elasticity. The test consists simply of measuring the force required to extend a sample, at some constant rate of deformation, and at the same time of observing the resulting deformation, usually by electronic, mechanical, or optical recording of the changes in length of some given gage length upon the specimen(*47*). From the observed loads and deformations, the nominal tensile stress and nominal strain, based on original values of the cross-sectional area and length of the specimen, are computed. The test sample may be a rod, or a strip, or a tube, but it usually has a central reduced section in which the strains are measured.

Recommended procedures for study of the tensile properties of rigid plastics are discussed in considerable detail in ASTM Standard D638-64T.† Different testing speeds are suggested depending upon the material being investigated. For most modulus measurements, a speed of testing of 0.20–0.25 in. per min is used. The tensile stress–strain curve for a typical thermoplastic material has a form such as that shown in Fig. 3-2; in some cases there is no marked yield region and in other cases the over-all ductility ϵ_u may not be much greater than the ductility at yield ϵ_y. For most polymers, at least at small strains,

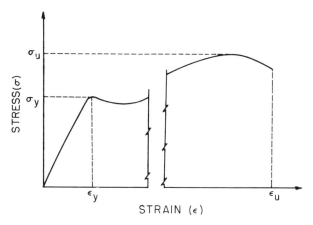

Figure 3-2. General form of tensile stress–strain curve of a rigid polymer.

there is a linear region in which stress is essentially directly proportional to strain. The tensile modulus E or E_t is determined from the slope of this portion, i.e.,

$$E_t = \frac{\Delta\sigma}{\Delta\epsilon} \tag{3-60}$$

For materials that do not show a significant linear region, the slope of the tangent at the origin or at very small stress values is recorded.

---

†All ASTM specifications cited in this chapter appear in ref. (*46*).

The recommended procedures are somewhat different if the polymer to be investigated is a rubberlike material or is in the form of a thin plastic sheet. The applicable ASTM specifications for these two cases are D412-64T and D882-64T. Additional standards are available for study of the tensile and compressive properties at subnormal and supernormal temperatures (D759-48, 1961), for study of plastics by use of microtensile specimens (D1708-59T), and for study of plastics at high speeds of loading (D2289-64T)(46).

It is also appropriate to represent tensile behavior in terms of a true stress–true strain relationship, especially if knowledge of the plastic region or of true ultimate strengths is desired(48). True stress and true strain are based on actual cross-sectional areas and actual gage lengths rather than initial values. When true stresses and strains are plotted rather than nominal ones, the general shape of the curve shown in Fig. 3-2 is changed. There is now no definite indication of a yield point and no apparent maximum in the σ–ϵ curve. Rather, the true stress–strain curve continues to rise steadily in the plastic range until fracture occurs. For knowledge of elastic modulus or of elastic behavior, either nominal or true stresses may be utilized.

A new method of measuring the static Young's modulus of materials, which claims high accuracy, has been reported by Sleeswyk(49). This method involves the testing of specimens of various lengths and correlating differences in strain with differences in gage length.

b. STRESS–STRAIN PROPERTIES IN SHEAR

Rather surprisingly there is, as yet, no standard ASTM test for determination of the static shear modulus G of rigid polymers. One method of determination which has been used for various materials is to measure the angle of twist, θ, of a circular rod or a thin-walled tube as it is subjected to an applied torque M. The behavior of the material in shear is then represented by the torque–twist curve or by the deduced shear-stress shear-strain curve. This curve, like that for tension, usually has a linear portion as well as a non-linear portion. If values of M and θ are taken for any point on the linear portion, the shear modulus is given by

$$G = \frac{ML}{\theta J} \qquad (3\text{-}61)$$

where L is the length of the specimen between grips and J is the polar moment of inertia of the cross section about the central axis.

A method somewhat similar to the above, but employing thin strips of thickness 1–3 mm, is recommended by ASTM for determination of the apparent rigidity modulus G for non rigid plastics. The procedure to be used is described in D1043-61T. Since for non rigid polymers Poisson's ratio ν is usually about $\frac{1}{2}$, this test will also give an approximate value for Young's modulus E since, from the relation given in Eq. (3-21),

$$E = 2G(1 + \nu) = 3G$$

It should be noted that some of the dynamic determinations of shear modulus, which will be considered later, can be carried out at such low frequencies that they also effectively provide knowledge of the "static" shear modulus. Apparatus for the determination of both Young's modulus and shear modulus over the temperature range $-25°$ to $100°C$ is described by Krosche and Treutsch(50). It has been pointed out (51) that the shear modulus of rubberlike materials can also be determined from observation of the indentation δ, produced by a cylindrical penetrator of radius r, subject to load P. The appropriate equation, for the case where Poisson's ratio is $\frac{1}{2}$, is

$$G = \frac{P}{8r\delta} \tag{3-62}$$

c. STRESS–STRAIN PROPERTIES IN BENDING

The behavior of plastics in flexure is frequently studied by the method described in ASTM D790-66. In this method the specimen, in the form of a horizontal rectangular beam, is supported by two knife edges, and a vertical concentrated load P is applied at the midpoint of the span. The deflection δ below the load point is recorded and a load-deflection curve then plotted. From the slope $m = P/\delta$ of the initial straight-line portion of this curve, the modulus of elasticity in bending, E_b, is computed using

$$E_b = \frac{ml^3}{48I} \tag{3-63}$$

where I is the moment of inertia of the cross section about the centroidal axis and l is the span length between supports. For low-modulus plastics, where the center deflection may approximate 10% of the span length, a correction to this equation is necessary(52).

Another method of test involves subjecting a specimen, in the form of a cantilever beam, to an applied bending moment and noting the angular deflection of the pendulum system used to apply the load. From the observed data, one can compute an apparent elastic modulus in the manner described in ASTM D747-63. For this test, it is customary to use specimens about 0.05 cm thick, 0.50 cm or more wide, and with a length/thickness ratio of 15 to 30. Values of E obtained from this test are generally in good agreement, for nonrigid polymers, with values of E computed from the measured G obtained from torsion testing according to D1043-61T.

d. STRESS–STRAIN PROPERTIES IN AXIAL COMPRESSION AND IN HYDROSTATIC COMPRESSION

A method for the determination of the properties of polymers under uniaxial compression is described in ASTM D695-63T. The specimen used in this test is a right circular cylinder with a length equal to twice its diameter. Both the applied compressive load and the compressive deformation between gage marks are recorded. Recommended testing speed is 0.5 in. per min. A stress–strain diagram is constructed and a compressive elastic modulus E_c is determined from the slope of the curve in the initial linear portion. For isotropic materials, the measured compressive modulus is usually the same, or almost the same, as the measured tensile modulus E_t.

A more significant material property is the response of the material to hydrostatic pressure, as in this case there is no shear component. The applicable modulus is now the bulk modulus K. Although there is no standard ASTM test for determination of the bulk modulus of polymers, the usual procedure is to measure either the axial compliance or the volume dilatation of a cylindrical specimen as the hydrostatic pressure is increased. Then K is computed from Eq. (3-10). Surland (*53*) used strain gage transducers to measure pressure changes and a differential transformer to measure axial changes. From his data, both K and Poisson's ratio ν can be computed. For rigid polymers, he finds K is comparable in value to E, but for nonrigid polymers K is orders of magnitude larger than E. He also finds that for materials containing voids, as rubbers or rocket propellants, K tends to increase with increasing pressure.

The bulk modulus, K, can also be computed from Eq. (3-28) if E and G are known and from Eq. (3-29) if E and ν are known. Some methods of measuring dynamic bulk modulus, such as that of Philippoff and Brodnyan(*54*), essentially also give values of static bulk modulus, as their method is applicable to frequencies as low as 10^{-4} Hz.

2. TRANSIENT METHODS

a. STRESS–STRAIN PARAMETERS IN CREEP

The standard method of studying creep, or the time dependence of deformation under constant load, is simply to subject a specimen to a constant load, usually in axial tension, and then monitor the resulting deformation as a function of time by means of a cathetometer or by electrical methods(6,55). Most investigators tend to work at low strains or stresses so as to remain in the range of linear viscoelastic behavior. The apparatus is frequently designed so that many specimens can be tested simultaneously. Measurements are generally made over a time period ranging from 10 sec to 10^3 or 10^4 hr. Recommended procedures for conducting creep tests are given in ASTM D674-56 (1961).

Creep measurements of polymers in tension have been discussed by Van Holde(56) and, at both low and high stresses, by Sauer et al.(57). Creep measurements in shear, using a sandwich arrangement, are described by Van Holde and Williams(58), and creep in torsion by Lethersich(59) and Plazek et al.(60). Recently Plazek(61), using a more sophisticated apparatus, with a magnetically suspended rotor, has measured creep compliances of a polystyrene fraction over the range from 10^{-10} to 10^4 cm²/dyn. Measurements of creep in tension, torsion, and bending have been carried out on polystyrene specimens by Marin(62). Creep and recovery properties of oriented materials have been reviewed by Ward(63).

b. STRESS–STRAIN PARAMETERS IN RELAXATION

It is usually possible to employ the same experimental arrangement for stress relaxation studies as for creep studies and the same ASTM standard, D674-56 (1961), applies. The only difference is that in creep we wish to measure the deformation $\epsilon(t)$ as a function of time for a given constant stress σ_0, while in stress relaxation we wish to measure the stress $\sigma(t)$ as a function of time for a given constant strain ϵ_0. This is usually done by means of some type of servomechanism which continually readjusts the applied stress so as to maintain the deformation constant. From $\sigma(t)$ and ϵ_0 values, the relaxation modulus $E_r(t)$ can then be computed. The relaxation modulus is a decreasing function of time. For representing the effects of temperature on relaxation phenomena, it is customary to use a so-called 10-sec relaxation modulus,

defined as
$$E_r(10) = \frac{\sigma(10)}{\epsilon_0} \qquad (3\text{-}64)$$

Stress relaxation has been measured under conditions of tension, torsion, and compression, and the constant strains employed have varied from fractions of 1% for rigid polymers to 50% or more for rubberlike materials.

Stress relaxation in tension has been described and discussed by many investigators, including Stern and Schaevitz(64) and Tobolsky (and McLoughlin)(7, 65–67). Measurements of stress relaxation in torsion have been carried out by Iwayanagi(68) and measurements of stress relaxation in compression by Wright(69). It is also possible to carry out both creep and relaxation studies under different types of stress by means of an Instron tester. Application of stress relaxation to soft polymers, rigid polymers, and fibers is discussed by Ferry(6).

Apparatus has been developed by Matsuoka and Maxwell(70) to monitor the hydrostatic pressure, as a function of time, required to maintain a given volume change. From these measurements, the bulk relaxation modulus $K_r(t)$ is determined.

3. DYNAMIC METHODS

Descriptions of the various dynamic methods of investigation of the stress–strain relations for viscoelastic polymers are given by Ferry(6) and Nielsen(55). These methods include free vibration methods, forced vibration methods, and pulse methods. The same experimental arrangement can frequently be used for both free decay studies and forced vibration studies. In the first case, the specimen is initially excited and then its displacement is monitored as a function of time, while in the second case the frequency of the excitation force is varied and the response is monitored as a function of this frequency.

a. LOW FREQUENCY METHODS ($<$ 0.1–100 Hz)

One of the most versatile instruments for low frequency dynamic studies of mechanical properties, especially for coverage of a wide temperature range, is the torsional pendulum. This instrument is designed to operate in the frequency range from about 0.1 to 10 Hz and it is generally closed in a chamber that can be cooled, heated, and sometimes evacuated. Instruments of this type have been described and used by many investigators, including Foppl(71), Ke(72), Nielsen(73), Schmeider and Wolf(74), Jenckel(75), Lethersich(76), Sinnott(77), McCrum(78), Fitzgerald et al.(79), and Koo et al.(80). A number of commercial variants are now on the market and ASTM standard

D2236-64T describes the procedure to be used. The recommended ASTM test specimen is a rectangular strip, with thickness from 0.015 to 0.100 in., width from 0.10 to 0.60 in., and length from 1 to 6 in., or a cylindrical specimen of comparable length and a radius of 0.30 in.

Although the method of recording the torsional displacement of the specimen varies from one type of apparatus to another, all effectively support the specimen between a fixed clamp and a second clamp which is rigidly attached to an inertial member. The test frequency can be changed by altering the inertial member or by adding additional suitable weights. A counterweight, or pulley device, is frequently used to compensate for the axial load that would otherwise be imposed. From the displacement–time curve, frequently recorded automatically, one can determine both the resonant frequency ν_0 and the log decrement. The torsion or shear modulus is then given by

$$G' = \frac{8\pi L \nu_0^2 I}{r^4} \qquad (3\text{-}65)$$

for a specimen of cylindrical shape, and by

$$G' = \frac{64\pi^2 L \nu_0^2 I}{bt^3\mu} \qquad (3\text{-}66)$$

for a specimen of rectangular shape. In these equations, L = length of specimen; I = moment of inertia of inertial member, b = specimen width; t = specimen thickness; r = specimen radius, and μ = shape factor which depends on the ratio of width to thickness.

A torsion pendulum in which the amplitude is detected electronically and which is designed for the study of polymers at high stresses is described by Heydemann and Zosel(81). This apparatus can also be used for relaxation studies. A variant of the torsion pendulum that is useful for soft specimens is torsion braid analysis. In this method, the test sample is a composite one. It consists of a multifilament inert substrate — usually glass fibers — upon which the polymer to be tested is deposited(82).

A dynamic system that operates in the low frequency region but which covers a much wider frequency range (0.001–100 Hz) is the rotating beam apparatus. This method of study was originally developed by Kimball(83) and applied to polymers by Maxwell(84). The specimen is in the form of a circular rod. It is fixed at one end and a load is applied at the other end. At the same time it is rotated about its axis. From the observed horizontal and vertical deflections of the free end, both components of the complex modulus can be computed.

An apparatus that operates at relatively low frequencies but at selected fixed frequencies (3.5, 11, 35, and 110 Hz) has been constructed by Takayanagi et al. (*85*) for measurement of elastic storage and loss modulus of polymer films or strips. A commercial version is available and has been used by Kwei et al. (*86*) to study thickness effects and thermal history effects on polyethylene and polypropylene.

Another apparatus that is designed to operate in the low frequency range (3×10^{-4}–6 Hz) is that of Philippoff (*87*). This apparatus permits direct measurement of shear stress and strain for viscoelastic liquids or non-rigid polymers, and, with suitable attachments, for measurements of bulk compression modulus. Measurements of sinusoidal stress and strain for shear, extension, torsion and flexure can also be accomplished with the apparatus of Koppelmann (*88*) by appropriate changes of specimen mounting. Another device, based on applying an alternating torque to a material enclosed between concentric cones, is used by Dobson (*89*) to determine complex shear modulus of very soft materials (10^5–10^9 dyn/cm^2).

An apparatus that permits study in the low frequency range as well as at higher frequencies (0.01–1000 Hz) is that of Wetton and co-workers (*90, 91*). In this apparatus a small cylindrical specimen is subjected to alternating torsion and the amplitude and phase of the response is recorded. From these one can then determine the complex shear modulus.

b. AUDIO FREQUENCY METHODS ($\sim$100–5000 Hz)

There are several different dynamic methods that operate successfully in this range. One of the most common methods is that of employing a specimen in the form of a cantilever reed. In order to study rubbery materials as well as rigid polymers, the specimen can be suspended vertically. The fixed end is oscillated at variable frequency and the displacement of the other end is determined usually by photoelectric means. From the observed resonance curve, the resonance frequency and the bandwidth are recorded and these are then used to compute the elastic storage modulus E' and the elastic loss modulus E''. This method has been used by Nolle (*92*) to study rubberlike materials, and by Becker (*93*) and Robinson (*94*) to study rigid polymers. For oscillation in the fundamental transverse mode the storage modulus is given by

$$E' = \frac{0.974 \rho L^4}{t^2} \left(\frac{\omega_0^2 + (\Delta\omega)^2}{2} \right) \qquad (3\text{-}67)$$

where ρ, t, and L are the density, thickness, and length of the cantilever reed, respectively, ω_0 is the resonant frequency in rad/sec and $\Delta\omega$ is the bandwidth at the half-power points.

Flexural vibrations of specimens in the form of loaded fixed–free rods can also be used to measure Young's modulus in the low audio frequency range. One such method is described by Bajeva(95).

Another method that is applicable in this frequency range is excitation of flexural vibrations of a specimen in the form of a free–free rod. This method has been described by Förster(96) and applied to polymers by Kline(97). It is particularly useful for studying the variation of the mechanical properties with temperature. The specimen is in the form of a circular rod, with length L about 10 cm and diameter d about 1 cm, and is supported by two cotton threads. One of these is attached to a transducer, which may be of the piezoelectric, magnetostrictive, or electromagnetic type. The other cotton support thread is connected to a detector, such as a phonograph pickup. A diagrammatic sketch of the necessary apparatus is shown in Fig. 3-3. The transducer is driven by a Hewlett-Packard oscillator and the response is amplified and fed to a recorder. The resonance curve is recorded automatically and is available for later study. The device operates well in the range from about 100–3000 Hz and has been employed successfully over the temperature range from $<100°$ to $>600°$K. For oscillation in a given transverse mode, the storage modulus is given by(98)

$$E' = \frac{6.48\rho L^4}{B_n^4 d^2}\nu_0{}^2 \tag{3-68}$$

where B_n is a parameter that depends on the vibration mode and the other symbols have the meanings already indicated. It is customary to operate at the fundamental mode. For this case $B = 1.505$ and

$$E' = \frac{1.26\rho L^4}{d^2}\nu_0{}^2 \tag{3-69}$$

Measurements of the real and imaginary parts of the dynamic bulk modulus are also possible in this frequency range by use of an apparatus such as that described by McKinney et al.(99). They impose periodic volume changes on a sample immersed in oil by means of a piezoelectric transducer and measure the associated pressure changes by a second transducer. Studies of dynamic compressibility carried out on polyvinylacetate(100) show that volume deformation, as well as shear deformation, may cause loss peaks and modulus dispersions.

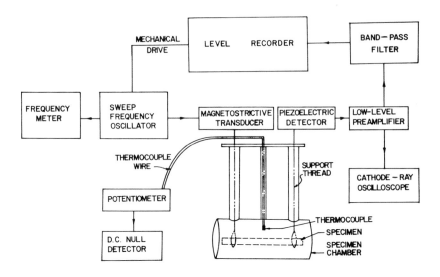

Figure 3-3. Diagrammatic sketch of dynamic mechanical properties apparatus (for use in audio frequency range).

An unusual method, employing specimens in the form of spheres, has been used by Lee and Smith(*101*) to determine complex Poisson's ratios and dilatational constants.

Resonant vibration methods have also been used to study behavior of rods in torsion and of beams or reeds in bending. Apparatus of this type is described by Koppelmann(*102*) and by Heydemann and Nägerl (*103*). Another apparatus(*104*), designed for study of the complex shear modulus of highly damped elastomers, is based on determination of resonant modes of a sandwich-type beam consisting of steel facings and a core of the soft polymer. The shear properties of rubberlike polymers have been studied by Hopkins(*105*) by noting the changes in frequency of a tuning-fork system to which the sample is coupled.

Nonresonance methods have also been employed in this frequency range to determine the real and imaginary parts of the shear modulus. An apparatus of this type is that described by Fitzgerald and Ferry (*106*) in which two samples in the form of small disks are simultaneously sheared between two surfaces, one of which is connected to a cylindrical driving tube and the other to a heavy, freely suspended mass. From measurements of the impedance presented to the driving system it is possible to determine both J' and J'' for both nonrigid and rigid polymers. The apparatus can be operated at constant temperature from $-60°$ to $150°C$ and over a variable frequency range from ~ 10 to ~ 6000 Hz.

Acoustic spectrometers(*107*) operating in the audio frequency range are also available for studying moduli and rheological properties of a wide range of materials, including liquids, adhesives, and both soft and hard solids. Shen et al.(*108*) have used this type of instrument to study properties of polymethacrylates from 77°K.

c. ULTRASONIC METHODS (~ 5000–$100,000$ Hz)

One of the principal methods used to measure mechanical behavior in this frequency range is to excite longitudinal resonant vibrations. Quimby(*109*) used this method to study metal rods at 40 kHz and Sack et al.(*110*) described a technique for studying reed-shaped samples. Parfitt(*111*) studied high-polymer samples over the range 5–60 kHz and Baccaredda and Butta(*112*) used a similar method to study Young's modulus in polyethylene rods. Crissman and McCammon(*113*) have applied this method to a study of the mechanical behavior of rigid rod-shaped samples. One advantage of this method is that only the length of the sample enters into the calculation and the elastic storage modulus is given simply by

$$E' = 4\rho L^2 v_0^2 \qquad (3\text{-}70)$$

where v_0 is the observed resonant frequency of the first longitudinal mode.

In the apparatus of Crissman and McCammon(*113*) a circular specimen, about 5 in. long, is supported by a thin low-loss glass fiber cemented to the specimen at one end and to the driving transducer at the other.

The displacement of the other end of the specimen is monitored as a function of the driving frequency and the usual type of resonance curve is recorded. Tests are carried out in an evacuated dewar vessel and accurate values of storage modulus and loss modulus can be made down to liquid helium temperatures. The component parts of the apparatus are identical with those illustrated in Fig. 3-3.

d. WAVE PROPAGATION METHODS (10^5–10^7 Hz)

These methods consist of measuring the transit time and the attenuation through the specimen of short pulses of duration of a few microseconds. From the variation of the amplitude of successive pulses one can calculate the attenuation or loss and from the transit time one can calculate the velocity of propagation and hence the applicable modulus.

Use of this method for bulk specimens is discussed by Mason and McSkimmin(*114*) and applied to polymers by Ivey et al.(*115*) and by Thurn(*116*). Bradfield(*117*) has used several different experimental arrangements in order to measure both shear and bulk modulus and their frequency dependence.

Wave propagation methods have also been applied to fibers and filaments. In these arrangements, the filament is excited at one end, where it is connected to the driving transducer; a piezoelectric detector, which can be moved along the filament, is used to detect the response. By observation of the relative phases and amplitudes as a function of distance, the wave velocity and attenuation can be computed. Kolsky and Hillier(*118,119*) have used this method to study both rubberlike materials and rigid high polymers; Ballou and Silverman(*120*) have employed it to investigate the behavior of nylon fibers. Commercial apparatus is now available.

Measurements of the dynamic bulk modulus of polymethylmethacrylate have been described by Pullen et al.(*121*). In their method, which makes use of an ultrasonic interferometer operating at 10^6 Hz, sound velocities are measured in certain liquids, such as silicon oil, both with and without a suspension of the polymer powder. From the recorded velocities the adiabatic bulk modulus can be determined.

B. Comparative Modulus Values of Polymers and Other Materials

Stress–strain properties, especially at low strains, can be characterized by various types of moduli (or compliance) values. The methods for determining these modulus values, both static and dynamic, were discussed in the preceding Section 3-3,A. In this and the next subsections we give an indication of the range of values of moduli for high polymers and also give some idea as to where these values stand relative to those for other common materials. To serve this purpose any one type of modulus value can be used; we shall most often use Young's modulus of elasticity, as measured in a tension or bending experiment, but shall also refer to other types.

Comparative values of tensile modulus for various polymers, for some common metals, and for several other materials of engineering interest are given in Table 3-3. These values are approximate, and are meant to give only relative rankings for plastics among themselves and in comparison with other materials. Actual measured values may differ considerably from those given depending upon the specific composition and orientation of the particular polymer, the degree of crystallinity and past thermal history of the sample, and the speed of

TABLE 3-3

Comparison of Tensile Moduli at Room Temperature
for Various Materials

Class	Substance	Approx. value of Young's modulus (dyn/cm^2)	(psi)
Metals	Lead	1.6×10^{11}	2.3×10^6
	Tin	4.7×10^{11}	6.8×10^6
	Aluminum	6.9×10^{11}	10×10^6
	Titanium	11×10^{11}	16×10^6
	Steel	20×10^{11}	29×10^6
	Beryllium	29×10^{11}	42×10^6
	Tungsten	35×10^{11}	51×10^6
Polymers	Rubber	1.0×10^7	1.5×10^2
	Polyethylene (low density)	1.0×10^9	1.5×10^4
	Polyethylene (high density)	1.0×10^{10}	1.5×10^5
	Cellulose acetate	2.0×10^{10}	2.9×10^5
	Polystyrene	3.1×10^{10}	4.5×10^5
	Phenolic	6.9×10^{10}	10×10^5
	Rayon (dry stretched)	44×10^{10}	63×10^5
	Native flax	100×10^{10}	150×10^5
Others	Wood ($\|$ to grain)	9×10^{10}	13×10^5
	Common brick	14×10^{10}	20×10^5
	Concrete	22×10^{10}	32×10^5
	Vitreous carbon	29×10^{10}	42×10^5
	Graphite (pyrolitic)	35×10^{10}	51×10^5
	Granite	52×10^{10}	75×10^5
	Glass	69×10^{10}	100×10^5

testing. These factors will be considered in greater detail later, along with the effects of temperature.

Inspection of Table 3-3 shows that the variation of modulus from one metal to another covers little more than one decade. Similarly, the variation among the other structural materials listed is encompassed by one decade. However, when we consider polymers the variation is very much greater, with rubbers having a modulus of the order of 10^7 dyn/cm^2, rigid plastics a modulus of the order of 10^{10} dyn/cm^2, and highly oriented polymers a modulus of the order of 10^{12} dyn/cm^2. Thus the range of modulus values for polymers covers five decades. However, if we omit rubbers from this tabulation and also highly oriented materials, then we see that many thermoplastic materials have a modulus of the order of $\frac{1}{100}$ that of steel. Rubbers have a modulus about three decades lower. Some highly oriented polymers, such as native flax, have rigidities approaching that of titanium and are above that of such rigid materials as glass and aluminum. In fact, as we have seen in the preceding section, the modulus of these very highly oriented fibers may approach the theoretical modulus as calculated for a fully extended chain.

C. Effects of Test Environment

1. VARIATION OF MODULUS WITH SPEED OF TESTING

It is well recognized that the static modulus, or the slope of the stress–strain curve, in a simple tension test is a function of testing speed. This is one reason why ASTM tests call for a standard rate of loading. For metals, the variation is generally not significant at room temperature, but it may be, at high strain rates or at elevated temperatures. Similarly, studies(122) on pyrolytic graphite at rates from 10^{-3} to 10^3 in./in. sec have shown that the stress–strain graphs of this material are, over this range, essentially strain-rate independent at room temperature. For polymers, however—even though the softening temperatures, T_g or T_m, may be above room temperature—the material is sensitive to time variations at room temperature and these variations must be known and considered for all design applications.

The degree to which the modulus of a polymer is affected by speed of testing will depend upon the particular polymer and upon how close the operating temperature is to the glass transition temperature. However, over fairly wide temperature ranges, crystalline polymers, as well as amorphous polymers, show a strong strain-rate dependence. For example, upon variation of testing speed from 0.2 to 2000 in./min it has been found(123) that Young's modulus increases from 20,000 to 70,000 psi for a low density polyethylene, from 91,000 to 174,000 psi for a high density polyethylene, and from 128,000 to 218,000 for a crystalline polypropylene. Changes also occurred in the ductility as measured by ultimate elongation. At low rates of loading, of the order of 2 in./min or less, the ductility was high ($\sim 200\%$) for all three materials and the samples would effectively cold-draw. However, at rates of loading of 20 in./min or higher, the ductility for polypropylene and the high density polyethylene dropped drastically to about 15%. Hence these polymers undergo a ductile-brittle transition at room temperature in the range of rates mentioned. The low density polyethylene, however, retained a ductility of 200% over all speeds tested and hence remained ductile even though the modulus increased some threefold or more, as noted. These marked variations of mechanical behavior with speed of testing emphasize the need for facilities that will permit studies to be carried out at both low and high speeds, and various types of apparatus and testing techniques have been devised to cope with this problem (*124*).

To illustrate the effects of testing speed on tensile stress–strain measurements, we present in Fig. 3-4 the data of Hall(*124a*) obtained at 20°C on a polypropylene monofilament drawn 5.5 times. Rates of straining ranged from a low value of 3.3×10^{-4} in./in./sec to a high value of 4.9×10^2 in./in./sec. Over this range there is, as the graph shows, a marked change in the mechanical properties of the oriented polypropylene fiber. At high rates of loading, the elastic modulus or slope of the curve is high, but the ductility, as measured by the elongation at break, is low. For low rates of loading, the elastic modulus is low, but the ductility is high.

Figure 3-5 provides an illustration from the data of Maiden and Green (*122*) of the effects of the rate of loading on an amorphous polymer. The stress–strain curves in this graph were obtained under compression

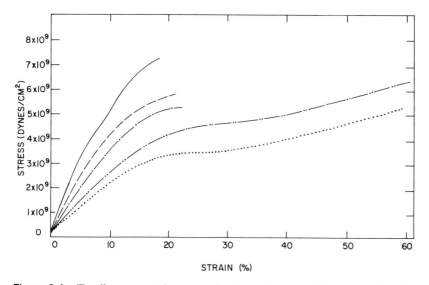

Figure 3-4. Tensile stress–strain curves of polypropylene monafilament as a function of strain rate. Data of Hall(*124a*). Code: ——— 4.9×10^2 sec^{-1}; ---- 6.3×10^1 sec^{-1}; —·—·— 0.23 sec^{-1}; —··—··— 4.17×10^{-3} sec^{-1}; ····· 3.3×10^{-4} sec^{-1}.

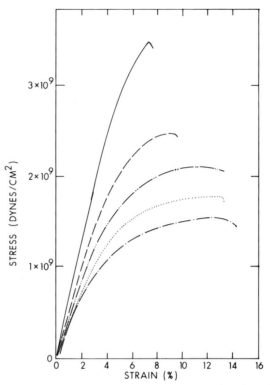

Figure 3-5. Compressive stress–strain curves of polymethyl methacrylate as a function of strain rate. Data of Maiden and Green(*122*). Code: ——— $1.2 \times 10^3 \text{ sec}^{-1}$; ---- 3 sec^{-1}; $-\cdot\cdot-\cdot\cdot-$ 0.5 sec^{-1}; $\cdots\cdots$ 0.07 sec^{-1}; $-\cdot-\cdot-$ 5.0×10^{-3} sec^{-1}.

loading and the polymer under investigation was polymethylmethacrylate. The rates of straining covered the range from 5×10^{-3} to $1\cdot2 \times 10^3$ in./in./sec. Once again, a marked increase in modulus is found to occur with an increase of the rate of loading. Variation of loading rates is also found to affect markedly the viscoelastic properties of elastomeric materials such as rubber(*125*).

The tendency for modulus values to increase with an increase in the rate of straining means that elastic constants measured under dynamic, or adiabatic, conditions will tend to be higher than values measured under low rates of straining or isothermal conditions. The value of the dynamic modulus will also vary somewhat with the frequency of the test and hence it is customary, when dynamic modulus values are given, also to state the frequency of the measurement. An example of the changes produced in dynamic tests by a variation of frequency is shown in Fig. 3-6. These data have been obtained on samples of poly-propyleneoxide by Wetton and Allen(*91*) at test frequencies varying from 10^{-2} to 10^3 Hz. Increased test frequency tends to shift the low-temperature relaxation near $-60°C$ to higher temperatures, while the melting transition near 70°C is not affected. There is also little effect on modulus values below the low-temperature relaxation, and appreciable effect on modulus values in the region between the glass and melting transitions, and a very large effect in the rubbery region above the melting temperature.

One advantage of making measurements at different frequencies, aside from obtaining needed information concerning the time dependence of the mechanical properties, is to ascertain how specific relaxations, as indicated by loss peaks and modulus inflections, vary with measurement frequency. From these differences, or directly from a plot of the frequency at the loss peak or at the modulus inflection vs. the reciprocal temperature, it is possible to compute an apparent activation energy for the relaxation process in question.

2. VARIATION OF MODULUS WITH ORIENTATION OF SPECIMEN RELATIVE TO LOAD AXIS

In metals where large-size single crystals can be produced, the appropriate elastic constants C_{ij} are usually determined by measurements of ultrasonic velocity in different directions. The individual elastic constants for the crystal may differ appreciably from the values for polycrystalline material; also the difference between the respective values is an indication of the anisotropy of the crystal. For example, polycrystalline aluminum is listed in Table 3-3 as having a modulus of about 6.9×10^{11} dyn/cm², whereas single crystals of aluminum have been recorded(*126*) with elastic constants of $C_{11} = 10.8 \times 10^{11}$, $C_{12} = 6.22 \times 10^{11}$, and $C_{14} = 2.84 \times 10^{11}$ dyn/cm².

It is difficult to measure elastic constants for polymer single crystals because of their small size ($\sim 1–10 \mu$) and very small thickness ($\sim 10^2$ Å). However, measurements have been made (*127*) for several polymers of the elastic constants of uniaxially drawn films and drawn fibers. Five independent elastic constants arise in this case. Also, as noted in Section 3-2,D, there have been some theoretical calculations made of the elastic constants of polymer crystals. Orientation markedly affects modulus values. For example, although unoriented crystalline polystyrene and amorphous polystyrene have about the same value of modulus below T_g, oriented crystalline polystyrene has a modulus about three times as high(*128*). There is also a large difference between

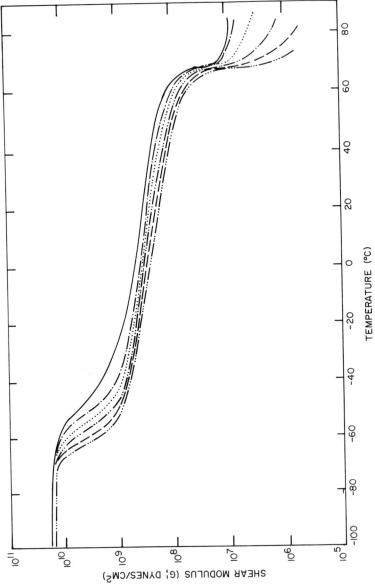

Figure 3-6. Shear modulus–temperature curves of polypropylene oxide as a function of frequency. Data of Wetton and Allen(*91*). Code: —— 10^3 cps; —·—·— 10^2 cps; ····· 10 cps; —··—··— 1 cps; —— 10^{-1} cps; ——·——·—— 10^{-2} cps.

the moduli measured in the direction of orientation, the so-called longitudinal modulus, and the modulus at right angles to this, the so-called lateral, or transverse, modulus. In Section 3-2, D, as well as in Table 3-3, we saw that natural highly oriented polymers such as native flax could approach a value of 10^{12} dyn/cm² for the modulus in the direction of orientation. Synthetic oriented polymers do not appear to reach as high a value, although they begin to approach it at high draw ratios and at low temperatures. For example, Vincent(*128a*) reports that the modulus of a high molecular weight linear polyethylene which was drawn to 16 times its original length reached a measured value of 0·62 × 10^{12} dyn/cm² (9 × 10^6 psi) when tested below the low temperature γ transition, i.e., near 100°K.

The lateral modulus for oriented polymers is near 10^{10} dyn/cm² rather than 10^{12} dyn/cm². Hence the lateral modulus of an oriented fiber is roughly comparable to the specimen modulus of isotropic polymers measured at temperatures below their glass transition. As noted in Section 3-2,D, the ratio of longitudinal crystal modulus to lateral modulus for straight chain polymers like polyethylene is of the order of 70, but is of the order of 14 for helical polymers like polypropylene.

For some materials such as wood, which consist of polymeric ingredients, nine elastic constants are required to describe the stress–strain behavior. These constants may be taken as the three Young's moduli in the longitudinal, radial, and tangential directions, three corresponding shear moduli, and three Poisson's ratios. As already noted in Table 3-3, the longitudinal modulus is about 13 × 10^5 psi. The moduli in the radial and tangential directions are essentially lateral moduli and are significantly less. For a specific wood, mahogany, Hearmon(*129*) gives 12.4, 0.97, and 0.48, × 10^5 psi for these three moduli, respectively. Hence in this case the ratio of the longitudinal modulus to the lateral modulus is about 13–26. Another cellulosic material with a high modulus parallel to the grain is bamboo. This has a reported value (*130*) of 49 × 10^5 psi, close to that of stretched rayon (Table 3-3).

Another material of interest in which the modulus values vary considerably with the method of preparation and the direction of loading is graphite. When produced in the form of a noncrystalline vitreous carbon its modulus is about 29 × 10^{10} dyn/cm²(*131*), about four times that of a phenolic material and of the order of that of pyrolytic graphite (Table 3-3). Carbon in filament form has a longitudinal modulus of about 41 × 10^{10} dyn/cm²(*130*). The highest recorded modulus of any material is found for graphite whiskers. The reported modulus values (*130*) here reach 10^{13} dyn/cm² (145 × 10^6 psi), or about five times that of steel and ten times that of aluminum single crystals or of highly oriented natural fibers.

3. VARIATION OF MODULUS WITH TEMPERATURE – GENERAL NATURE OF VARIATION

The temperature variation of the modulus of polymers not only gives considerable information as to the possible usefulness of polymers at different temperatures, but also information concerning their mechanical relaxation behavior. The modulus–temperature behavior of each polymer is characteristic of its particular chemical and physical structure. Due to thermal expansion effects, there is, in all solid polymers, a slow decrease of modulus with increasing temperature. However, depending upon the particular polymer being studied, there may also occur with increasing temperature one or more characteristic drops in modulus (as well as one or more characteristic peaks in the associated loss modulus). These changes result from the onset of internal relaxation processes. This effect will be illustrated here for several different types of polymers, but a detailed discussion of the specific relation between the mechanical behavior and structural factors will be reserved for the next section.

Figure 3-7 shows data taken from Schmeider and Wolf(*132*) on the temperature dependence of the shear modulus of various samples of vulcanized rubber. The glass transition temperature for these materials is in the vicinity of $-50°C$. Below this temperature the modulus value is of the order of 10^{10} dyn/cm^2 and varies only slightly with temperature. Here the rubber is behaving essentially like a glassy polymer. Near $-50°C$, the modulus drops sharply, falling from $\sim 10^{10}$ to $\sim 10^7$ dyn/cm^2, or by about three decades of 10. This drop is indicative of the onset of large-scale segmental motions, restrained only by cross-links or molecular entanglements that are present. Above the transition region, the modulus is again almost independent of temperature but, for the cross-linked samples, actually increases somewhat in value with increasing temperature. This is the behavior predicted on the basis of the theory of rubber elasticity; in fact, from the slope of the modulus–temperature curve, the degree of cross-linking of the sample can be computed using formulas given in Section 3-2,C.

The effects of temperature on the relaxation modulus of polystyrene (*7*) are shown in Fig. 3-8. For the cross-linked sample as well as for the two atactic samples (A and C) the modulus curve shows a marked drop of three decades or more in the vicinity of 100°C, which is close to the glass transition temperature of this polymer. Below this tem-

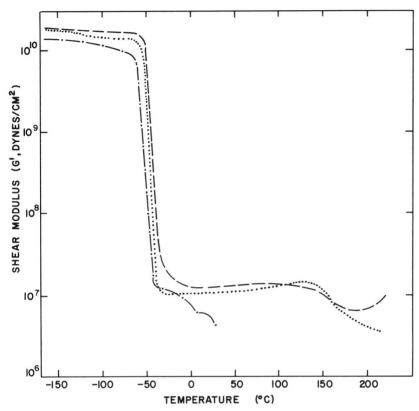

Figure 3-7. Shear modulus–temperature curves of vulcanized rubber for various amounts of sulfur. Data of Schmieder and Wolf(*132*). Code: $-\cdot-\cdot-$ 0% *S*; $\cdots\cdots$ 2.0% *S*; $----$ 5.0% *S*.

perature, the modulus varies little with temperature and has a value of about 2×10^{10} dyn/cm² for the atactic sample. After the transition region, the cross-linked sample has a modulus of about 0.5×10^7 dyn/cm², and it is almost independent of temperature to well above 200°C. For the two atactic samples, there is a small rubbery plateau region followed by a rubbery flow region. The partly crystalline sample shows two temperature regions in which the modulus shows marked decreases. The first drop occurs in the vicinity of T_g and is due to the increased flexibility of the amorphous regions of the polymer. However, the magnitude of the drop is considerably reduced from that for the atactic polymer because of the increased rigidity of the crystalline portions of the sample. The second marked drop in relaxation modulus,

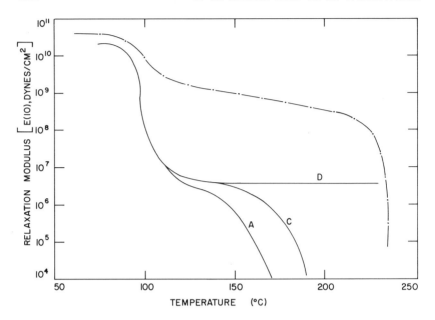

Figure 3-8. Relaxation modulus (10 sec) vs. temperature for various polystyrene samples. Data of Tobolsky and Yu(7). Code: — ·— ·— isotactic crystalline sample; ___D___ atactic, lightly cross-linked sample; ___C___ atactic sample, $\bar{M}_n = 2.17 \times 10^5$; ___A___ atactic sample, $\bar{M}_n = 1.4 \times 10^5$.

which occurs in the vicinity of the melting temperature, essentially reflects the greatly increased chain mobility that arises as the crystalline regions disorder. One other point to notice is the increased stiffness with increasing temperature of the higher molecular weight sample (C vs. A).

Recently Plazek(61) has studied the mechanical behavior of specific fractions of polystyrene by measuring creep compliance rather than relaxation modulus. Some of his measurements, made as a function of time at various temperatures in the vicinity of T_g, are shown in Fig. 3-9. For a given time, it is evident that there is a marked increase in compliance (or decrease in modulus) with increasing temperature, while for a given temperature there is a marked increase in compliance with log time. Attempts were made by Plazek to reduce these data to one master curve, but this was not found to be possible for the creep compliance. However, when account was taken of the viscous flow term, he was able to obtain a single master curve (see Fig. 3-10) for recoverable compliance vs. reduced time.

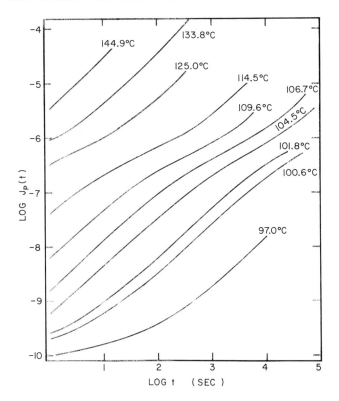

Figure 3-9. Creep compliance $J_p(t)$ vs. time for polystyrene fraction ($\overline{M}_n = 4.69 \times 10^4$) at various temperatures. Data of Plazek (*61*).

The effects of temperature on the shear modulus G and on the bulk modulus K, as well as on Poisson's ratio ν, are shown in Fig. 3-11 for a polypropylene sample tested at a frequency of 5 MHz. The data, obtained by H. A. Waterman[see (*133*)], show that the relaxation that occurs near room temperature is present in both the shear and bulk moduli but is more prominent in the former. Below this transition Poisson's ratio is about 0·33 and is almost independent of temperature. Above the transition, Poisson's ratio increases rapidly toward the ideal rubberlike value of 0.50.

Additional examples of the effect of temperature on relaxation modulus, creep compliance, or elastic storage modulus will be exhibited in later sections in connection with discussion of the influence of various factors on modulus–temperature behavior. The temperature range investigated now extends, for some polymers, from 4°K to well above

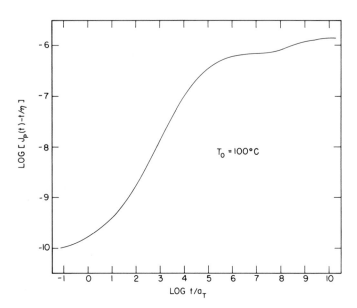

Figure 3-10. Master curve of recoverable compliance vs. reduced time for polystyrene fraction ($\bar{M}_n = 4.69 \times 10^4$). Reference temperature 100°C. Data of Plazek(*61*).

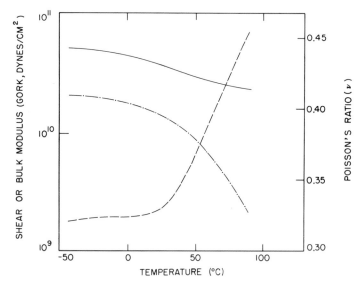

Figure 3-11. Bulk modulus, shear modulus, and Poisson's ratio for polypropylene as function of temperature at test frequency of 5 mHz. Data of Waterman; see Staverman and Heijboer(*133*). Code: ——— bulk modulus K'; —·—·— shear modulus G'; --- Poisson's ratio ν.

164

the melting point. When a wide temperature range is covered, the experimental data frequently show several relaxation or dispersion regions, in addition to the principal dispersion appearing in the vicinity of T_g. These relaxation regions are believed to be associated with the onset of certain types of molecular mobility, such as hindered rotation of relatively small molecular groups, which may be situated, depending upon the polymer, either in the main backbone chain or in the side chain of the polymer.

4. COMPARATIVE MODULUS VALUES OF POLYMERS OF VARYING COMPOSITION

In this section we give experimental values of modulus that have been obtained from polymers of different composition and structure when measurements are made at very low temperatures, at room temperature, and at high temperatures. From such data one can attempt to correlate modulus values with polymer structure and also see the marked influence on modulus values of the presence of relaxation processes.

Rather than attempting to cite all recorded modulus data, we have, instead, tried to collect data on a variety of polymers of different structures which have been studied by means of one type of apparatus. Otherwise it is hard to make comparisons, as with one apparatus the elastic modulus E' is obtained, with another the shear modulus G' is found, with another the relaxation modulus E_r is found, etc. Also the frequencies of measurement vary markedly from one apparatus to another. For a given apparatus, there may be some variation of frequency with type of material studied, but this variation is usually small compared to that involved in going from, say, a transverse bending type of apparatus to a torsion pendulum.

a. VALUES AT LOW TEMPERATURES (6° and 77°K)

Table 3-4 lists the modulus of some 15 representative polymers and of vitreous carbon measured at 6° and 77°K. For each material the approximate test frequency of measurement is also cited. All of the modulus values recorded in this table were measured by use of a longitudinal vibration apparatus of the type discussed in Section 3-3,A, 3,c, in which a rodlike specimen was excited in its first longitudinal vibration mode.

The list of materials given in this table includes highly crystalline polymers such as linear polyethylene, isotactic polypropylene, and poly-4-methyl-pentene, as well as wholly amorphous polymers such

TABLE 3-4

Comparative Modulus Values at 6°K and 77°K for Various High Polymers

Polymer	Measurements at 6°K		Measurements at 77°K		
	Elastic modulus E' (10^{10} dyn/cm²)	Frequency f_0 (10^4 Hz)	Elastic modulus E' (10^{10} dyn/cm²)	Frequency f_0 (10^4 Hz)	Ref.
Polyethylene (linear)	10.3	(1.1)	9.7	(1.0)	(134)
Nylon 6-6	9.2	(0.9)	8.6	(0.9)	(134)
Poly-D-L-propylene oxide	8.4	(1.1)	7.6	(1.0)	(134)
Poly-ethyl methacrylate	8.3	(0.9)	6.3	(0.8)	(134)
Polybutene-1	8.1	(1.0)	7.7	(1.0)	(134)
Poly-methyl methacrylate	7.8	(0.9)	7.5	(0.9)	(134)
Polypropylene (isotactic)	7.5	(1.0)	7.0	(1.0)	(134)
Polyisobutyl methacrylate	7.4	(0.9)	6.9	(0.8)	(134)
Polyvinyl chloride	6.8	(0.7)	6.4	(0.7)	(134)
Poly-α-methyl styrene	6.6	(0.7)	6.0	(0.7)	(135)
Polyimide	6.2	(~1)	5.9	(~1)	(136)
Polystyrene (crystalline)	6.1	(0.8)	5.0	(0.7)	(135)
Polystyrene (isotactic amorphous)	5.6	(0.8)	4.6	(0.7)	(135)
Polystyrene (atactic)			4.6	(0.6)	(135)
Poly-4-methyl pentene	4.9	(1.1)	4.1	(1.0)	(134)
Vitreous carbon	29.2	(2.2)	29.1	(2.2)	(131)

as atactic polystyrene and polymethylmethacrylate. All modulus value at 6°K fall between $\sim 5 \times 10^{10}$ and $\sim 10 \times 10^{10}$ dyn/cm², except for the vitreous carbon. Of the polymers tested, linear polyethylene has the greatest low temperature modulus value (10.3×10^{10} dyn/cm²) and nylon 6-6 is next with 9.2×10^{10} dyn/cm².

The relative order of stiffness of these polymers at 77°K is somewhat the same as at 6°K. In general there is about a 6% drop between 6° and 77°K and this is attributed to thermal expansion effects, which act to reduce the intermolecular forces of cohesion. However, three materials, crystalline P4MP1, amorphous PS, and amorphous PEMA, all show much larger reductions, of the order of 20%. This indicates that a relaxation process is present for these materials in the temperature range between liquid helium and liquid nitrogen values. In fact, it is known from the references cited that all three of the materials mentioned show a modulus dispersion and an associated peak in elastic loss modulus in the interval from 6° to 77°K.

b. VALUES AT HIGHER TEMPERATURES (100°, 300°, 373°, and 473°K)

In Table 3-5 we have listed measured dynamic modulus values for a series of 18 different polymers at four selected temperatures: 100°, 300°, 373°, and 473°K. Highly crystalline types, partially crystalline types, and fully amorphous polymers are included. All of the recorded values were obtained with a transverse beam apparatus of the type described in Section 3-3,A,3,b. The frequencies of measurement are given in parentheses after the listing of the modulus values.

From inspection of Table 3-5, one can notice the following facts:

(1) At 100°K, linear PE has the highest modulus and nylon 6-6 the next highest of the various polymers listed. Crystalline isotactic polypropylene has a modulus some 60% above that of the atactic PP.

(2) At 300°K, the rating is no longer the same as at 100°K. The modulus of polyethylene has fallen drastically, with the room temperature value being less than one-third the value at 77°K. This drop is a direct result of the presence of the well-known γ relaxation which, at these measuring frequencies, is usually centered near 170°K. In contrast to polyethylene, the polyimide modulus has fallen less than 30% in passing through the same 200° interval. The reason is that the polyimide, especially in the dry state, has no major transition in this temperature interval. In fact the modulus–temperature plot of polyimide is almost a straight line from about 150° to past 400°K. Some of the other polymers exhibit even a greater modulus variation with increasing temperature than polyethylene. The room temperature modulus for polyvinyl stearate, which has a melting point near 300°K, has dropped by a factor of 7 compared to the 100°K value, and that for polypentene, for which the glass transition is 233°K, shows similar behavior. On the other hand, the two polystyrene samples show only a very small drop between 100° and 300°K. This drop is even less than that of polyimide, or about 20%. Since polystyrene is known to undergo no significant relaxation in this temperature interval, the observed small drop is essentially due to thermal expansion.

TABLE 3-5

Comparative Modulus Values at 100°K, 300°K, 373°K, and 473°K for Various High Polymers

Polymer	100°K Elastic modulus E' (10^{10} dyn/cm²)	100°K Freq. f_0 Hz	300°K Elastic modulus E' (10^{10} dyn/cm²)	300°K Freq. f_0 Hz	373°K Elastic modulus E' (10^{10} dyn/cm²)	373°K Freq. f_0 Hz	473°K Elastic modulus E' (10^{10} dyn/cm²)	473°K Freq. f_0 Hz	Ref.
Polyethylene (linear)	9.6	(1500)	2.9	(800)	0.73	(400)			(137)
Nylon 6-6	9.3[a]	(1700)	4.1	(1100)	2.3	(730)	0.34	(234)	(138)
Nylon 6	7.7	(1130)	3.3	(740)	1.0	(405)			(139)
Nylon 6-10	7.5	(1500)	2.8	(900)	0.85	(500)			(138)
Nylon 10-10	7.1[a]	(1500)	2.4	(880)	0.55	(430)			(138)
Polypropylene (isotactic)	6.6	(1800)	2.4	(1000)	0.50	(500)			(140)
Polypropylene (isotactic)	5.8[a]	(2100)	1.8	(1200)	0.44	(590)			(141)
Polyvinyl chloride	6.1	(~1000)	3.0	(~700)					(142)
Polybutene-1	6.8	(3800)	2.0	(690)	0.35	(290)			(143)
Poly-α-methyl styrene	5.6	(1300)	4.5	(1200)	4.2	(1100)			(144)
Polystyrene (crystalline)	5.4	(2400)	4.4	(1200)	3.3	(1100)	0.10	(180)	(145)
Polypentene-1	5.1	(2700)	0.66	(300)					(143)
Polyimide (dried)	4.8	(840)	3.4	(700)	3.0	(660)	2.6	(610)	(139)
Polyvinyl stearate	4.4	(1280)	0.6	(480)					(139)
Polystyrene (atactic)	4.1	(1300)	3.3	(2100)	2.4	(1800)			(145)
Poly-4-methyl pentene	3.8	(1700)	2.3	(1400)	0.16	(360)			(143)
Polypropylene (atactic)	3.8	(1800)							(141)
Poly-3-methyl butene	3.2	(1700)	2.5	(1500)	1.2	(1000)	0.19	(430)	(143)

[a]Measurement made at 110°K.

168

(3) At 100°C, the amorphous polymer, poly-a-methyl styrene, has the highest modulus value of the polymers listed. For the crystalline poly-4-methyl pentene, there ia a marked reduction in modulus between 0° and 100°C due to the presence, in this interval, of its glass transition. This is also the situation for the four polyamide specimens, but for the polyimide there is very little change.

(4) Modulus measurements for only a few of the polymers listed were possible, or were made, at 200°C. Polyimide, which is known to be one of the most stable polymers of all, clearly has the highest modulus at 200°C. In fact, it retains a high modulus value, viz., 1.9×10^{10} dyn/cm² (530 Hz), even at 300°C (139).

c. Values of Characteristic Viscoelastic Parameters

As indicated in Section 3-2,B, there are various ways in which to define viscoelastic parameters for polymers. One method, discussed by Tobolsky and Takahashi(146), is based on measurements of relaxation modulus as a function of time for various temperatures. From the $\log E_r(t)$ vs. $\log t$ plot, stress relaxation master curves can be constructed by a horizontal shift along the log time axis. Two parameters of importance are then the horizontal asymptotes of the master curve at the short and long time ends. These are respectively the "glassy" modulus called E_1 and the "rubbery" modulus called E_2. Since the measurements are usually made in shear, rather than tension, $E_2 = 3G_2$, but this simple relation does not hold in the glassy region. Also, since Poisson's ratio is not the same for different solid polymers, the relation between the tensile modulus and the shear modulus will vary. For this reason we simply arbitrarily take $3G_1$ as a comparative measure of the glassy modulus.

Three other important viscoelastic parameters can be readily defined. One, n, is taken as the negative slope of the master curve at the reference value $E_r(t) = 10^9$ dyn/cm². According to the molecular theory of viscoelasticity discussed in Section 3-2, this value should be $\frac{1}{2}$. A second, s, is taken as the negative slope of the 10-sec modulus–temperature curve, i.e., the $3G(10)$ vs. T curve, at the value of 10^9 dyn/cm². A third, denoted T_i, is comparable to a glass transition temperature, but is arbitrarily defined as the temperature at which the 10-sec modulus $3G(10)$ reaches 10^9 dyn/cm².

Values of these five viscoelastic parameters are given in Table 3-6 for a series of linear amorphous polymers, a series of lightly cross-linked amorphous polymers, a series of amorphous copolymers, and a

TABLE 3-6

Characteristic Viscoelastic Parameters for Relaxation Modulus–Temperature Curves (147)

Polymer	$3G_1$ dyn/cm²	$3G_2$ dyn/cm²	n dyn/cm²/sec	s dyn/cm²/°C	T_i °C
Amorphous linear					
Natural rubber (unvulcanized)	2.5×10^{10}	4×10^7	1.25	0.2	-67
Polyisobutylene	3.5×10^{10}	1×10^7	0.75	0.15	-62
Polypropylene (atactic)	2.0×10^{10}	2.5×10^7		0.2	-16
Polymethyl acrylate	3×10^{10}	1.5×10^7		0.2	$+16$
Polystyrene	2×10^{10}	0.5×10^7	0.85	0.2	101
Polymethyl methacrylate	1.5×10^{10}	2×10^7	0.55	0.15	107
Polycarbonate	1.5×10^{10}	5×10^7	1.1	0.3	150
Amorphous lightly cross-linked					
Natural rubber (vulcanized)	3.5×10^{10}	4×10^7	1.1	0.2	-57
Polymethoxyethyl methacrylate	2×10^{10}	1.5×10^7		0.1	23
Poly-n-propyl methacrylate	2×10^{10}	2×10^7	0.5	0.1	56
Polyethyl methacrylate	2.5×10^{10}	2.5×10^7		0.1	77
Poly-2-hydroxyethyl methacrylate	3×10^{10}	2.5×10^7	0.55	0.1	96
Amorphous copolymers					
Ethylene propylene (2-1)[a]	1×10^{10}	7×10^7		0.15	-59
Butadiene styrene (3-1)[a]	2×10^{10}	4.5×10^7	0.70	0·15	-48
Ethylmethacrylate-n-propylmethacrylate (1-1)[a]	2×10^{10}	2×10^7		0.1	68
2-Hydroxyethylmethacrylate-n-propylmethacrylate (27-73)[b]	2.5×10^{10}	2×10^7		0.05	68
2-Hydroxyethylmethacrylate-n-propylmethacrylate (55-45)[b]	3×10^{10}	3×10^7		0.05	83
2-Hydroxyethylmethacrylate-n-propylmethacrylate (75-25)[b]	4×10^{10}	2×10^7		0.05	86
Styrene acenaphthalene (80-20)[b]			0.65	0.15	134
Styrene acenaphthalene (20-80)[b]			0.65	0.1	252

[a] Mol ratios.

[b] Numbers in parenthesis represent weight ratios of the respective monomers.

TABLE 3-6 (cont.)

Polymer	$3G_1$ dyn/cm²	$3G_2$ dyn/cm²	n dyn/cm²/sec	s dyn/cm²/°C	T_i °C
Plasticized polymers					
Polyvinylchloride-dioctylphthalate (44.4%)	3×10^{10}	2.5×10^7	0.30	0.05	-33
Polyvinylchloride-dioctylphthalate (37.5%)	2×10^{10}	2×10^7	0.30	0.05	-14
Polyvinylchloride-dioctylphthalate (28.6%)	2.5×10^{10}	4×10^7	0.30	0.05	15
Polyvinylchloride-dioctylphthalate (23.1%)	4×10^{10}	2×10^7	0.35	0.05	26
Polyvinylchloride-dioctylphthalate (16.7%)	3.5×10^{10}	3×10^7	0.50	0.1	35
Polyvinylchloride-dioctylphthalate (9.1%)	3×10^{10}	2.5×10^7	0.55	0.2	52
Polyvinylchloride-dioctylphthalate (0.0%)	4×10^{10}	2×10^7	0.60	0.25	78

series of plasticized polymers(*147*). From the table, it may be noted that:

(1) The values of the "tensile" modulus below the glass transition temperature do not vary greatly with structure and composition. For the polymers cited all values fall in the range from 1×10^{10} to 4×10^{10} dyn/cm².

(2) The rubbery plateau modulus is approximately three decades lower in value than the glassy modulus.

(3) The value of n is seldom the theoretically expected value of $\frac{1}{2}$ that is predicted on the basis of the Rouse molecular theory of viscoelasticity. However, for some amorphous polymers, such as polymethyl methacrylate and poly-n-propyl methacrylate, the observed value of n is in accord with the theoretical value.

(4) The value of s, which is a measure of the breadth of the transition, does not show any significant variation in any one group, even though the transition temperature may vary by 200°C or so.

(5) For copolymers, the degree of copolymerization appears to have a greater effect on the "glassy" modulus than on the "rubbery" modulus or on s or n.

(6) For the plasticized polyvinyl chloride, the degree of plasticization has a much greater and more direct effect on the transition temperature than on the other viscoelastic parameters.

3-4 FACTORS AFFECTING THE MODULUS–TEMPERATURE
RELATIONSHIP

A. General Considerations

As a consequence of the long-chain nature of polymeric substances there are three principal structural features on which the value of the modulus depends. These are the amount of chain flexibility as governed by the forces between connected units in the polymer chain, the strength and regularity of the molecular attractive forces between nonconnected groups of segments, and the molecular weight or, for cross-linked material, the molecular weight between cross-links. The first two features also determine the glass transition temperature T_g, the crystallizability, and the melting temperature T_m of polymeric substances and the third feature principally affects T_g. As pointed out in the previous section, the elastic modulus for a noncross-linked, noncrystalline material at temperatures below T_g is of the order of 10^{10} dyn/cm^2 and the material is rigid and glassy, while at a temperature 50°C or so above T_g, it has a value of the order of 10^7 dyn/cm^2 and the material is rubbery or liquidlike with a high degree of segmental mobility. One example of such behavior has been shown in Fig. 3-7. Other examples are given in Figs. 3-12 and 3-13. Highly crystalline polymeric materials will maintain, at temperatures below T_g, an elastic modulus in the 10^{10}–10^{11} dyn/cm^2 range, as the data of Tables 3-4 and 3-5 show. The behavior of many partially crystalline polymers can be best described in terms of separate amorphous and crystalline regions. This implies that in the temperature range where the amorphous parts have a high flexibility and the crystalline parts a high rigidity the modulus has values of 10^8–10^{10} dyn/cm^2, intermediate between that for a rigid and that for a rubbery solid. Above the melting temperature, the modulus falls to values of 10^5–10^7 dyn/cm^2. One example of this type of behavior has been illustrated in Fig. 3-6. Other examples will be seen later.

For partially crystalline polymers the melting point is always found at temperatures above T_g. Therefore the modulus of a partially crystalline material will remain at values characteristic of a rigid solid to temperatures well above that at which a completely amorphous material with the same T_g will attain rubbery values. This is apparent in Fig. 3-8, where the modulus of a noncrystallizable specimen and the modulus of a crystalline isotactic specimen are shown.

The chemical composition and structure of the repeat units in the polymer chain will affect the forces between atoms on adjacent connected and nonconnected units. For unsymmetrical units such as those

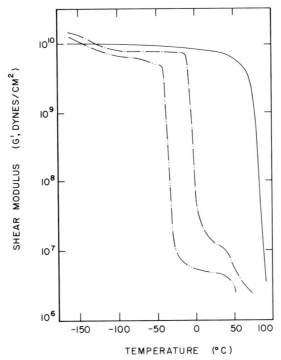

Figure 3-12. Dynamic shear modulus vs. temperature of three polyvinyl ethers at 1–10 Hz. Data of Schmieder and Wolf(*132*). Code: ─··─··─ *n*-butyl; ─·─·─ isobutyl; ─────── ter butyl.

in poly(methyl methacrylate)

$$\left[\!-CH_2-\underset{\underset{\underset{CH_3}{O}}{\overset{\overset{CH_3}{|}}{\underset{|}{C=O}}}{C}\!-\right]$$

polystyrene,

$$-\!(CH_2\!-\!CH)\!-$$

and polypropylene,

$$\left[\!-CH_2\!-\!\underset{\underset{CH_3}{|}}{CH}\!-\right]$$

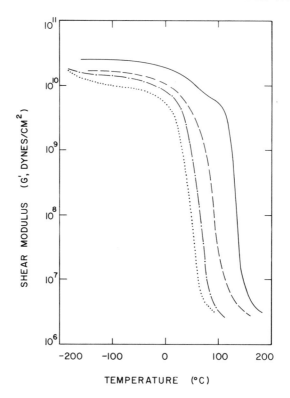

Figure 3-13. Dynamic shear modulus vs. temperature of four poly(methacrylate) esters at 1 Hz. Data of Heijboer(*148*). Code: ——— methyl; ——— ethyl; —·—·— propyl; ···· butyl.

the exact way the repeat units are connected is important. This is usually expressed in terms of the placement of three consecutive repeat units. The isotactic structure has the side chain of all three units projecting from the same side of the zigzag chain conformation, the syndiotactic structure has an alteration of this projection from one side to the other, and the heterotactic structure has no such regularity. Also of importance is the exact way the chains are packed in the crystal or glass. Different conformations are possible, including the planar zigzag and various helical conformations. Upon crystallizing from the melt, a number of polymers in the unoriented state form aggregates called spherulites, which in turn appear to consist of thin sheets or lamellae 100–400 Å thick(*149*). Since the chain direction is approximately perpendicular to the lamellar surface some chain folding must occur. The thickness between folds and fold density, the number of dislocations and defects, and the way the lamellae are connected together are dependent on the thermal history of the sample; all these parameters are expected to affect physical properties such as the modulus.

Some polymers which give essentially amorphous specimens when cooled from the melt yield crystals when precipitated from dilute solution. Such polymers include highly isotactic and syndiotactic poly-(methyl methacrylate), commercial polyacrylonitrile, and poly(vinyl chloride).

The ease with which a crystallizable polymer will crystallize from the melt appears to depend mainly on the stiffness of the main chain and the bulkiness of the sidechains. For example, highly isotactic and highly syndiotactic poly(methyl methacrylate) as well as isotactic polystyrene do not crystallize from the melt, although reheating to a temperature above T_g will cause isotactic polystyrene to crystallize; poly(ethylene terephthalate), polypropylene, and natural rubber can be easily quenched, yielding a product of low crystalline order; and for polyisobutylene to be crystallized it must be stretched. Upon annealing quenched samples, crystallinity is developed which will cause a subsequent rise in modulus at all temperatures below the annealing temperature.

B. The Glass Transition Temperature and Related Modulus Changes

1. STRUCTURAL EFFECTS

Prediction of the glass transition temperature from a knowledge of the repeat unit, the tacticity, the crystal structure, and the over-all morphology is not yet possible, although some generalizations can be made. Literature values of T_g and T_m for some selected polymers are given in Table 3-7. It should be pointed out that the values of T_g given here can only be considered exact for the particular polymer sample under study and for the particular test conditions. Many factors other than structural ones will influence the values of T_g, as discussed in a recent review (*150*).

The following structural factors are found to increase T_g: (1) the presence of rigid groups, such as benzene rings, in the main chain; (2) bulky, nonflexible side chains, such as benzene rings and terebutyl groups; and (3) polarity in the main chain (ether, carboxyl, amide), next to the main chain, or farther removed from the main chain. Some

TABLE 3-7

Glass Transition Temperatures, Melting Temperatures, and Approximate Crystallinities of Melt-Formed Samples for Various Polymers

Polymer	Repeat unit	T_g °C	Ref.	T_m °C	Ref.	Crystal-linity^a
Polyethylene	—CH_2CH_2—	?		137	(55)	High
Polytetrafluoroethylene	—CF_2CF_2—	?		327	(55)	High
Polyoxymethylene	—CH_2—O—	?		181	(55)	High
Poly(hexamethylene sebacamide)	—$NH(CH_2)_6NHC(CH_2)_8C$— (with two C=O groups)	40	(55)	227	(55)	Medium
Poly(hexamethylene adipamide)	—$NH(CH_2)_6NHC(CH_2)_4C$— (with two C=O groups)	50	(55)	265	(55)	Medium
Poly(ethylene terephthalate)	—$O(CH_2)_2OC$—⟨benzene⟩—C— (with two C=O groups)	70	(55)	267	(55)	Medium
Polycarbonate	—O—⟨benzene⟩—$C(CH_3)_2$—⟨benzene⟩—OC— (with C=O group)	150	(151)			Low
Poly(vinyl alcohol)	—CH_2—CH— with OH	85	(55)	Decomp.		Medium
Isotactic polypropylene	—CH_2—CH— with CH_3	−20	(152)	162	(153)	High
Atactic polypropylene	—CH_2—CH— with CH_3	−20	(154)	—		None
Isotactic poly(butene-1)	—CH_2—CH— with CH_2, CH_3	−25	(55)	125	(153)	Medium
Isotactic poly(pentene-1)	—CH_2—CH— with $(CH_2)_2$, CH_3	−40	(153)	70	(153)	Medium
Isotactic poly(4-methylpentene-1)	—CH_2—CH— with CH_2, CH, CH_3 CH_3	20	(55)	250	(55)	Medium

TABLE 3-7 (cont.)

Polymer	Repeat unit	T_g °C	Ref.	T_m °C	Ref.	Crystal-linity[a]
Polyisobutylene	—CH$_2$—C$\overset{\diagup \text{CH}_3}{\underset{\diagdown \text{CH}_3}{}}$	−75	(155)	—		None
Cispolyisoprene	—CH$_2$—$\overset{\text{CH}_3}{\overset{\mid}{\text{C}}}$=CH—CH$_2$—	−70	(156)	28	(55)	Low
Poly(vinyl chloride)	—CH$_2$—$\overset{}{\underset{\overset{\mid}{\text{Cl}}}{\text{CH}}}$—	80	(156)	212	(55)	Low
Poly(chlorotri-fluoroethylene)	—CF$_2$—$\overset{}{\underset{\overset{\mid}{\text{Cl}}}{\text{CF}}}$—	45	(156)	220	(55)	Medium
Poly(vinylidene chloride)	—CH$_2$—C$\overset{\diagup \text{Cl}}{\underset{\diagdown \text{Cl}}{}}$	−15	(55)	198	(55)	Medium
Commercial polystyrene	—CH$_2$—CH— ⬡	100	(157)	—		None
Isotactic polystyrene	—CH$_2$—CH— ⬡	105	(55)	240	(55)	Medium
Poly(vinyl acetate)	—CH$_2$—CH— O—C=O—CH$_3$	30	(156)	—		None
Poly(vinyl stearate)	—CH$_2$—CH— O—C=O—(CH$_2$)$_{17}$—CH$_3$	?		53	(139)	High
Poly(vinyl ethyl ether)	—CH$_2$—CH— O—CH$_2$—CH$_3$	−40	(158)	86	(55)	None

TABLE 3-7 (cont.)

Polymer	Repeat unit	T_g °C	Ref.	T_m °C	Ref.	Crystal-linity[a]
Poly(vinyl n-butyl ether)	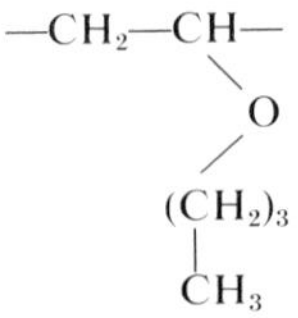 —CH₂—CH— / O / (CH₂)₃ / CH₃	−55	(158)	64	(55)	None
Poly(vinyl isobutyl ether)	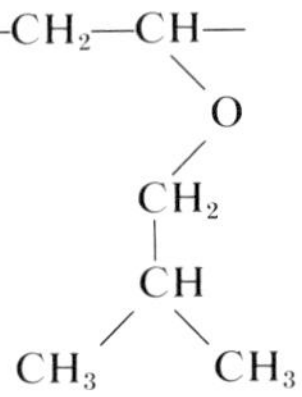 —CH₂—CH— / O / CH₂ / CH / CH₃ CH₃	−20	(158)			None
Poly(vinyl tertiary butyl ether)	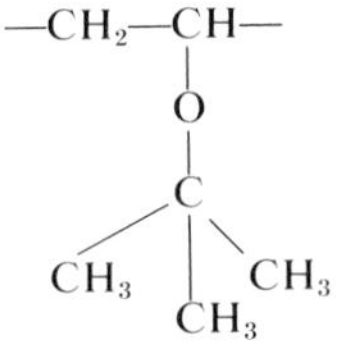 —CH₂—CH— / O / C / CH₃ CH₃ / CH₃	90	(158)	260	(55)	None
Poly(methyl acrylate	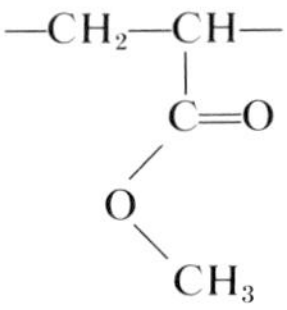 —CH₂—CH— / C=O / O / CH₃	10	(156)	—		None
Poly(ethyl acrylate)	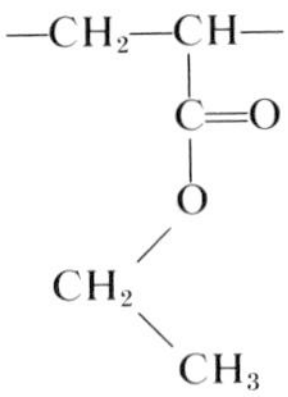 —CH₂—CH— / C=O / O / CH₂ / CH₃	−20	(156)	—		None
Poly(n-propylacrylate)	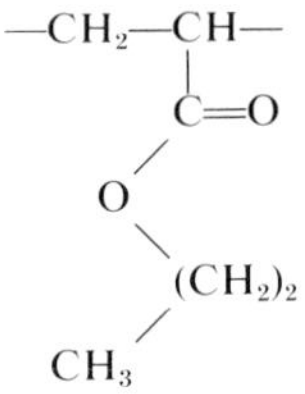 —CH₂—CH— / C=O / O / (CH₂)₂ / CH₃	−45	(159)	—		None

178

TABLE 3-7 (cont.)

Polymer	Repeat unit	T_g °C	Ref.	T_m °C	Ref.	Crystal-linity[a]
Poly(n-butyl acrylate)	$-CH_2-CH-$ $\|$ $C=O$ O $(CH_2)_3$ CH_3	−55	(156)	—		None
Commercial poly (methyl methacrylate)	CH_3 $-CH_2-C-$ $\|$ $C=O$ O CH_3	105	(156)	—		None
Isotactic poly(methyl methacrylate)	CH_3 $-CH_2-C-$ $\|$ $C=O$ O CH_3	45	(160)	160	(55)	Very low
Syndiotactic poly (methyl methacrylate)	CH_3 $-CH_2-C-$ $\|$ $C=O$ O CH_3	115	(160)	> 200	(55)	Very low
Poly(ethyl methacrylate)	CH_3 $-CH_2-C-$ $\|$ $C=O$ O CH_2 CH_3	65	(161)	—		None

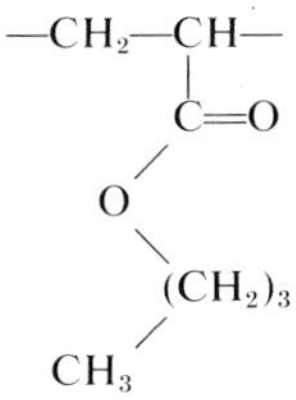

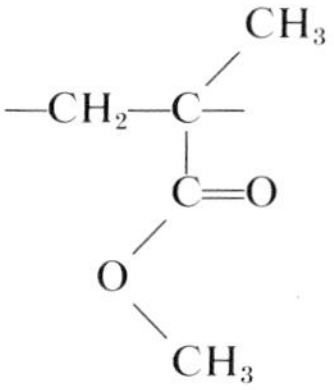

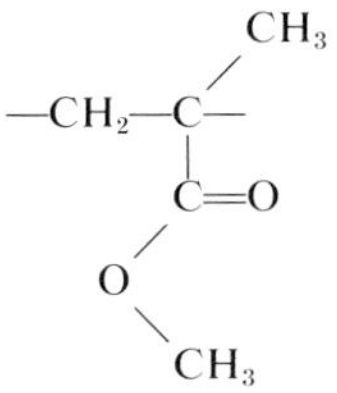

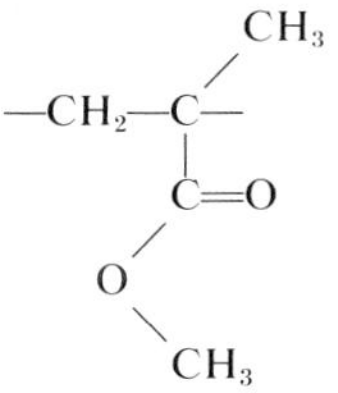

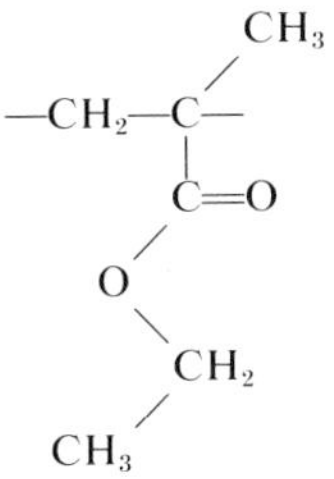

179

TABLE 3-7 (cont.)

Polymer	Repeat unit	T_g °C	Ref.	T_m °C	Ref.	Crystal-linity[a]
Poly(propyl methacrylate)	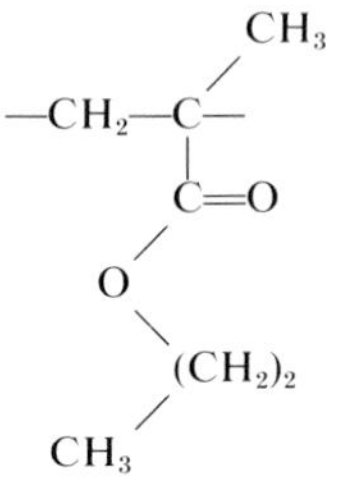	45	(*108*)	—		None
Poly(*n*-butyl methacrylate)	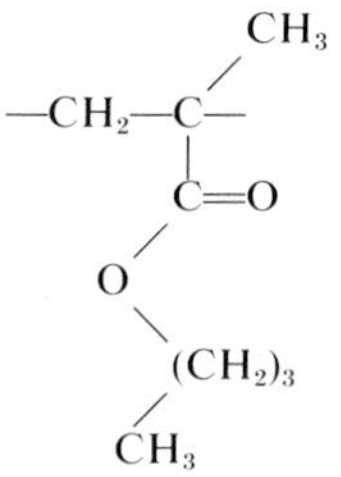	15	(*108*)	—		None
Poly(isobutyl methacrylate)	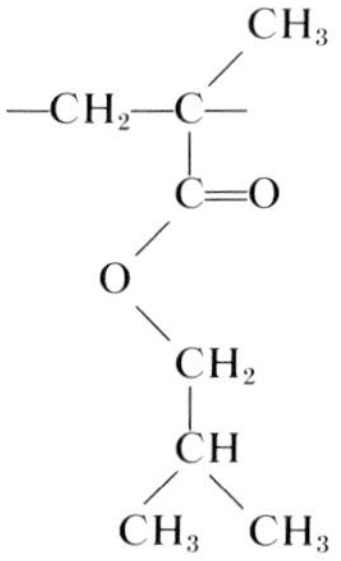	50	(*108*)	—		None
Poly(2-hydroxyethyl methacrylate)	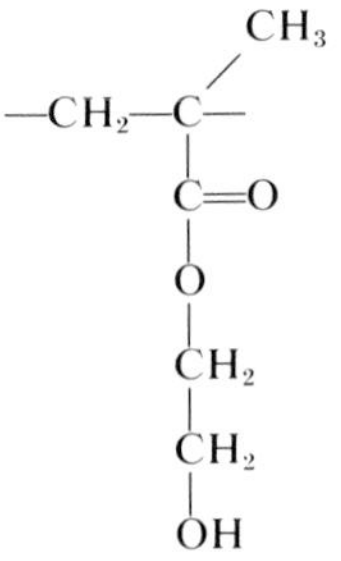	85	(*108*)	—		None

Poly(propyl methacrylate):

$$-CH_2-C(CH_3)- \quad C=O \quad O-(CH_2)_2-CH_3$$

Poly(*n*-butyl methacrylate):

$$-CH_2-C(CH_3)- \quad C=O \quad O-(CH_2)_3-CH_3$$

Poly(isobutyl methacrylate):

$$-CH_2-C(CH_3)- \quad C=O \quad O-CH_2-CH(CH_3)(CH_3)$$

Poly(2-hydroxyethyl methacrylate):

$$-CH_2-C(CH_3)- \quad C=O \quad O-CH_2-CH_2-OH$$

180

TABLE 3-7 (cont.)

Polymer	Repeat unit	T_g °C	Ref.	T_m °C	Ref.	Crystal-linity[a]
Poly(2-hydroxypropyl methacrylate)	CH_3 | —CH_2—C— | C=O | O \\ CH_2 | CH / \\ OH CH_3	70	(108)	—		None

[a]Approximate value of melt-formed samples.

structural factors which act to decrease T_g are: (1) an increase in side-chain length when nonpolar units such as methylene are being added; and (2) an increase of symmetry, at least for some substituents, in the monomer unit. Generally, an increase in molecular weight leads to an increase in T_g, the value of which levels off at high molecular weight values (of the order of 10^5 or smaller) with the exact T_g-molecular weight relationship depending on the particular polymer under investigation.

As pointed out above for noncrystalline polymers, a precipitous decrease in modulus with increasing temperature is found somewhat above T_g. Therefore any alteration of structural factors which changes T_g in a series of polymers will also shift the position of this dispersion. This effect is demonstrated in Figs. 3-12 and 3-13, where modulus data for a series of three poly(vinyl butyl ethers)(132) and four poly(alkyl methacrylates) with linear hydrocarbon side chains(148), respectively, are given. The modulus drop is seen to shift to lower temperatures with an increase in side-chain length and with a decrease in side-chain bulkiness, as does also the T_g value. More extensive modulus results on the poly(alkyl methacrylates) and on some poly(alkyl chloroacrylates) which bear out these same effects have been reported(162,163). Sound-velocity measurements for poly(vinyl acetate) and poly(vinyl proprionate) also show a shift of the T_g-related dispersion to lower temperatures with increase in side-chain length(164).

Changes in tacticity may also cause large changes in T_g and therefore in the position of the T_g-associated modulus dispersion. This is seen, for poly(methyl methacrylate), in Fig. 3-14(*165*). However, this marked effect of tacticity on T_g has not been demonstrated for materials such as polypropylene and polystyrene(*166, 167*).

When a methyl group in the side chain is replaced by a hydroxyl group, such as for some of the poly(alkyl methacrylates), T_g increases (see Table 3-7) and the temperature position of the modulus drop shifts in like manner, due to the introduction of hydrogen bonds between adjacent polymer chains(*108*).

2. COPOLYMERIZATION

When copolymers of the random or alternating type are studied it is found that for a homogeneous product T_g depends on the composition, shifting from that for pure component A to that for pure B(*150*). If the product is not homogeneous, the glass transition can become diffuse; if the degree of heterogeneity is high, more than one distinct T_g may be indicated. To demonstrate these effects on the modulus–temperature

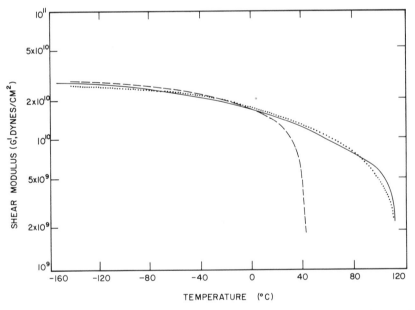

Figure 3-14. The effect of tacticity on the shear modulus–temperature relation of poly(methyl methacrylate) at frequencies ~1 Hz. Data of Gall and McCrum(*165*). Code: ——— commercial; · · · · syndiotactic; ---- isotactic.

plot, copolymer composition data for four vinyl chloride-2-ethyl hexyl acrylate copolymers and for pure poly(vinyl chloride) are given in Fig. 3-15(*168*). Only one modulus dispersion is found for the 50/50 copolymer. This dispersion shifts to a higher temperature with increasing vinyl chloride content, with a second dispersion at higher temperatures becoming evident. The occurrence of two dispersions indicates considerable heterogeneity of the product. The results of Fitzgerald and Nielsen(*169*) for copolymers of styrene and methacrylic acid and for sodium salts of methacrylic acid show only one modulus dispersion, which shifts to higher temperatures with a decrease in styrene content.

If long sequences of one monomer are attached to a chain made up from another monomer the resulting system usually acts differently

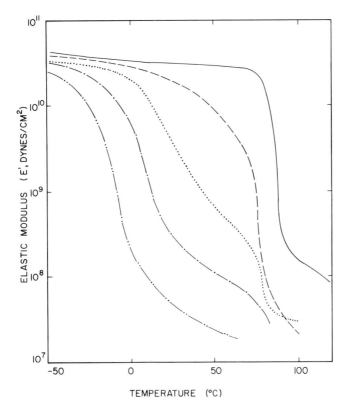

Figure 3-15. Elastic modulus vs. temperature curves for polyvinylchloride and various vinylchloride-2-ethyl hexyl acrylate copolymers at test frequencies of 0.25–15 Hz. Data of Bohn(*168*). Code: ———— 100/0 vinylchloride-2-ethyl hexyl acrylate; ----85/15; ···· 75/25; –·–·– 65/35; –··—··– 50/50.

than a homogeneous alternating or random copolymer. Such a system generally has two modulus dispersions, each associated with the T_g of a separate component, as expected for a blend of two polymers which are incompatible and therefore form separate regions of the two materials(*170–174*) [see Neilsen(*55*) for earlier references]. Modulus temperature plots for two graft copolymers, one block copolymer, and a blend of poly(4-vinylbiphenyl) and polyethylene oxide are given in Fig. 3-16, along with that for pure poly(4-vinylbiphenyl)(*174*). Two distinct drops are seen for the copolymers and the blend, although there are some differences in these curves. The exact position of the modulus dispersions can depend on the method of sample preparation; if the polymer specimen is cast from solution, the manner in which the two parts of the graft or block copolymer are dispersed will depend on the solvent chosen(*55*).

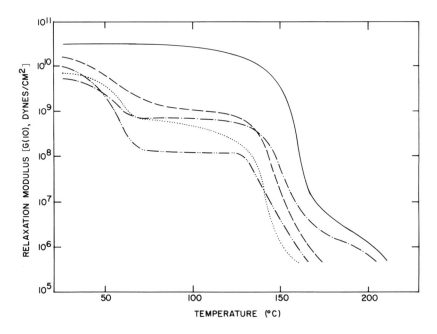

Figure 3-16. Relaxation shear modulus vs. temperature for various graft and block copolymers. Data of Rembaum et al.(*174*). Code: ——— poly(4-vinyl biphenyl); - - - - graft copolymer, 80% poly(4-vinyl biphenyl) – 20% ethylene oxide; – · – · – graft copolymer, 33% 4-vinyl biphenyl – 67% ethylene oxide; – · · – · · – block copolymer, 50% vinyl biphenyl – 50% ethylene oxide; · · · · · blend, 50% 4-vinyl(biphenyl) – 50% ethylene oxide.

3. BLENDS

As with graft and block copolymers, the exact behavior of the modulus–temperature plot depends on the compatibility of the two polymers being blended. Data(*175*) for a compatible system — poly-(vinyl chloride) blended with a butadiene-acrylonitrile copolymer — are given in Fig. 3-17; in this case only one modulus dispersion, which shifts with composition of the blend, is observed. On the other hand, results for blends of nitrile-butadiene rubber with a styrene-acrylonitrile copolymer show two modulus–temperature dispersions indicative of the two pure components(*175*). Numerous other examples of this latter case have been reported(*55,171,174,176*). One example of this latter case is given in Fig. 3-16.

4. CROSSLINKING

For amorphous polymers the addition of cross-links should act to hold the primary chains together. If the cross-links are close enough together to restrict the chain motion which occurs at T_g, then a shift of

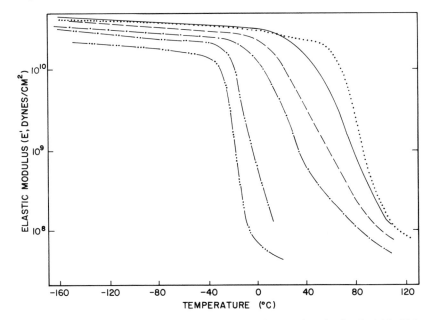

Figure 3-17.   Elastic modulus–temperature curves for a series of poly(vinylchloride)-butadiene-acrylonitrile copolymer rubber blends at frequency of 138 Hz. Data of Takayanagi(*175*). Code: ···· 100/0 poly(vinylchloride)-nitrile-butadiene rubber blend; ——— 83/17; ---- 67/33; –·–·– 50/50; –··–··– 20/80; –···–···– 0/100.

T_g to higher temperatures should take place. This shift of T_g with cross-linking has received some study and approximate relationships were ascertained(55). The T_g-related modulus dispersion for sulfur-vulcanized natural rubber shows a shift to higher values after several per cent sulfur has been added (Fig. 3-7); a phenol–formaldehyde resin cured with 4% of hexamethylene tetramine has the T_g-related modulus drop shifted by approximately 30°C to higher temperatures from that for a resin cured with 2% amine(55); a recent study on polyurethane cross-linked with various agents shows a shift of the T_g-connected modulus drop with increased cross-linking agent(177).

5. FILLERS

Investigations of the modulus–temperature relationships for TiO_2-filled poly(vinyl acetate) (up to 40% filler)(178), polyurethane rubber plus NaCl (up to 41% by volume of filler)(179), and aluminum-filled epoxy resin(180) all indicate that the temperature position of the T_g-related modulus drop is independent of filler content.

On the other hand, the use of mica, or asbestos, and of calcium carbonate as fillers for polystyrene increases the temperature of the T_g-related modulus drop(55). The addition of glass beads to polyisobutylene(181) and to a polyurethane rubber(182) causes an increase in T_g, by 0.25°C per volume per cent of beads for polyisobutylene(181). Data for the polyisobutylene-glass bead system(181) are given in Fig. 3-18.

6. DILUENTS

The addition of a soluble diluent to a completely or partially amorphous polymer results in a lowering of T_g(150). Numerous studies have shown this also to be the case for the modulus dispersion associated with T_g. Among the systems showing this behavior are poly(vinyl chloride)-diethyl phthalate(183), 6-6 nylon-water(184), polyurethane-ethanol(185), and polyurethane-ethyl acetate(186). Modulus–temperature curves for 6-6 nylon with varying amounts of water up to saturation and for a methanol-saturated sample are given in Fig. 3-19; a shift of the T_g-related modulus drop to lower temperatures with increasing amount of diluent is found.

7. CRYSTALLINITY

The effects of crystalline order on the T_g-related modulus dispersion can be studied for polymers which do not crystallize too rapidly on cooling and can therefore be quenched into an essentially amorphous condition. Upon annealing these materials, crystallinity can be

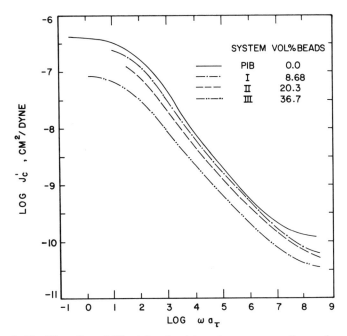

Figure 3-18. The effect of filler (glass beads) on the creep compliances for polyiso-butylene. Data of Landel(*181*).

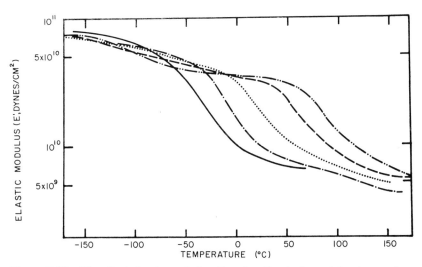

Figure 3-19. The effect of water and of methanol on the elastic modulus–temperature relation of poly(hexamethylene adipamide) nylon 6-6 at frequencies ~ 10^3 Hz. Data of Woodward, et al.(*184*). Code: $-\cdots-\cdots-$ 0% H_2O or CH_3OH; ---- 0.9% H_2O; ⋯⋯ 3.3% H_2O; $-\cdot-\cdot-$ 6.4% H_2O; ——— 10.5% CH_3OH.

187

developed. The T_g-related modulus drop for poly(ethylene terephthalate) at ~ 80°C for completely amorphous material is found to shift to higher temperatures, to decrease in magnitude, and to broaden with increasing crystallinity(*187,188*). Other polymers for which similar results have been found include poly(ε-caprolactam)(*188*), poly(methyl pimelic acid hexamethylene diamine)(*132*), poly(vinyl alcohol)(*188*), a polycarbonate of bisphenol A(*55*), and isotactic polystyrene(*167*).

C. The Melting Temperature and Related Modulus Changes

1. STRUCTURAL EFFECTS

In general, the melting temperature is affected by the same structural factors as T_g, although the magnitude of the effect can be quite different [see Table 3-7 and Nielsen(*55*)]. Approximate relationships between T_g and the melting point T_m have been given as follows:

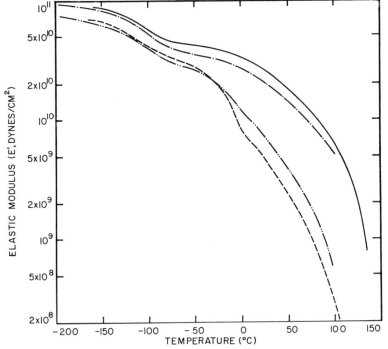

Figure 3-20. The effect of short-chain branching on the elastic modulus–temperature curve for polyethylene at frequency of ~ 10^3 Hz. Data of Kline et al.(*190*); Merrill et al.(*191*). Code: ---- 3.2 CH$_3$/100 CH$_2$; –··–··– 1.6 CH$_3$/100 CH$_2$; –·–·– < 0.1 CH$_3$/100 CH$_2$; —— < 0.1 CH$_3$/100 CH$_2$ (Marlex 50).

for polymers with unsymmetrical chain units, $T_g/T_m \sim \frac{2}{3}$; and for polymers with symmetrical chain units, $T_g/T_m \sim \frac{1}{2}$, with all temperatures in degrees Kelvin. The change in the T_m-related modulus drop with chemical repeat unit is apparent upon comparison of the modulus–temperature curves for different crystalline polymers. Data are given for polyoxymethylene (Fig. 3-21)(*189*) for some polyethylenes (Fig. 3-20)(*190,191*), for some polyamides (Fig. 3-22)(*184*), for poly(vinyl stearate) (Fig. 3-23)(*192*), and for polytetrafluoroethylene (Fig. 3-24) (*193*). It should be kept in mind that changes in crystal structure, including chain conformation and packing, and in crystallinity take place when the chemical structure is changed, and these physical changes may affect the melting temperature. When polymers formed from monosubstituted monomers or nonsymmetrical disubstituted monomers are being considered, tacticity may be an important factor in determining the melting temperature as it is for determination of T_g in PMMA. Increasing the side-chain length in polymers with flexible nonpolar substituents, such as *n*-paraffin ones, causes a decrease in melting point for the polymer until a length in the vicinity of C_8 is reached, and then the melting point increases. This latter effect is caused by crystallization of the side chains. In the case of poly(vinyl stearate) (of unknown molecular weight), the melting point is only $\sim 30°$ above that for the monomer (298°K), crystallization therein principally involving forces between side-chain atoms.

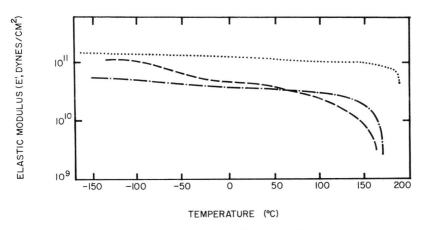

Figure 3-21. The effect of method of crystallization on the modulus–temperature behavior of polyoxymethylene at frequency of 138 Hz. Data of Takayanagi et al.(*189*). Code: ····· radiation-induced solid state polymer of tetraoxane; --- drawn sample; –·–·– single crystal mat.

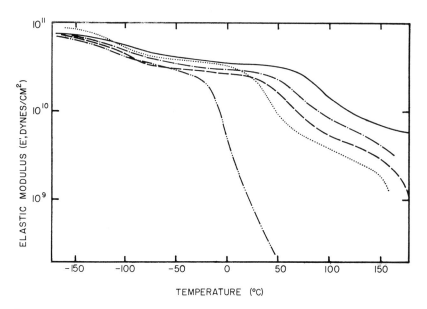

Figure 3-22. The elastic modulus–temperature relation of various polyamides at frequencies of $\sim 10^3$–10^2 Hz. Data of Woodward et al.(*184*). Code: ——— 6-6 nylon; —·—·— 6-10 nylon; - - - - 10-10 nylon; ····· 17% N-CH$_3$ 10-10 nylon; —··—··— 58% N-CH$_3$ 10-10 nylon.

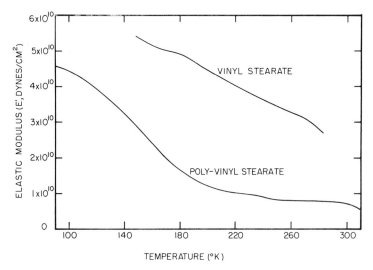

Figure 3-23. Elastic modulus–temperature plots of vinyl stearate and poly(vinyl stearate) at frequencies of $\sim 10^3$ Hz. Data of Lim and Sauer(*192*).

190

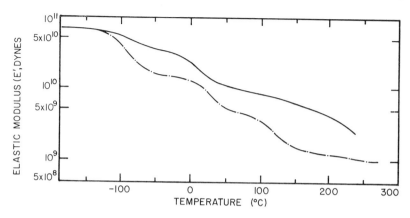

Figure 3-24. The effect of irradiation on the elastic modulus–temperature behavior of poly(tetrafluoroethylene) at frequencies $\sim 10^3$–10^2 Hz. Data of Bernier et al.*(193)*. Code: —— 196×10^6 rad (Co^{60}); $-\cdot-\cdot-$ unirradiated.

2. COPOLYMERIZATION

As mentioned in an earlier section, the melting point depends on the regularity of the chain packing. Therefore, unlike the effect on T_g, copolymerization is expected to lead to a lowering of T_m if the introduction of a foreign repeat unit in the chain acts principally to disrupt the crystalline sequence. For a random copolymer, the melting temperature T_m is related to T_m°, the melting point for pure homopolymer; ΔH_u is the heat of fusion per mole of homopolymer repeat unit; and X_A is the mole fraction of the crystallizable monomer in the polymer. The appropriate equation is

$$\frac{1}{T_m} - \frac{1}{T_m^\circ} = -\frac{R}{\Delta H_u}(\ln X_A) \tag{3-71}$$

The T_m-related modulus dispersion should be affected in a similar fashion. A lowering of the temperature region in which this dispersion occurs has been found for copolymers of ethylene with units having either methyl or propyl sidechains up to $\sim 4\%$ of comonomer*(194)*, and for copolymers of ethylene with vinyl acetate and vinyl chloride *(195)*. High pressure polymerization of polyethylene leads to polymers believed to have various amounts of short-chain branching; it is found that as the amount of short-chain branching, as exemplified by the number of methyl groups per 100 methylene groups, increases, the T_m-related modulus drop shifts to lower temperatures. This effect is seen in Fig. 3-20*(190,191)*.

The T_m-related modulus drop is affected by irradiation, which generally acts to decrease the crystallinity because of the cross-links being formed. This type of behavior is evident for linear polyethylene(*191*) as seen in Fig. 3-25, for branched polyethylene(*196*), and for poly-(ethylene terephthalate)(*197*).

3. DILUENTS

The melting temperature may also be lowered by the presence of low molecular weight substances which can enter the crystalline parts of the system. A similar effect on the T_m-connected modulus dispersion is expected; however, no data on this are available.

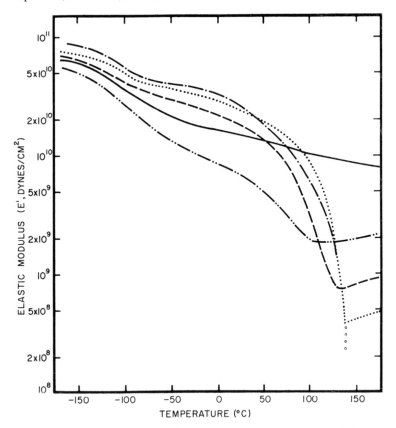

Figure 3-25.   The effect of pile irradiation on the modulus–temperature behavior of a high density polyethylene at frequencies of $\sim 10^3$ Hz. Data of Merrill et al.(*191*). Code: —·—·— unirradiated; ···· 0.6×10^{18} nvt; ---- 1.1×10^{18} nvt; —··—··— 1.5×10^{18} nvt; ——— 2.9×10^{18} nvt.

4. CRYSTAL MORPHOLOGY

Although extensive data are lacking concerning the dependence of the melting temperature and the corresponding modulus drop on the crystal morphology, there are results to indicate that it is important. The melting point of melt-crystallized samples of linear polyethylene is reported to depend on the crystallization temperature, differing by 5–10° for samples crystallized at 0°C and 124°C; the modulus–temperature drop is also shifted to higher temperature with higher annealing temperature(189). For polyoxymethylene, the temperature position of the T_m-connected modulus drop differs by 20°–30° for a mat of single crystals prepared from dilute solution and a single crystal formed by radiation-induced solid state polymerization of tetraoxane(189) (see Fig. 3-21). This latter sample has the molecular axes almost completely in the direction parallel with the long axis of the crystal and in the test the stress was applied parallel to the molecular axis. In addition, the melting point of the solid state polymerized sample was reported as 10° higher than that for melt-crystallized samples.

D. Modulus–Temperature Relationships below the Glass Transition Temperature and the Melting Temperature

1. STRUCTURAL EFFECTS

In the "glassy" state at temperatures below T_g, a comparison of modulus–temperature curves for noncrystalline polymer samples shows differences ascribed principally to the differences in the chemical structure of the repeat unit. A large number of noncrystalline polymers have side-chain substituents on every other carbon atom. The effect of a change of the bulkiness of the hydrocarbon portion of such a substituent on the modulus–temperature relationship is shown by Fig. 3-12, where data for three poly(vinyl butyl ethers) have been given(132). The polymer with the most flexible side chain—the n-butyl ether—has the lowest shear modulus at temperatures extending from the region just below T_g to $\sim -120°C$. In the $-120°C$ region a modulus dispersion, much smaller in magnitude than the one in the vicinity of T_g, is observed for the two polymers with flexible hydrocarbon portions in the side chain—the n-butyl and the isobutyl ethers—causing the modulus–temperature plots for them to cross that for the tertiary butyl ether in the $-120°$ to $-150°C$ range. Similar behavior is also exhibited by poly(methylacrylate esters) with propyl as well as butyl side chains($162,163$). For polymers containing linear paraffin groups in the side chain, an increase in hydrocarbon length at least up to C_4 leads to a decrease in modulus at temperatures from below T_g to a value $< -150°C$. Below $-150°C$ modulus dispersions can occur for the materials with the lower modulus values, causing a crossing over of the curves. This type of behavior is seen in Fig. 3-13, where data for the methyl, ethyl, n-propyl, and n-butyl poly(methacrylate esters) are given(148). Results similar to these were published previously by Hoff et al.(163) for poly(methylacrylate esters) and poly(chloroacrylate esters). Results obtained below $-200°C$ show that a dispersion of smaller magnitude than those for the n-propyl and n-butyl esters occurs for the ethyl ester, leading to a crossing of the modulus curve for this polymer over that for the methyl ester at $\sim -230°C$ at 10^4 Hz(198).

Sound velocity data for two poly(vinyl esters), the acetate and the proprionate, show that the acetate—with the shorter side chain— is the more rigid at temperatures down to $-100°C$ at a frequency of 2×10^6 Hz(164), in keeping with the results discussed above for the poly(methyl acrylate esters).

A recent study(162) has indicated that hydrogen bonding involving the side chain can be of importance in determining the modulus value below T_g. In that study, results for two poly(methacrylate esters) with hydroxyl groups terminating the ester side chains were compared with those for the esters with a methyl group in place of the hydroxyl. It was found that in both cases the modulus value at any temperature below T_g is greater for the hydroxyl-containing polymer by a factor ranging from 1.5 to 3.

The motional processes leading to the modulus dispersion below $-120°C$ described above for the poly(vinyl ethers), poly(methacrylate esters), and poly(chloroacrylate esters) are believed to involve mainly the hydrocarbon portion of the ester or ether side chain. Although the exact nature of these processes is not known, the onset of side-chain hindered rotations is a possibility.

This process is also found for the poly(alpha olefins) containing ethyl, propyl, isobutyl, isopropyl, butyl, pentyl, and hexyl side chains (199,200), but not for polypropylene—the polymer with methyl side chains—which indicates side chain motion as the cause of the dispersion observed.

Small modulus dispersions(201) are found for polystyrene at $\sim -220°C$ and for poly(alpha methylstyrene) at $\sim -130°C$ at 10^4 Hz; these processes are believed to involve oscillations and/or rocking of the phenyl side groups; for the latter polymer NMR results show that methyl group reorientations at this frequency take place at this temperature as well(*202*).

Poly(γ-benzyl-L-glutamate), a polymer with long flexible side chain substitutents

$$-CH_2CH_2\overset{\displaystyle O}{\overset{\displaystyle \|}{C}}-O-CH_2-\!\!\!\!\!\bigcirc\!\!\!\!-$$

on an alpha amino acid backbone, shows a drop in the modulus of a decade at about 290°K (10⁻¹ Hz)(*203*). The process responsible for this is believed to involve principally side-chain reorientations due to the tightly hydrogen-bonded nature of the backbone structure of this alpha helix-forming polymer.

Poly(cyclohexyl acrylate) and poly(cyclohexyl methacrylate) have modulus dispersions at ~ −30°C (200 Hz)(*204.205*), attributed to a change in the cyclohexyl side-group chain from one form to the other.

There are a number of polymers, which are usually partially crystalline, that do not have flexible side chains but do have one or more modulus dispersions at low temperatures (< 0°C). Such phenomena are evident in Fig. 3-6 for poly(propylene oxide), in Figs. 3-20 and 3-26

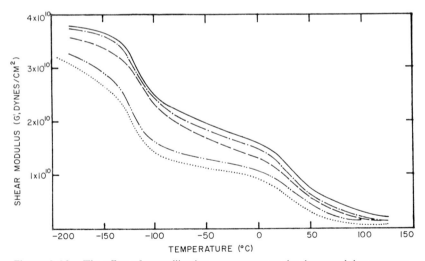

Figure 3-26. The effect of crystallization temperature on the shear modulus–temperature behavior for linear polyethylene at frequency of 1 Hz. Data of Peckhold et al. (*206*). Code: ——— 129.7°C, $\rho = 0.986$ g/cm³; –·–·– 128.0°C, $\rho = 0.985$ g/cm³; ---- 126.5°C, $\rho = 0.983$ g/cm³; –··–··– 124.5°C, $\rho = 0.978$ g/cm³; ···· quenched, $\rho = 0.959$ g/cm³.

for linear polyethylene, in Fig. 3-21 for polyoxymethylene, in Fig. 3-19 for 6-6 nylon, in Fig. 3-22 for 6-10 nylon, 10-10 nylon, and N-methylated 10-10 nylon, and in Fig. 3-24 for polytetrafluoroethylene. Other polymers for which low temperature modulus dispersions have been reported are shown in Table 3-8.

Assignment of mechanisms to explain these modulus dispersions is complicated by the fact that most of these materials are partially or highly crystalline. However, it is believed that only a small number of consecutive main-chain units enters into the motion responsible. Since

TABLE 3-8

Low Temperature Secondary Modulus Dispersions[a]

Polymer	Temp. value °C	Freq. Hz	Ref.
Poly(ethylene terephthalate)	~ −70	1	(187)
Poly(ethylene oxide)	~ −130	1	(207)
Poly(trimethylene oxide)	−110	10^2	(208)
Poly(tetramethylene oxide)	−110	10^2	(208)
Polyurethane from hexane-1,6 diiso-cyanate and butane-1,4 diol	~ −120	1	(185)
Nylon-4	−140	0.3	(209)
Nylon-6	−120, −55	10	(132)
Nylon-8	−130, −50	10	(132)
Nylon-11	−115, −55	10	(132)
6-7 Nylon	−115, −50	10	(132)
6-8 Nylon	−120, −50	10	(132)
6-12 Nylon	−120, −50	10	(132)
Polyethylene isophthalate	−70	10^2	(210)
Poly(*trans*-quinitol adipate)	−40	10^2	(210)
Poly(*trans*-quinitol sebacate)	−50	10^2	(210)
Poly(hydroquinone adipate)	< −80	10^2	(210)
Poly(hydroquinone sebacate)	< −80	10^2	(210)
Polyimide	−90	1	(211)
Poly(tetramethylene sebacate)	−120	10^2	(212)
Polycarbonate of 4,4′ dioxy-diphenyl 2,2′ propane	−100	10^2	(213)
Polycarbonate of 1,5 naphthylene-di (β oxyethyl ether)	−90	10^3	(213)
Poly(1,4-*cis*-butadiene)	−130	10	(214)
Poly(1,4 *trans*-butadiene)	−145	10^2	(189)
Poly(trifluoromonochloroethylene)	−35	1	(215)
Epoxy resin	−30	10^3	(216)

[a]The temperature values reported here are those for which the mechanical loss is a maximum.

single crystal mats of polyethylene(*206,217,218*) and of polyoxymethylene(*189,219*) show such dispersions, it appears that at least one mechanism which contributes involves motion within crystal defects (*219a*). A more inclusive discussion of this has been recently published (*220*).

The plots given in Figs. 3-20, 3-26, and 3-24 for polyethylene and poly(tetrafluoroethylene) clearly show modulus dispersion regions above 0°C but below T_m. For polyethylene there is evidence that the process at ~30°C is caused by more than one mechanism(*221*). The mechanisms responsible for these dispersions are believed to involve motion in or of crystalline parts(*189,219a*). It has been found by optical studies(*222*) that spherulite deformation can take place at temperatures of 0°C and above for polyethylene, and nuclear magnetic resonance studies(*223*) indicate that torsional motion in the crystalline regions can occur in the temperature range of these dispersions. The exact nature of the modulus dispersions at ~25°C and ~130°C (10^3 Hz) for poly(tetrafluoroethylene) are still not completely known. X-ray studies show that a crystal–crystal transition and a crystal disordering process take place at 20°C and 30°C respectively for this polymer(*224,225*), involving an unwinding of the helical chains; therefore the modulus dispersion in this region may be due to a torsional motion in the crystalline parts.

A number of other crystalline polymers show modulus drops above the T_g-related one but prior to that at T_m; these include poly(vinyl alcohol)(*218*), polyoxymethylene (see Fig. 3-21), polypropylene(*226*), and polybutene(*227*), and appear to be due to motion in or of crystalline regions.

The modulus dispersion around 0°C for branched polyethylene noticed in Fig. 3-20 appears to be associated with the branched parts of the polymer chain, and therefore the amorphous disordered regions; however, in addition to the change of branching for these samples, the crystallinity also is changed, which complicates the explanation of the mechanism.

Poly(1,4 *trans*-butadiene) has a crystal–crystal transition at ~60°C (*228*) and an annealed single crystal mat of this polymer shows greater than a twofold decrease in modulus in this temperature region(*189*).

2. CRYSTAL MORPHOLOGY

A number of studies has shown that the modulus–temperature relationship below T_m can be significantly affected by the amount of crystalline perfection, by the organization of the polymer chains in the crystalline units or regions, and by the organization of the crystalline units within the macroscopic sample. When modulus–temperature plots are compared for melt-formed samples of the same polymer that have been given different thermal histories, and therefore different crystallinities and densities, it is usually found that an increase in the modulus value takes place, at temperatures below that where significant recrystallization can occur, with an increase in density and therefore of crystalline order. An example of this type of behavior is shown in Fig. 3-26, where modulus–temperature plots are given for linear polyethylene samples crystallized at various temperatures below T_m. Similar effects are also exhibited by poly(tetrafluoroethylene)(*188*), poly(ethylene terephthalate)(*187,188,210*), isotactic polypropylene(*229,230*), nylon-6(*188*), polyoxymethylene(*231*), and polyethylene oxide(*207*).

A number of recent investigations have been carried out on mats of polymer single crystals grown from dilute solution; such studies have been made on polyethylene(*189,206,217*), polyoxymethylene(*189, 219*), poly(ethylene oxide)(*232*), polypropylene(*226*), poly(butene-1) (*227*), poly(1,4 *trans*-butadiene)(*189*), and poly(4-methyl-pentene-1) (*220,233*). Sizable differences in the modulus between single crystal mats and melt-formed specimens can occur, but the exact relationship depends on the polymer studied.

The effect of crystallization temperature and, therefore, lamellar thickness, on the modulus–temperature relationship has been studied for linear polyethylene crystals(*189*) and for polypropylene crystals (*234*). For polyethylene the modulus in the region 0° to 100°C increases with increasing growth temperature, and for polypropylene an increase in the modulus at all temperatures is found. The effect of annealing single crystals at temperatures above the crystallization temperature on the modulus behavior has been reported for linear polyethylene(*217*) and for poly(1,4 *trans*-butadiene)(*189*). For polyethylene the principal effect appears to be at temperatures above 0°C, where an increase in modulus with increasing annealing temperature is found, but for poly (1,4 *trans*-butadiene) the modulus values in the −150°C to ~ +60°C region are increased by annealing.

For polyoxymethylene, solid state polymerized samples are found to have modulus values which are higher than those for any other sample at all temperatures below T_m (see Fig. 3-21)(*189,219*). The high degree of crystal perfection and orientation is believed to be responsible for this.

Changes in crystal morphology brought about by orientation of a specimen would be expected to bring about alterations in the modulus–

temperature plot. Some elastic modulus data(210) at 10^2 Hz are given
in Fig. 3-27 for poly(ethylene terephthalate). The sample was initially
of low crystallinity, and the vibration of the sample was probably at
right angles to the stretch direction. For draw ratios of 3, 5, and 7,
an increase in the elastic modulus over that for an undrawn specimen
with increasing draw ratio is seen. For poly(oxymethylene) drawn
tenfold, the elastic modulus at a frequency of ~ 10^2 Hz and at temperatures from 10° to ~ 150°C increases with increasing draw temperature,
reaching values (for a draw temperature of 160°C) close to those for
the solid state polymerized crystal of poly(tetraoxane)(188). For
drawn polyethylene, the elastic modulus at all temperatures below
T_m obtained by vibrating the sample parallel to the stretch direction,
is greater than that when the sample is vibrated at right angles to the
stretch direction; when the sample is cold-drawn and then annealed at
130°C, the modulus is greater for perpendicular vibrations than for
parallel vibrations at temperatures above about 50°C, but is reversed
at temperatures below −120°C(235). For polypropylene annealed at
155°C after stretching, perpendicular vibrations yield a higher elastic
modulus than parallel ones above ~ 0°C(235).

Increases in elastic modulus with orientation have also been found
for nylon 6-6, viscose rayon, polyacrylonitrile(236), nylon-6(237), and

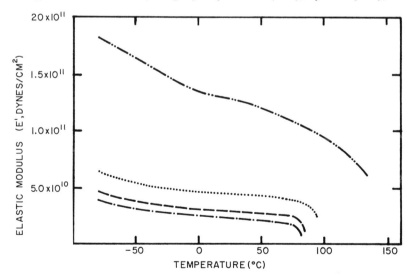

Figure 3-27.   Effect of orientation on the elastic modulus–temperature behavior of
poly(ethylene terephthalate) at frequencies of 100 Hz. Data of Kawaguchi(210). Code:
     − ·− ·− draw ratio 1; ---- draw ratio 3; · · · · draw ratio 5; − · ·− · ·− draw ratio 7.

isotactic polystyrene(*167*). For isotactic polystyrene, the elastic modulus obtained in the stretch direction is higher, as already noted in Section 3-3.C.2, than that for the unoriented specimen, while the elastic modulus found perpendicular to the stretch direction is lower in value than for the unoriented.

The shear modulus at 1 Hz measured parallel to the stretch direction for high pressure polyethylene stretched 400% is found to be higher than that for unstretched polymer below about $-20°C$ (*238*). For low pressure polyethylene the effect of stretching 650% is to increase the parallel shear modulus by factors up to ~3–4 at temperatures below 20°C. On the other hand, for a polyamide film the parallel shear modulus is not increased below 0°C (*238*), and for polytetrafluoroethylene it has been reported that drawing of an annealed sample 2.2 times causes a decrease in shear modulus at all temperatures, whereas drawing quenched samples first causes a decrease, then an increase (*239*).

The mechanical properties of some long-chain but low molecular weight substances have been studied. These substances, which include the *n*-paraffins(*206*) and vinyl stearate(*192*), are highly crystalline. The modulus–temperature plot for such substances can be similar to that for polymers, as is shown in Fig. 3-23, where results for vinyl stearate and poly(vinyl stearate) are compared. The polymer has a higher melting point and therefore a higher modulus in the region between T_m for the monomer and that for the polymer. However, at lower temperatures the modulus for the monomer is higher than that of the polymer, with the modulus for the polymer undergoing a dispersion at ~ $-120°C$. Side-chain crystallization in the polymer should lead to similarities in the crystal structures for the monomer and polymer, except that in the polymer the hydrocarbon backbone links adjacent side chains. The crystalline order in the polymer is not expected to be as high as that for the monomer(*240*), which may partially account for the lower modulus and greater segmental mobility for the polymer below T_m.

3. COPOLYMERIZATION

For a highly crystalline polymer like polyethylene, it is expected that the addition of a small amount of a comonomer will decrease the extent of crystalline order and thereby lower the modulus at temperatures below T_m. This is apparent from the data in Fig. 3-20, where small amounts (1–3%) of short-chain branching units lead to marked reductions in the modulus–temperature curve below T_m as well as reductions in the crystallinity ($\sim 90\%$ to $\sim 50\%$). This same effect is found when small amounts of comonomers which yield methyl and propyl side chains are added to polyethylene(*194*), when vinyl acetate and vinyl chloride are used as comonomers(*195*) with ethylene, and when hexafluoropropylene (10.7%) is used as comonomer for tetrafluoroethylene(*241*).

When methyl methacrylate is grafted onto high density polyethylene film, using high energy irradiation to initiate the grafting, the elastic modulus at 20 Hz from $-20°$ to $100°–150°C$ increases with increasing methyl methacrylate up to wt ratios of MMA/ethylene of 188(*242*). When low density polyethylene film is used, the modulus–temperature plot first decreases (wt MMA/wt PE = 27), then increases (wt MMA/ wt PE = 69, 89, 122).

4. IRRADIATION

When irradiation acts mainly to cross-link primary chains it is expected that the modulus–temperature curve will be increased. However, for crystalline polymers irradiation disrupts the order(*243*) and even when cross-linking takes place the modulus–temperature curve below T_m may drop to lower values until the crystallinity is destroyed and then increase again as for polyethylene(*191*) (see Fig. 3-25). Irradiation of nylon 6-6 also causes a drop in the modulus–temperature curve below T_m(*244*), while for poly(ethylene terephthalate) irradiation in a reactor facility to 37×10^{10} erg/g causes a drop in the modulus curve above T_g(*197*). On the other hand, irradiation of polytetrafluoroethylene at low dosages acts to increase the crystallinity, probably due to chain scission and reduction of molecular weight, thereby raising the modulus–temperature curve between $-120°$ and $\sim 530°C$, as is observed from the results shown in Fig. 3-24. McLaren (*245*) has reported that when annealed polytetrafluoroethylene is irradiated at doses from 0.5 to 5×10^6 rads in a Co^{60} source, the modulus decreases slightly below $\sim 30°C$ with increasing dose; for quenched samples an increase in the modulus level occurs with increasing dose.

5. FILLERS

The addition of inert fillers to polymers acts to increase the modulus (decrease the compliance) at temperatures below T_g, as has been shown for mica and asbestos-filled polystyrene(*246*), for aluminum-filled epoxy resin(*180*), and for glass bead-filled polyisobutylene(*181*) (see Fig. 3-18).

6. DILUENTS

For partially crystalline polymers with polar groups such as

$$\text{—OH} \quad \text{and} \quad \text{—NH}\overset{\text{O}}{\underset{}{\text{C}}}\text{—}$$

the addition of diluents which enter the disordered regions can act to enhance greatly or possibly to bring about the appearance of a dispersion region at temperatures below T_g. In addition to this the modulus level in the temperature region of the dispersion in question and below is increased, as is seen in Fig. 3-19 for 6-6 nylon with varying amount of water added. These effects are also found for 6-12 nylon-water(247), 6-12 nylon-ethanol(185), nylon 6-ϵ-caprolactam (monomer)(188), and poly(vinyl alcohol)-water(188). For poly-(ethylene terephthalate)-water up to 1.2% water, the modulus increases at temperatures below the $\sim -80°C$ dispersion(213), while for an epoxy resin no change in modulus occurs upon addition of 0.9% water to a dry sample(180).

The addition of water to an amorphous polymer, poly(methyl methacrylate), leads to a new but small dispersion region below T_g (165).

E. Modulus–Temperature Relationships above the Glass Transition Temperature and/or the Melting Temperature

1. MOLECULAR WEIGHT

The modulus above T_g for an amorphous polymer or above T_m for a crystalline polymer in an uncross-linked condition depends on the molecular weight, as is seen in Fig. 3-8 for polystyrene. Similar results for bisphenyl A polycarbonate have been found where samples with molecular weights of 90,000 have a higher 10-sec relaxation modulus than those with a 40,000 molecular weight above 140°C (151). For polyisobutylene it was found that for a molecular weight of 5×10^5 the modulus curve drops precipitously at 0°C, for a molecular weight of 9×10^5 the drop is at $\sim 20°C$, and for a molecular weight of $\sim 2 \times 10^6$ at 130°C with the modulus value of this temperature reaching about 10^7 dyn/cm²(132). This dependence on molecular weight has been explained in terms of the number of entanglements a polymer chain undergoes with other chains, this number increasing with the length of the chain.

2. CROSS-LINKING

Cross-linking to low degrees but to amounts giving an infinite network causes an increase in the modulus–temperature values at temperatures above T_g for amorphous polymers and above T_m for crystalline polymers. In this rubbery region the modulus increases with increasing temperature, as is evident in Fig. 3-7, where data for sulfur-vulcanized rubber is given, and in Fig. 3-25, where results showing the effect of high energy irradiation of polyethylene on the elastic modulus are found. Similar results have been given for phenol-formaldehyde resin cross-linked with hexamethylene tetramine(248), and for 6-6 nylon cross-linked with high energy irradiation(243). As the amount of cross-linking is increased the modulus–temperature curve continues to rise to higher levels, but at high cross-linking degrees the modulus no longer increases with increasing temperature but decreases slowly(132,248) (see Fig. 3-25). This occurs because at higher degrees of cross-linking the chain flexibility is decreased, the material can no longer act like a rubber, and therefore has the properties of a rigid solid.

3. FILLERS

The addition of a filler to a rubbery solid acts to increase the modulus or decrease the compliance, as is seen in Fig. 3-18 for glass bead-filled polyisobutylene. Similar results have been reported for rubber–carbon black(55), urethane rubber–glass beads(182), urethane rubber–sodium chloride(179), and poly(vinyl acetate–titanium dioxide)(178).

4. ORIENTATION

The effect of orientation on the elastic modulus and/or the relaxation spectrum has been investigated for natural rubber vulcanizate (sulfur-vulcanized)(249–251), butyl rubber(249), gutta percha, GRS, perbunan, and neoprene(251). Wave propagation studies at 10^3 Hz and 20°C on natural rubber showed that the whole relaxation spectrum, $L(\tau)$, is shifted to longer times with increasing extension ratio in the 100–600% range(249); in another study, the wave velocity at 20°C was found to increase with increasing strain when strains up to 300% were used. When these studies are carried out at temperatures below 0°C, a decrease is found in the elastic modulus with increasing extension ratio to values of ~ 2 and then an increase is found for extension ratios up to 7. At temperatures greater than 0°C (up to 50°C) only an increase in modulus is observed. For butyl rubber tested at temperatures in the region from $-10°$ to $50°C$ only an increase is found for extension ratios up to 7. This increase is not as large in magnitude as for natural rubber vulcanizate, and the modulus–strain plot has two regions, the first of lesser slope than the second. The wave velocity at $30°C$ for neoprene plus carbon black and for GRS and perbunan at $20°C$ increases with increasing strain, while that for gutta percha at $40°C$ decreases and then increases.

For most rubberlike materials, at high elongations (600%) an increase in dynamic elastic modulus of the order of 100 times is found (251–253).

3-5 CORRELATION OF MODULUS DATA WITH OTHER PHYSICAL MEASUREMENTS

A. Mechanical Loss Modulus

As discussed in Section 3-2,B,4, the phenomenological theory of viscoelasticity predicts that for each relaxation process characterized by a dispersion in the storage modulus–frequency or storage modulus–temperature plots there should also be a peak in the loss modulus or loss tangent plots. The peak in loss tangent is usually found at somewhat higher temperatures than the midpoint of the modulus–temperature dispersion. For purely viscous processes which lead to decreases in the storage modulus, such as those occurring at the melting point of crystalline polymers, no change in loss modulus occurs. Since the storage modulus decreases and the loss modulus remains unchanged, an upswing in loss tangent is found.

Experimentally, the features indicated from phenomenological theory are verified (55,132,162). It is also found that weak processes are usually more easily detected in the loss modulus or loss tangent plots than in the storage modulus plot, due partly to the fact that the modulus also changes with temperature due to thermal expansion and that a modulus change due to a more predominant mechanism may obscure that of the weaker one.

There appears to be no consistent correlation between the mangitude of the loss modulus peak and the storage modulus drop. As an example, for the poly(alpha olefins) poly(butene-1) and poly(pentene-1), the loss modulus peak is of greater magnitude for the $\sim -120°C$ process when compared with that at $\sim 25°C$, while the storage modulus drop is greater for the $\sim 25°C$ process than for the $-120°C$ one (254). It has been noted that, in general, loss tangent peaks have heights in about the same ratio as storage modulus drops. However, it is not evident from the experimental data which specific parameter, such as loss modulus, loss tangent, area under peak, elastic modulus change, etc., if any, is the best criterion for assignment of motional mechanisms. In some instances, as for the variation of the γ relaxation process in teflon with degree of crystallinity, several different measures appear to give similar information, while for the high temperature alpha relaxation in the same material, one measure shows a marked change in relaxation strength with increase of crystallinity, while a second measure shows no change (193).

B. Dielectric Constant and Loss†

The in-phase component of the complex dielectric constant ϵ' has low values when the atomic or molecular dipoles in the material under study are unable to follow an applied ac voltage. As the ability of the dipoles to follow the field increases, ϵ' increases. If the polar groups in the material under study are part of polymer chains, then the dipole moment will depend on the mobility of the segment containing the dipole as well as on the mobility of adjacent segments. At a given temperature the dipoles can follow the field if the frequency is low and hence the dielectric constant is high; upon an increase of frequency, ϵ' decreases until the limiting high frequency value is reached. At a given frequency, as the temperature is increased from low to high values, there will be an increase in ϵ' as the relaxation region is traversed. This increase will occur at those temperatures where the internal relaxation time is comparable to the period of the applied field and it will be accompanied by a maximum in the loss curve.

The real part, ϵ', of the complex dielectric constant thus acts analogously to the in-phase part of the complex compliance J'; as is the case for J', if a wide enough temperature range is traversed, more than one dispersion in ϵ' can usually be observed for a given material. Whether or not the relative magnitudes of any dispersion in ϵ' are the same as those for the dispersion in J' depends on the placement of the dipoles in the polymeric repeat unit. If the dipole is incorporated in the main chain, as it is in poly(vinyl chloride), the nylons, the polyesters, the poly(alkylene oxides), the polyurethanes, and poly(vinyl alcohol), then the relative magnitudes will be similar for related dispersions in ϵ' and J'. When the dipole is part of the side chain removed

†For a detailed discussion of this method and best results, see Curtis(255) and Ref.(162).

from the main chain, such as in poly(alkyl methacrylate esters), the principal dielectric constant dispersion will correspond to side-chain movement and not to the T_g-related process; therefore for this type of polymer the relative magnitudes of any two dispersions will be different for ϵ' and J' if one of the dispersions involves side-chain motion and the other main-chain motion. Dielectric constant results for one polymer, poly(trifluoromonochloroethylene), are given in Fig. 3-28 as a function of both temperature and frequency (256).

Correlation between dynamic mechanical and dielectric properties is usually attempted by comparison of the respective loss tangents, ϵ''/ϵ' and E''/E'. In general this type of comparison is successful, although the maximum in the electrical loss tangent is sometimes at somewhat higher temperatures than the corresponding maximum in the mechanical loss tangent at the same frequency. As with the comparison of ϵ' and J', the magnitude of the respective loss tangents will depend on the placement of the dipolar groups. The temperatures of maximum loss for dynamic mechanical and electrical studies for a variety of polymers have been compiled (162,257), and activation energies for the various relaxation processes have been estimated.

The reduced-variables method discussed in Section 3-2,B,5 has been

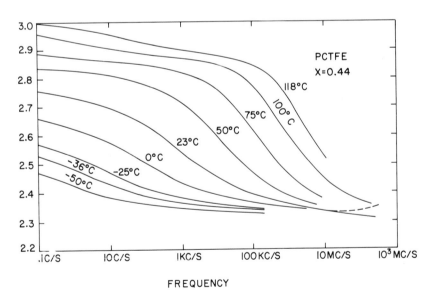

Figure 3-28. Dielectric constant-frequency curves at various temperatures for poly-(trifluoromonochloroethylene) (sample 44% crystalline). Data of Scott et al. (256).

successfully applied to superpose electrical data taken at different temperatures and the shift factors are in agreement with those found upon superposing mechanical data for the same polymer(*258–261*). The distribution of relaxation times is similar but not identical for electrical and mechanical measurements, which is one reason for the difference in the values of the temperature of maximum loss for the two methods.

C. Nuclear Magnetic Resonance†

Nuclear magnetic resonance experiments can be carried out with material containing nuclei which have magnetic moments with values other than zero. Polymers with hydrogen or fluorine nuclei fall in this category. When such a material is placed in a strong static magnetic field, transitions from one nuclear spin energy level to another can be induced by a radio-frequency field of appropriate frequency. However, this steady-state absorption, or NMR line, is broadened by local interactions of a given spin with neighboring spins. Motion of the interacting nuclei at frequencies $\gtrsim 10^4$ Hz leads to a narrowing of this absorption envelope. Therefore, when transformation from a rigid to a more flexible condition occurs in a polymer upon increase of temperature, the NMR absorption, as given by the "line width" or by the "second moment" of the absorption, will narrow. In cases of crystalline polymers a narrow line component may become visible along with the broad component at some specific temperature. The narrow component is usually attributed to nuclear spins that are attached to more mobile (amorphous or disordered) chain segments. The narrow component usually appears in the vicinity of T_g and undergoes further narrowing as the temperature is increased. The broad component for crystalline polymers narrows precipitously at temperatures approaching T_m; for amorphous polymers, this narrowing occurs at or above T_g.

In addition to the line width and second moment, another useful parameter which can be measured is the spin-lattice relaxation time, T_1, the time constant for energy transfer from nuclei in the higher spin energy states to the surrounding lattice. Motion of the lattice at frequencies near the resonance frequency, which for most apparatus is in the 10^7–10^8 Hz range, leads to a more efficient transfer of energy and therefore a shorter T_1. Therefore, in traversing a temperature region where a motional process is being activated, T_1 will go through a minimum. This minimum will be at higher temperatures than the mid-

---

†For a detailed discussion of this method, see ref.(*262*).

point of the line width or second moment change, due to the higher frequency of the motion affecting T_1.

Some second-moment and T_1 results for poly(4-methyl-pentene-1) are shown along with elastic storage modulus and loss modulus results in Fig. 3-29(263). All four parameters show the T_g-related relaxation process which is located at ~ 50°C (~ 10^4 Hz) and at 150°C (~ 10^7 Hz). At low temperatures, however, the process which strongly affects the NMR results, such as the marked drop in ΔH^2 near 80°K, is not the same as that affecting E' and E''. The low temperature NMR process is attributed principally to methyl group reorientation, whereas the −120°C (~ 10^3 Hz) process that affects the mechanical properties and gives rise to a definite maximum in E'', as the figure shows, is probably due to isobutyl-group oscillations.

Unless some other motion occurs along with it, methyl-group reorientations are not expected to cause a very noticeable change in the mechanical properties, whereas since considerable movement of a large number of protons is involved the change seen by the NMR methods is significant. The assignment of the majority of the low-temperature NMR processes to methyl reorientations has been based on comparisons of experimental values of second moments with calculated rigid lattice values and with estimated values for the case where the methyl groups are reorientating; comparison is also sometimes made with experimental results on deuterated materials, since deuterons do not give a nuclear resonance signal under the conditions in which protons respond.

The similarities and differences between NMR and mechanical results seen for poly(4-methyl-pentene-1) in Fig. 3-29 are found to occur in many other polymers. The mechanical method and the NMR method clearly show the T_g-related process, but where other processes are concerned the intensity of response depends on the method used. A number of papers discussing such comparisons has appeared(220, 263–265).

In the case of poly(propylene oxide) and poly(alpha methyl styrene), mechanical-loss maxima are found at ~ 10^4 Hz in the temperature regions where methyl reorientation processes are found by NMR (198,201); it is believed, however, that some main-chain motion in the case of poly(propylene oxide) and phenyl-group motion in the case of poly(alpha methyl styrene) are taking place along with methyl reorientations, causing the changes in the mechanical properties. In one investigation at 10^7 Hz small loss maxima have been found for PMMA, PEMA, PiBMA, and PPr in the temperature region where T_1 minima

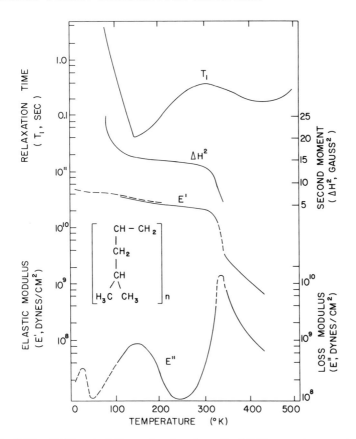

Figure 3-29. NMR spin lattice relaxation time, T_1, NMR second moment, ΔH^2, dynamic storage modulus, E', and dynamic loss modulus, E'', as functions of temperature for poly(4-methyl pentene-1). Data of Woodward(263).

attributed to methyl reorientations also exist(265a). The authors attribute these maxima to motion of methyl groups plus other parts of the polymer chain. However, for the poly(methacrylate esters), traces of water can lead to such maxima in the same temperature–frequency region(165).

The second moment–temperature plots for a number of polymers — various poly(alpha olefins), poly(ethyl vinyl ether), and polyvinyl stearate — although not showing abrupt changes, do show steady decreases in the temperature ranges where the mechanical properties show modulus dispersions and loss peaks attributed to side-group movement(265b, 266).

D. Specific Volume

The measurement of specific volume as a function of temperature is one of the principal methods used to measure T_g. However, the use of this method to locate secondary transitions has not met with as much success. It has recently been used, together with thermal expansion and dynamic mechanical methods, to provide increased understanding of the glass transition in highly crystalline polymers(267a).

Nielsen(267b) has found that for a series of six polyethylenes of varying density, the specific volume $V(T)$ is related to the shear modulus G' by a linear expression:

$$\log_{10} G' = 26.67 - 16.27\, V(T)$$

at any temperature. A plot of this relation is given in Fig. 3-30.

E. Specific Heat

Low temperature specific heat studies have been reported for polyethylene to $\sim -220°C$ (268), for natural rubber to $\sim -250°C$ (269), for

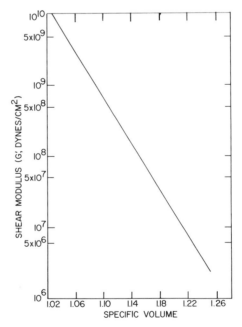

Figure 3-30.   Correlation of shear modulus and specific volume of polyethylene. From Nielson(267).

atactic polypropylene to $\sim -250°C$ (268), for isotactic polypropylene to $\sim -180°C$ (270), for poly(4-methyl-pentene-1) to $\sim -190°C$ (268), for polyisobutylene to $\sim -220°C$ (268), for poly(butene-1) to $\sim -220°C$ (268), for isotactic, syndiotactic, and commercial poly(methyl methacrylate) to $-30°C$ (268), for atactic polystyrene to $\sim -250°C$ (268,271), for isotactic polystyrene $20°-300°K$ (272), for poly(ethylene terephthalate) to $\sim -180°C$ (270), for polytetrafluoroethylene to $\sim -130°C$ (270), for polycarbonate to $\sim -100°C$ (270), and for plasticized PVC to $\sim -30°C$ (270). In general, abrupt changes in slope occur in specific heat–temperature plots in the T_g region. This is shown, for example, by Fig. 3-31 for data obtained on polypropylene (268). Changes also occur, as for poly(tetrafluoroethylene), in the temperature regions in which crystal–crystal transitions are found. However, the relaxation processes at lower temperatures which cause noticeable changes in the storage and loss moduli and in the electrical loss and dielectric constant do not bring about abrupt changes in the specific heat–temperature plot (268,270). Also, changes in crystallinity do not appreciably affect the specific heat below T_g (268) as they do the storage modulus–temperature plot.

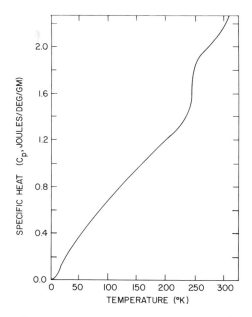

Figure 3-31.   Specific heat vs. temperature for polypropylene. Data of O'Reilly and Karasz (268).

F. Thermal Conductivity†

In a paper published by Steere(270) thermal conductivity results obtained by a transient method are given for poly(ethylene terephthalate), poly(tetrafluoroethylene), polypropylene, polycarbonate, and poly(vinyl chloride). For poly(ethylene terephthalate) a discontinuity is found near T_g and a plateau in the $-50°$ to $0°C$ range indicative of a secondary process. In Fig. 3-32, drawn from Steere's data on poly(tetrafluoroethylene), two sharp discontinuities are seen at $19°$ and $30°C$, the temperatures of known crystal–crystal and crystal–disorder transitions. An inflection point is found for polypropylene at $10°C$, indicative of a T_g-related process. For plasticized poly(vinyl chloride) a maximum in the thermal conductivity in the vicinity of T_g was found which shifted to lower temperatures with increasing plasticizer amount. Therefore, although changes in conductivity do occur near T_g, it appears that they can occur as discontinuities, inflection points, or peaks.

G. Impact Strength

Comparisons of impact strength of unnotched specimens with shear modulus (~ 1 Hz) and damping have been reported by Heijboer(274)

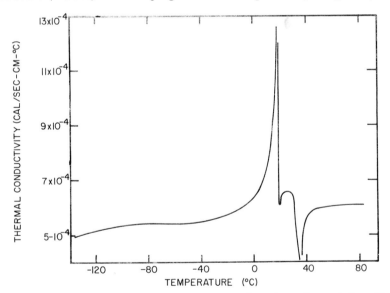

Figure 3-32.   Thermal conductivity vs. temperature for polytetrafluoroethylene. Data of Steere(270).

†For a detailed discussion of this topic see Ref. (273).

for poly(methyl methacrylate), poly(propyl methacrylate), a 40:60 (wt%) copolymer of methyl methacrylate and cyclohexylmethacrylate, a 50:50 copolymer of methyl methacrylate and acrylonitrile, poly(2, 6-dimethyl-p-phenylene oxide), polycarbonate of bisphenol, polyoxymethylene, and high density polyethylene; the results of these impact studies for the latter two polymers are reproduced in Fig. 3-33. Both materials show a rise in impact strength with increasing temperature in the vicinity of the low temperature modulus dispersion (see Figs. 3-21 and 3-26). Polycarbonate also exhibits an increase in impact strength in the vicinity of, but below, the low temperature modulus dispersion at ~ − 80°C. However, poly(2,6-dimethyl-p-phenylene oxide) (~ − 150°C) and the 50:50 methyl methacrylate acrylonitrile copolymer (~ 50°C) both show increases in impact strength by a factor of two or greater which are not correlated with modulus dispersions (or damping maxima). In addition, poly(propyl methacrylate), which has a modulus dispersion at −185°C (1 Hz), and the 40:60 copolymer of methyl methacrylate and cyclohexylmethacrylate with a dispersion at −80°C (1 Hz) do not show corresponding increases in impact strength. For the latter two copolymers the motions responsible for the changes in dynamic mechanical properties are believed to take place principally in the side chain and therefore little effect on the

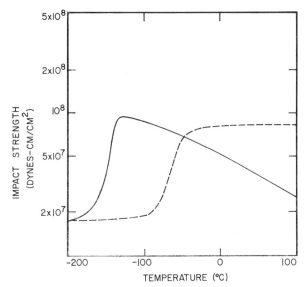

Figure 3-33. Impact strength vs. temperature for high density polyethylene(————) and polyoxymethylene (- - - -). Data of Heijboer(274).

impact properties is expected. The presence of an impact strength change with no change in dynamic properties has been explained(*274*) as due to the importance of nonlinear viscoelastic effects on the high strain impact strength measurement.

The impact strength of polycarbonate from bisphenol A has also been studied for notched specimens as a function of temperature, and the results(*275*) are similar to those found for an unnotched specimen (*274*).

3-6 SUMMARY

It has been shown that the mechanical properties of high polymers are not only a function of the particular chemical composition, physical structure, and texture, but also of the external environment. Depending upon this environment, polymers may behave as elastic rigid solids, as viscoelastic materials, or as rubberlike materials.

For elastic solids, the stress–strain relationships have been stated for the case of linear behavior, and the effect of symmetry considerations on the number of independent elastic constants required to define mechanical behavior has been discussed. For isotropic solids, the interrelationships between the various elastic constants that come into play, depending upon the nature of the loading conditions, have been given.

For linear viscoelastic solids, the appropriate parameters defining stress–strain behavior are also time dependent. The various manifestations of viscoelasticity, such as relaxation, creep, and the nature of response to dynamic loading, are described both in terms of behavior of suitable models and also in terms of a relaxation or retardation distribution function. In general, and especially for amorphous polymers, a time–temperature equivalence principle has been found to be very useful in correlating and predicting behavior as a function of both temperature and frequency.

A discussion has been given of the molecular theories that have been developed for both viscoelastic materials and rubberlike materials. The latter appears to be much more successful that the former. One difficulty with the molecular theories of viscoelasticity is that they ignore local structure and the nature of energy barriers that restrict bond rotation. Instead, they assume a given molecule is free to take on all possible conformations. As a result of these rather unrealistic assumptions, the predictions of the theory can at best be expected to hold only when these conditions are approximately met, as for the case of dilute solutions or for the temperature range above the glass transition. Clearly more sophisticated theories are needed, even for the case of amorphous polymers, in order to provide more insight into the meaning of the monomeric friction coefficient and to take more appropriately into account local mode motions and restraints. Some steps in this direction have already been taken(*6,7,20,276,277*).

The classical theory of rubber elasticity, on the other hand, does appear to predict correctly the main features of rubberlike behavior. Here, too, however, there are some unanswered questions. First, there is as yet no final agreement on the nature of the correction terms required to take due account of the concentration of cross-links. Second, it appears that, in some applications, it may be necessary to take account of possible energy changes with changes of conformation. Developments have recently taken place relative to both of these questions(*278–282*).

Although the linear theories of elasticity and viscoelasticity do permit the correlation of a vast array of experimental data obtained by different techniques, they are not able to provide an explanation for behavior at high strains where nonlinear effects arise. A more general nonlinear theory is needed in these applications and progress along these lines has taken place(*127,283–286*).

Attempts have been made to calculate theoretical values of elastic moduli from known or assumed force constants, and these theoretical values have been compared both with measured lattice moduli obtained from X-ray data and specimen moduli obtained from numerical stress–strain curves. For some polymers, there is fair agreement between the X-ray longitudinal modulus and the modulus calculated on the basis of an extended zigzag chain. For other polymers, the agreement is rather poor. Additional experimental data are needed, especially of moduli values at low temperatures. Also more appropriate potential functions appear to be required in order properly to take care of intermolecular effects.

It is noted that the possible range of modulus values under normal temperature conditions is much greater for high polymers than for metals, or other common materials. The stiffness and elasticity of polymers is also more susceptible to environmental variables such as loading speed, test temperature, and specimen orientation. Although the specific modulus values thus depend on composition, prior history, and test environment, many polymers have an elastic modulus that is of the order of 10^{10} dyn/cm^2 at temperatures below T_g and of the order of 10^7 dyn/cm^2 at temperatures above T_g.

As discussed in some detail in Section 3-4, marked changes in modulus will occur both in the vicinity of the glass transition temperature and in the vicinity of the melting temperature. It should also be noted that all of the factors that affect T_g and/or T_m, such as structure, polarity, tacticity, molecular weight, chain stiffness, side-chain length, cross-linking, branching, copolymerization, etc., will also markedly affect the modulus–temperature relation. Many of the above factors also have some influence on the values of the modulus at temperatures below T_g. The nature of the modulus–temperature relation at temperatures below the primary transition also depends on whether or not additional secondary transitions are present and this, in turn, appears to depend to a great extent on the nature of the polymer repeat unit.

Although our understanding of the nature of modulus dispersions in polymers has been greatly enhanced as a result of the many investigations that have been made to date, there is still some uncertainty concerning the specific molecular mechanisms involved in the various observed transitions. It is also not clear why some particular factor, such as tacticity or orientation, may have one effect for a given polymer but a different effect for another polymer. Additional experimental and theoretical studies are needed, and more complete characterization of test specimens, as to structure, texture, molecular weight, past history, etc., is essential.

Some of the specific areas where additional study would enhance our knowledge and understanding of modulus–temperature behavior and perhaps remove some of the present uncertainties are: low molecular weight analogs of polymers and of sharp polymer fractions; the effects of orientation in both single crystal elements and in drawn polymers; the role of crystal defects and imperfections; the effects of diluents on both low temperature transitions and the T_m-related modulus drop; the effect of pressure as well as of temperature; the nature of modulus dispersions at very low temperatures; and the relation between observed mechanical relaxation processes and the magnitudes of intra- and intermolecular energy barriers to reorientation.

The degree of correlation between results obtained by study of the stress–strain parameters in high polymers and results obtained by study of other physical methods is, as noted in Section 3-5, sometimes quite high and sometimes quite low. The physical properties that apparently do correlate, to some degree, with mechanical modulus measurements include: mechanical loss, or internal friction measurements, dielectric measurements, nuclear magnetic resonance measurements, specific volume measurements, specific heat measurements, and impact strength measurements. One difficulty with attempts at relating these different manifestations of physical behavior is that the property being measured may be more or less sensitive to specific molecular features than is mechanical behavior. Another is that the available data have generally been acquired on specimens that are not strictly comparable as to composition, structure, past history, and test environment. To enhance our present understanding of the relationship between the various physical properties or the relationship between any given physical property and the polymer composition and structure, it is essential that new data be acquired by various physical methods on comparable, well-characterized specimens, and that these investigations be carried out over wide ranges of external environment.

ACKNOWLEDGMENT

Acknowledgment is hereby given to the U.S. Atomic Energy Commission and to the National Science Foundation for the support which helped to make this study possible. Our thanks are given also to Mr. David Liu for his aid in the preparation of the diagrams.

REFERENCES

1. I. S. Sokolnikoff, *Mathematical Theory of Elasticity*, McGraw-Hill, New York, 1946.
2. A. P. Boresi, *Elasticity in Engineering Mechanics*, Prentice-Hall, Englewood Cliffs, New Jersey, 1965.
3. J. F. Nye, *Physical Properties of Crystals*, Oxford University Press, London, 1957.
4. H. P. Huntingdon, *The Elastic Constants of Crystals*, Academic Press, New York, 1958.
5. J. W. Dally and W. F. Riley, *Experimental Stress Analysis*, McGraw-Hill, New York, 1965.
6. J. D. Ferry, *Viscoelastic Properties of Polymers*, Wiley, New York, 1961.
7. A. V. Tobolsky, *Properties and Structure of Polymers*, Wiley, New York, 1960.
8. B. Gross, *Mathematical Structure of the Theories of Viscoelasticity*, Hermann & Cie., Paris, 1953.
9. H. Leaderman, *Elastic and Creep Properties of Filamentous Materials and Other High Polymers*, The Textile Foundation, Washington, D.C., 1943.
10. M. L. Williams, R. F. Landel and J. D. Ferry, *J. Am. Chem. Soc.*, 77, 3701 (1955).
11. K. Nagamatsu, *Kolloid Z.*, 172, 141 (1960).
12. M. Takayanagi, *Mem. Fac. Eng'g. Kyushu Univ.*, 23, 41 (1963).
13. I. M. Ward, *Polymer*, 5, 59 (1964).
14. A. K. Doolittle, *J. Appl. Phys.*, 22, 1471 (1951); 23, 236 (1952); 23, 418 (1952).
15. P. E. Rouse, *J. Chem. Phys.*, 21, 1272 (1953).
16. F. Bueche, *J. Chem. Phys.*, 22, 603 (1954).
17. B. H. Zimm, *J. Chem. Phys.*, 24, 269 (1956).
18. P. Mears, *Polymer Structure and Bulk Properties*, D. Van Nostrand, London, 1965.
19. F. Bueche, *J. Chem. Phys.*, 25, 599 (1956); *Physical Properties of Polymers*, Interscience, New York, 1962.
20. Y. H. Pao, in *Relaxation Phenomena in Polymers*, (R. Longworth, ed.), Interscience, New York (to be published); *J. Macromol. Sci.*, Part B, 1, 289 (1967).

21. P. J. Flory, *Principles of Polymer Chemistry*, Cornell University Press, Ithaca, New York, 1953.

22. L. R. G. Treloar, *The Physics of Rubber Elasticity*, 2d ed., Clarendon Press, Oxford, 1959.

23. A. Ciferri, *J. Polymer Sci.* **54**, 149 (1961).

24. W. J. Dalmage and L. E. Contois, *J. Polymer Sci.*, **28**, 275 (1958).

25. I. Sakurada, T. Ho, and K. Nakamae, *J. Polymer Sci.*, **C15**, 75 (1966).

26. H. Mark and R. Raff, *High Polymeric Reactions, Their Theory and Practice*, p. 14, Interscience, 1941.

27. K. H. Meyer and W. Lotmar, *Helv. Chim. Acta*, **19**, 68 (1936).

28. W. J. Lyons, *J. Appl. Phys.*, **30**, 796 (1959).

29. W. J. Lyons, *J. Appl. Phys.*, **29**, 1429 (1958).

30. L. R. G. Treloar, *Polymer*, **1**, 95 (1960).

31. L. R. G. Treloar, *Polymer*, **1**, 290 (1960).

32. L. R. G. Treloar, *Polymer*, **1**, 279 (1960).

33. M. Asahina and S. Enomoto, *J. Polymer Sci.*, **59**, 101 (1962).

34. S. Enomoto and M. Asahina, *J. Polymer Sci.*, **59**, 113 (1962).

35. A. Odajima and T. Maeda, *Rept. Polymer Phys. Japan*, **8**, 33 (1965); **9**, 169 (1966); *J. Polymer Sci.*, Part C, **No. 15**, 55 (1966).

36. M. Born and T. Huang, *Dynamical Theory of Crystal Lattices*, Clarendon Press, Oxford, 1956.

37. T. Shimanouchi, M. Asahina, and S. Enomoto, *J. Polymer Sci.*, **59**, 93 (1962).

38. T. Miyazawa, Paper presented at 13th Symp. High Polymer Chem., Tokyo, Nov. (1964).

39. S. Newman and R. L. Miller, *J. Polymer Sci.*, **60**, 514 (1962).

40. T. Shimanouchi and S. Mizushima, *J. Chem. Phys.*, **17**, 1102 (1949).

41. S. Mizushima and T. Shimanouchi, *J. Am. Chem. Soc.*, **71**, 1320 (1949).

42. R. F. Schaufele and T. Shimanouchi, *J. Chem. Phys.*, **47**, 3605 (1967).

43. S. Enomoto and M. Asahina, *J. Polymer Sci.*, **A2**, 3523 (1964).

44. T. Miyazawa and T. Kitagawa, *J. Polymer Sci.*, **B2**, 395 (1964).

45. R. J. Samuels, *J. Polymer Sci.*, **A3**, 1741 (1965).

46. *ASTM Standards, Part 27, Plastics*, Amer. Soc. for Test. Mats., Philadelphia, 1966.

47. J. Marin, *Engineering Materials, Their Mechanical Properties and Applications*, Prentice–Hall, New York, 1952.

48. N. H. Polakowski and E. J. Ripling, *Strength and Structure of Engineering Materials*, Prentice–Hall, New York, 1966.

49. A. W. Sleeswyk, *Brit. J. Appl. Phys.*, **15**, 985 (1964).

50. G. Krosche and G. Treutsch, *Plask. Kautschuk (Germany)*, **14**, 27 (1967).

51. H. Sekiguchi, K. Sugawara, T. Ashida, and M. Nishimoto, *Proc. 4th Japan Congress on Testing Materials*, Kyoto, Japan, 1961.

52. D. C. West, *Experimental Mechs.*, **21**, 185 (1964).

53. C. S. Surland, *Experimental Mechs.*, **20**, 112 (1963).

54. W. Philippoff and J. Brodnyan, *J. Appl. Phys.*, **26**, 846 (1955).

55. L. E. Nielsen, *Mechanical Properties of Polymers*, Reinhold Publishing, New York, 1962.

56. K. Van Holde, *J. Polymer Sci.*, **24**, 417 (1957).

57. J. A. Sauer, J. Marin, and C. C. Hsiao, *J. Appl. Phys.*, **20**, 507 (1949).

58. K. Van Holde and J. W. Williams, *J. Polymer Sci.*, **11**, 243 (1953).

59. W. Lethersich, *J. Sci. Inst.*, **24**, 66 (1947).

60. D. J. Plazek, M. N. Vrancken, and J. W. Berge, *Trans. Soc. Rheology*, **2**, 39 (1958).
61. D. J. Plazek, *J. Phys. Chem.*, **69**, 3480 (1965).
62. J. Marin, *Proc. ASTM*, **49**, 1158 (1949).
63. I. M. Ward, *Appl. Math. Res.*, **3**, 208 (1964).
64. R. S. Stern and H. Schaevitz, *Rev. Sci. Inst.*, **19**, 835 (1948).
65. J. R. McLoughlin, *Rev. Sci. Inst.*, **23**, 459 (1952).
66. A. V. Tobolsky and J. R. McLoughlin, *J. Polymer Sci.*, **8**, 543 (1952).
67. A. V. Tobolsky, *J. Appl. Phys.*, **27**, 673 (1956).
68. S. Iwayanagi, *J. Sci. Res. Inst. Japan*, **49**, 4 (1955).
69. E. E. Wright, *ASTM Bulletin*, **184**, 47 (1952).
70. S. Matsuoka and B. Maxwell, *J. Polymer Sci.*, **32**, 131 (1958).
71. O. Foppl, *J. Iron Steel Inst.*, **134**, 393 (1936).
72. T. S. Ke, *Phys. Rev.*, **71**, 533 (1947).
73. L. E. Nielsen, *Rev. Sci. Inst.*, **22**, 690 (1951).
74. K. Schmieder and K. Wolf, *Kolloid Z.*, **127**, 65 (1952).
75. E. Jenckel, *Kolloid Z.*, **136**, 142 (1954).
76. W. Lethersich, *Brit. J. Appl. Phys.*, **1**, 294 (1950).
77. K. M. Sinnott, *J. Appl. Phys.*, **29**, 1433 (1958).
78. N. G. McCrum, *J. Polymer Sci.*, **34**, 355 (1959).
79. J. R. Fitzgerald, K. M. Laing, and G. S. Bachman, *Trans. Soc. Glass Technol.*, **36**, 90 (1962).
80. G. P. Koo, M. N. Riddell, and J. L. O'Toole, *Polymer Eng'g. Sci.*, **6**, 363 (1966).
81. P. Heydemann and A. Zosel, *Acustica*, **15**, 49 (1965).
82. J. K. Gillham, *Appl. Polymer Symposia*, **No. 2**, 45 (1966); also Chap. 4 of this volume.
83. A. L. Kimball, *J. Appl. Mchs.*, **8**, 437 (1941).
84. B. Maxwell, *J. Polymer Sci.*, **20**, 551 (1956).
85. M. Takayanagi, H. Harima, and Y. Iwata, *Memoirs Fac. Eng'g. Kyushu Univ.*, **23**, 1 (1963).
86. T. K. Kwei, H. Schonbrun, and H. L. Frisch, *J. Appl. Phys.*, **38**, 2512 (1967).
87. W. P. Philippoff, *J. Appl. Phys.*, **24**, 685 (1953).
88. J. Koppelmann, *Rheol. Acta*, **1**, 20 (1958).
89. G. R. Dobson, *J. Sci. Inst.*, **44**, 375 (1967).
90. P. Lord and R. E. Wetton, *J. Sci. Inst.*, **38**, 385 (1961).
91. R. E. Wetton and G. Allen, *Polymer*, **7**, 331 (1966).
92. A. W. Nolle, *J. Appl. Phys.*, **19**, 753 (1948).
93. G. W. Becker, *Kolloid Z.*, **140**, 1 (1955).
94. D. W. Robinson, *J. Sci. Inst.*, **32**, 2 (1955).
95. K. D. Bajeva, *J. Sci. Inst.*, **41**, 662 (1964).
96. F. Förster, *Z. Metallkunde*, **29**, 109 (1937).
97. D. E. Kline, *J. Polymer Sci.*, **22**, 449 (1956).
98. P. M. Morse, *Vibration and Sound*, McGraw-Hill, New York, 1936.
99. J. E. McKinney, S. Edelman, and R. S. Marvin, *J. Appl. Phys.*, **27**, 425 (1956).
100. J. E. McKinney and H. V. Belcher, *J. Res. NBS*, **A67**, 43 (1963).
101. T. M. Lee and J. L. Smith, *J. Acoust. Soc. Am.*, **37**, 54 (1965).
102. J. Koppelmann, *Kolloid Z.*, **144**, 12 (1955).
103. P. Heydemann and H. Nägerl, *Acustica*, **14**, 70 (1964).
104. T. Nicholas and R. H. Heller, *Experimental Mechs.*, Mar. 1 (1967).
105. I. L. Hopkins, *Trans. ASME*, **73**, 195 (1951).

220   J. A. SAUER AND A. E. WOODWARD

106. E. R. Fitzgerald and J. D. Ferry, *J. Colloid Sci.*, **8**, 1 (1953).
107. R. H. Muller, *Anal. Chem.*, **35**, 115A (1963).
108. M. C. Shen, J. D. Strong, and F. J. Matusik, *J. Macromol. Sci. (Phys.)*, **B1**, 15 (1967).
109. S. L. Quimby, *Phys. Rev.*, **25**, 558 (1925); also, **32**, 345 (1932).
110. H. S. Sack, J. Metz, H. L. Raub, and R. N. Work, *J. Appl. Phys.*, **18**, 450 (1947).
111. C. G. Parfitt, *Nature*, **164**, 489 (1949).
112. M. Baccaredda and E. Butta, *J. Polymer Sci.*, **22**, 217 (1956).
113. J. M. Crissman and R. O. McCammon, *J. Acoust. Soc. Am.*, **34**, 1703 (1962).
114. W. P. Mason and H. J. McSkimmin, *J. Acoust. Soc. Am.*, **19**, 464 (1947).
115. D. G. Ivey, B. A. Mrowca, and E. Guth, *J. Appl. Phys.*, **20**, 486 (1949).
116. H. Thurn, *Z. Angew. Phys.*, **7**, 44 (1955).
117. G. Bradfield, *Acustica*, **17**, 184 (1966).
118. K. W. Hillier and H. Kolsky, *Proc. Phys. Soc.*, **B62**, 111 (1949).
119. H. Kolsky, *Stress Waves in Solids*, Clarendon Press, Oxford, 1953.
120. J. W. Ballou and S. J. Silverman, *J. Acoust. Soc. Am.*, **16**, 113 (1944).
121. W. J. Pullen, J. Roberts and T. E. Whall, *Polymer*, **5**, 471 (1964).
122. C. J. Maiden and S. J. Green, *J. Appl. Mchs.*, **33**, 496 (1966).
123. S. Strella and S. Newman, *Polymer*, **5**, 107 (1964).
124. A. G. H. Dietz and F. R. Eirich (eds.), *High Speed Testing*, Vol. 5, Interscience, 1965.
124a. I. H. Hall, *J. Polymer Sci.*, **54**, 505 (1961).
125. W. E. Wolstenholme, *High Speed Testing: The Rheology of Solids* (A. G. H. Dietz and F. R. Eirich, eds.), Vol. 6, Interscience, 1967.
126. W. Boas and J. K. MacKenzie, *Progress in Metal Physics*, Vol. 2, Pergamon Press, 1950.
127. I. M. Ward and P. R. Pinnock, *Brit. J. Appl. Phys.*, **17**, 3 (1966).
128. G. M. Bryant, *Textile Res. J.*, **37**, 552 (1967).
128a. P. I. Vincent, *Proc. Roy. Soc.*, **A282**, 113 (1964).
129. R. F. S. Hearmon, *Building Materials—Their Elasticity and Inelasticity*, (M. Reiner, ed.), p. 189, North Holland, Amsterdam, 1964.
130. E. Scala, *Fiber Composite Materials*, Ch. 7, Am. Soc. for Metals, 1965.
131. R. E. Taylor and D. E. Kline, *Carbon (Oxford)*, **5**, 607 (1967).
132. K. Schmieder and K. Wolf, *Kolloid Z.*, **134**, 149 (1953).
133. A. J. Staverman and J. Heijboer, *Kunststoffe*, **50**, 23 (1960).
134. J. M. Crissman, J. A. Sauer, and A. E. Woodward, *J. Polymer Sci.*, **A2**, 5075 (1964).
135. J. M. Crissman, A. E. Woodward, and J. A. Sauer, *J. Polymer Sci.*, **A3**, 2693 (1965).
136. G. A. Bernier and D. E. Kline, *J. Appl. Polymer Sci.*, **12**, 593 (1968).
137. C. W. Deeley, J. A. Sauer, and A. E. Woodward, *J. Appl. Phys.*, **29**, 1415 (1958).
138. A. E. Woodward, J. M. Crissman, and J. A. Sauer, *J. Polymer Sci.*, **44**, 23 (1960).
139. T. Lim, Ph. D. Thesis, Rutgers, The State University, New Brunswick, New Jersey, 1967.
140. J. A. Sauer, L. J. Merrill, and A. E. Woodward, *J. Polymer Sci.*, **58**, 19 (1962).
141. J. A. Sauer, N. Fuschillo, R. A. Wall, and A. E. Woodward, *J. Appl. Phys.*, **29**, 1385 (1958).
142. R. P. Kreahling and D. E. Kline, *Kolloid Z. und Z. für Poly.*, **206**, 1 (1965).
143. A. E. Woodward, J. A. Sauer and R. A. Wall, *J. Chem. Phys.*, **30**, 854 (1959); *J. Polymer Sci.*, **50**, 117 (1961).
144. J. A. Sauer and D. E. Kline, *Proc. 9th Intern. Congr. Appl. Mechs., Brasseos*, **5**, 368 (1957).

145. R. A. Wall, J. A. Sauer, and A. E. Woodward, *J. Polymer Sci.*, **35**, 281 (1959).
146. A. V. Tobolsky and M. Takahashi, *J. Appl. Polymer Sci.*, **7**, 1341 (1963).
147. M. C. Shen and A. V. Tobolsky (unpublished).
148. I. J. Heijboer, *Proc. Intern. Conf. Phys. of Non-crystalline Solids, Delft, 1964* (J. A. Prins, ed.), pp. 231–250, North Holland, Amsterdam, 1965.
149. P. H. Geil, *Polymer Single Crystals*, Interscience, New York, 1963.
150. M. C. Shen and A. Eisenberg, *Progress in Solid State Chemistry*, Vol. 3, p. 407, Pergamon Press, New York, 1966.
151. J. P. Mercier, J. J. Aklonis, M. Litt, and A. V. Tobolsky, *J. Appl. Polymer Sci.*, **9**, 447 (1965).
152. M. L. Dannis, *J. Appl. Polymer Sci.*, **1**, 121 (1959).
153. N. Fuschillo, A. E. Woodward, and J. A. Sauer, *J. Appl. Phys.*, **30**, 1488 (1959).
154. B. Ke, *Polymer Letters*, **1**, 167 (1963).
155. R. F. Boyer and R. S. Spencer, *Advances in Colloid Science*, Vol. 2, p. 1, Interscience, New York, 1946.
156. L. A. Wood, *J. Polymer Sci.*, **28**, 319 (1958).
157. T. G. Fox and S. Loshaek, *J. Polymer Sci.*, **40**, 371 (1955).
158. J. Lal and G. S. Trick, *J. Polymer Sci.*, **A2**, 4559 (1964).
159. K. H. Illers, *Bunsengesellschaft für Physikalische Chemie Berichte*, **70**, 353 (1966).
160. T. G. Fox, B. S. Garrett, W. E. Goode, S. Gratch, J. F. Kinkaid, A. Spell and J. D. Stroupe, *J. Am. Chem. Soc.*, **80**, 1768 (1958).
161. A. F. Lewis, *J. Polymer Sci.*, **B1**, 649 (1963).
162. N. G. McCrum, B. E. Read, and G. Williams, *Anelastic and Dielectric Effects in Polymeric Solids*, Wiley, New York, 1967.
163. E. A. Hoff, A. W. Robinson, and A. H. Willbourn, *J. Polymer Sci.*, **17**, 161 (1955).
164. H. Thurn and K. Wolf, *Kolloid Z.*, **148**, 16 (1956).
165. W. G. Gall and N. G. McCrum, *J. Polymer Sci.*, **50**, 489 (1961).
166. G. Natta, F. Danusso, and G. Moraglia, *Makromol. Chem.*, **28**, 166 (1958).
167. S. Newman and W. P. Cox, *J. Polymer Sci.*, **46**, 29 (1960).
168. L. Bohn, *Kunststoffe*, **53**, 93 (1963).
169. W. E. Fitzgerald and L. E. Nielson, *Proc. Roy. Soc.*, **A282**, 137 (1964).
170. H. Tanaka and A. Matsumoto, *Rept. Progr. Polymer Phys. Japan*, **5**, 151 (1962).
171. M. Baccaredda, E. Butta, and V. Frosini, *J. Polymer Sci.*, **C4**, 605 (1964).
172. P. Lebel and C. Job, *J. Polymer Sci.*, **C4**, 649 (1964).
173. T. Soen, T. Horino, Y. Ogawa, and H. Kawai, *Rept. Progr. Polymer Phys. Japan*, **9**, 315 (1966).
174. A. Rembaum, J. Moacanin, and E. Cuddihy, *J. Polymer Sci.*, **C4**, 529 (1964).
175. M. Takayanagi, *Mem. Fac. Eng'g. Kyushu Univ.*, **28**, 1 (1963).
176. K. Fujino, Y. Ogawa, and H. Kawai, *Rept. Progr. Polymer Phys. Japan*, **7**, 215 (1964).
177. K. Shibayama and M. Kodama, *Rept. Progr. Polymer Phys. Japan*, **8**, 255 (1965).
178. I. Galperin and T. K. Kwei, *J. Appl. Polymer Sci.*, **10**, 673 (1966).
179. C. W. van der Waal, H. W. Bree and F. A. Schwartzl, *J. Appl. Polymer Sci.*, **9**, 2143 (1965).
180. D. E. Kline and J. A. Sauer, *Soc. Plastics Engs. Trans.*, **2**, 21 (1962).
181. R. F. Landel, *Trans. Soc. Rheology*, **2**, 53 (1958).
182. K. W. Bills, Jr., K. H. Sweeney, and F. S. Salcedo, *J. Appl. Polymer Sci.*, **4**, 259 (1960).

183. K. Wolf, *Kunststoffe*, **41**, 89 (1951).

184. A. E. Woodward, J. M. Crissman, and J. A. Sauer, *J. Polymer Sci.*, **44**, 23 (1960).

185. K. H. Illers and H. Jacobs, *Makromol. Chem.*, **39**, 234 (1960).

186. K. Shibayama and M. Kodama, *Rept. Progr. Polymer Phys. Japan*, **9**, 327 (1966).

187. K. H. Illers and H. Breuer, *J. Colloid Sci.*, **18**, 1 (1963).

188. M. Takayanagi, *Mem. Fac. Eng'g. Kyushu Univ.*, **23**, 41 (1963).

189. M. Takayanagi, K. Imada, A. Nagai, T. Tatsumi, and T. Matsuo, *J. Polymer Sci.*, **C16**, 867 (1967).

190. D. E. Kline, J. A. Sauer, and A. E. Woodward, *J. Polymer Sci.*, **22**, 455 (1956).

191. L. Merrill, J. A. Sauer, and A. E. Woodward, *Polymer*, **1**, 351 (1960).

192. T. Lim and J. A. Sauer (to be published); *Bulletin APS*, *Ser.* 2, **11**, 213 (1966).

193. G. A. Bernier, D. E. Kline, and J. A. Sauer, *J. Macromol. Sci. (Phys.)*, **B1**, 335 (1967).

194. J. B. Jackson, P. J. Flory, R. Chaing, and M. J. Richardson, *Polymer*, **4**, 237 (1963).

195. L. E. Nielsen, *J. Polymer Sci.*, **42**, 357 (1960).

196. C. W. Deeley, D. E. Kline, J. A. Sauer, and A. E. Woodward, *J. Polymer Sci.*, **28**, 109 (1958).

197. D. E. Kline and J. A. Sauer, *Polymer*, **2**, 401 (1961).

198. J. M. Crissman, J. A. Sauer, and A. E. Woodward, *J. Polymer Sci.*, **Part A, 2**, 5075 (1964).

199. R. A. Wall, J. A. Sauer, and A. E. Woodward, *J. Polymer Sci.*, **50**, 117 (1961).

200. T. F. Schatzki, *Polymer Preprints*, **6**, 645 (1965).

201. J. M. Crissman, A. E. Woodward, and J. A. Sauer, *J. Polymer Sci.*, **A3**, 2693 (1965).

202. A. Odajima, A. E. Woodward, and J. A. Sauer, *J. Polymer Sci.*, **55**, 181 (1961).

203. R. G. Saba, J. A. Sauer, and A. E. Woodward, *J. Polymer Sci.*, **A1**, 1483 (1963).

204. I. J. Heijboer, *Kolloid Z.*, **171**, 7 (1960).

205. I. J. Heijboer, *Kolloid Z.*, **148**, 36 (1956).

206. W. Peckhold, U. Eisele, and G. Knauss, *Kolloid Z. Z. Polymeren*, **196**, 27 (1964).

207. B. Read, *Polymer*, **3**, 529 (1962).

208. A. H. Willbourn, *Trans. Faraday Soc.*, **54**, 717 (1958).

209. A. H. Lawson, J. A. Sauer, and A. E. Woodward, *J. Appl. Phys.*, **34**, 2492 (1963).

210. T. Kawaguchi, *J. Polymer Sci.*, **32**, 417 (1958).

211. V. Zaleckas, R. G. Saba, and D. Morrow (unpublished).

212. T. Kawaguchi, *J. Appl. Polymer Sci.*, **2**, 56 (1959).

213. K. H. Illers and H. Breuer, *Kolloid Z.*, **176**, 110 (1961).

214. K. Wolf, *Elektrochem. Z.*, **65**, 604 (1961).

215. A. K. Schulz, *J. Chem. Phys.*, **53**, 933 (1956).

216. D. E. Kline, *J. Polymer Sci.*, **47**, 237 (1960).

217. K. M. Sinnott, *J. Appl. Phys.*, **37**, 3385 (1966).

218. M. Takaganagi, *Kautschuk Gummi Kunststoffe*, **17**, 164 (1964).

219. N. Yamada, Z. Orito, and S. Minami, *Rept. Progr. Polymer Phys. Japan*, **8**, 259 (1965).

219a. J. D. Hoffman, G. Williams, and E. Passaglia, *J. Polymer Sci.*, **Part C, No. 14**, 173 (1966).

220. A. E. Woodward, *Adv. Chem.*, **63**, 298 (1967).

221. H. Nakayasu, A. Markovitz, and D. J. Plazek, *Trans. Soc. Rheol.*, **5**, 261 (1961).

222. S. Hoshino, J. Powers, D. C. LeGrand, H. Kawai and R. S. Stein, *J. Polymer Sci.*, **58**, 185 (1962).

223. A. Odajima, J. A. Sauer, and A. E. Woodward, *J. Phys. Chem.*, **66**, 718 (1962).

224. H. A. Rigby and C. W. Bunn, *Nature*, **164**, 583 (1949).
225. R. H. H. Pierce, E. S. Clark, W. M. B. Bryant, and J. F. Whitney, American Chemical Society Meeting, September, 1956; see C. A. Sperati and H. W. Starkweather, Jr., *Advan. Polymer Sci.*, **2**, 465 (1961).
226. S. Minami and M. Takayanagi, *Rept. Progr. Polymer Phys. Japan*, **7**, 241 (1964).
227. H. Yasuda and M. Takayanagi, *Rept. Progr. Polymer Phys. Japan*, **7**, 245 (1964).
228. G. Natta and P. Corradini, *Rend. Accad. Nazl. Lincei 8*, **19**, 229 (1955).
229. E. Passaglia and G. M. Martin, *U.S. Bur. Stds. J. Res. Phys. Chem.*, **68A**, 519 (1964).
230. N. Kishi, Z. Orito, and M. Uchida, *Rept. Progr. Polymer Phys. Japan*, **7**, 233 (1964).
231. N. G. McCrum, *J. Polymer Sci.*, **54**, 561 (1961).
232. S. Minami, Z. Orito, and N. Yamada, *Rept. Progr. Polymer Phys. Japan*, **9**, 381 (1966).
233. M. Takayanagi and N. Kawasaki, *J. Chem. Soc. Japan, Ind. Chem. Sec.*, **69**, 1971 (1966).
234. S. Minami, Z. Orito, and N. Yamada, *Rept. Progr. Polymer Phys. Japan*, **9**, 333 (1966).
235. T. Kajigama, K. Imada and M. Takayanagi, *Rept. Progr. Polymer Phys. Japan*, **9**, 345 (1966).
236. W. W. Mosely, Jr., *J. Appl. Polymer Sci.*, **3**, 266 (1960).
237. N. Tokita, *J. Polymer Sci.*, **20**, 515 (1956).
238. K. H. Hellwege, R. Kaiser, and K. Kuphal, *Kolloid Z.*, **157**, 27 (1958).
239. K. Taguchi and K. Yamagata, *Rept. Progr. Polymer Phys. Japan*, **9**, 303 (1966).
240. D. A. Lutz and L. P. Witnauer, *Polymer Letters*, **2**, 31 (1964).
241. R. K. Eby and F. C. Wilson, *J. Appl. Phys.*, **33**, 2951 (1962).
242. M. Sato and E. F. Fukada, *Rept. Progr. Polymer Phys. Japan*, **6**, 129 (1963).
243. A. Charlesby, *Effects of Radiation on Materials*, Chap 10, Reinhold, New York, 1958.
244. C. W. Deeley, J. A. Sauer, and A. E. Woodward, *J. Appl. Phys.*, **28**, 1124 (1957).
245. K. G. McLaren, *Brit. J. Appl. Phys.*, **16**, 185 (1965).
246. L. E. Nielsen, R. A. Wall, and P. G. Richmond, *Soc. Plastics Eng. J.*, **11**, 22 (1955).
247. K. Illers, *Makromol. Chem.*, **38**, 168 (1960).
248. M. F. Drumm, C. W. H. Dodge, and L. E. Nielsen, *Ind. Eng. Chem.*, **48**, 76 (1956).
249. W. P. Mason, *J. Appl. Polymer Sci.*, **1**, 63 (1959).
250. W. P. Mason, *J. Appl. Polymer Sci.*, **5**, 428 (1961).
251. K. W. Hillier, *Trans. Inst. Rubber Ind.*, **26**, 64 (1950).
252. K. W. Hillier and H. Kolsky, *Proc. Phys. Soc. London*, **62**, 111 (1949).
253. P. Mason, *Physical Properties of High Polymers, Soc. Chem. Ind.*, *Monograph No. 5*, p. 262, Macmillan, New York, 1959.
254. A. E. Woodward, *Rheology*, (F. Eirich, ed.), Vol. 5, Academic Press (in press).
255. A. J. Curtis, *Progress in Dielectrics*, Vol. 2, pp. 29–76, Wiley, New York, 1960.
256. A. H. Scott, D. J. Schieber, A. J. Curtis, J. I. Lauritzen, Jr., and J. D. Hoffman, *J. Res. Natl. Bur. Stds.*, **66A**, 269 (1962).
257. A. E. Woodward and J. A. Sauer, *Physics and Chemistry of the Organic Solid State* (D. Fox, et al. eds.), Vol. 2, p. 635, Interscience, New York, 1965.
258. J. D. Ferry and S. Strella, *J. Colloid Sci.*, **13**, 459 (1958).
259. E. R. Fitzgerald and J. D. Ferry, *J. Colloid Sci.*, **8**, 1 (1953).

260. A. R. Payne, *Physical Properties of High Polymers*, Soc. Chem. Ind. Monograph #5, p. 273, Macmillan, New York, 1959.

261. M. L. Williams, *J. Phys. Chem.*, **59**, 95 (1955).

262. D. E. O'Reilly and J. H. Anderson, *Physics and Chemistry of the Organic Solid State* (D. Fox et al., eds.), Vol. 2, pp. 121–341, Interscience, New York, 1965.

263. A. E. Woodward, *Pure Appl. Chem.*, **12**, 341 (1966).

264. J. A. Sauer and A. E. Woodward, *Rev. Mod. Phys.*, **32**, 88 (1960).

265. A. E. Woodward, *Trans. Acad. Sci.*, Ser. 2, **24**, 250 (1962).

265a. H. Hirose and Y. Wada, *Rept. Progr. Polymer Phys. Japan*, **9**, 287 (1966).

265b. A. E. Woodward, A. Odajima, and J. A. Sauer, *J. Phys. Chem.*, **65**, 1384 (1961).

266. L. J. Merrill, J. A. Sauer, and A. E. Woodward, *J. Polymer Sci.*, **A3**, 4243 (1965).

267a. F. C. Stehling and L. Mandelkern, *Polymer Lett.*, **7**, 255 (1969).

267b. L. E. Nielson, *J. Appl. Phys.*, **25**, 1209 (1954).

268. J. M. O'Reilly and F. E. Karasz, *J. Polymer Sci.*, **C14**, 49 (1966).

269. N. Bekkedahl and H. Matheson, *J. Res. Natl. Bur. Stds.*, **15**, 503 (1935).

270. R. C. Steere, *J. Appl. Polymer Sci.*, **10**, 1673 (1966).

271. I. V. Sochava and O. N. Trapeznikova, *Vestn. Lening. Univ. Ser Fizi Khim*, **13**, #16, 65 (1958); **16**, #10, 70 (1961); **19**, #10, 56 (1964).

272. F. S. Dainton, D. M. Evans, F. E. Hoare, and T. P. Media, *Polymer*, **3**, 263 (1962).

273. D. E. Kline and D. Hansen (see Chap. 6 of this volume).

274. I. J. Heijboer, *J. Polymer Sci.*, **C, No. 16**, 3755 (1968).

275. S. Turley, *Polymer Preprints*, **8**, 1524 (1967).

276. A. V. Tobolsky and J. J. Aklonis, *J. Phys. Chem.*, **68**, 1970 (1964).

277. R. S. Marvin and H. Oser, *J. Res. Natl. Bur. Stds.*, **B66**, 171 (1962).

278. M. V. Vol'kenshtein and O. B. Ptityn, *Zh. Tekh. Fiz.*, **25**, 649 (1955).

279. N. R. Krigbaum and M. Kaneko, *J. Chem. Phys.*, **36**, 99 (1962).

280. P. J. Flory, A. Ciferri, and C. A. Hoeve, *J. Polymer Sci.*, **45**, 235 (1960).

281. M. Shen, W. F. Hall, and R. E. DeWames, *J. Macromol. Sci., Rev. Macromol. Chem.*, **2**, 183 (1968).

282. K. Dusek and W. Prins, *Advan. Polymer Sci.*, **6**, 1 (1969).

283. A. E. Green and R. S. Rivlin, *Arch. Rat. Mech. Anal.*, **1**, 1 (1957).

284. R. S. Rivlin, *Proc. 1st Symp. Naval Structural Mechs.*, Oxford, p. 169, Pergamon Press, London, 1960.

285. H. Leaderman, F. McCrackin, and D. Nakada, *Trans. Soc. Rheol.*, **7**, 111 (1963).

286. I. M. Ward and E. T. Onat, *J. Mech. Phys. Solids*, **11**, 217 (1963).

CHAPTER 4

Torsional Braid Analysis: A Semimicro Thermomechanical Approach to Polymer Characterization

J. K. GILLHAM

POLYMER MATERIALS PROGRAM
DEPARTMENT OF CHEMICAL ENGINEERING
PRINCETON UNIVERSITY
PRINCETON, NEW JERSEY

4-1 INTRODUCTION

Torsional braid analysis (TBA)(*1,2*) is an extension of the torsion pendulum method (see Chapter 3) for examining materials. A specimen is prepared by impregnation of a multifilament glass braid substrate with a solution of the material which is to be tested, followed by thermal removal of the solvent. Less than 100 mg of polymer per experiment suffices. In contrast to the use of the conventional torsion pendulum, this approach permits investigation of materials which cannot support their own weight so that it is suitable for studies of such processes as resin curing and environmental degradation, and since thermoplastic samples may be melted, TBA allows the *in situ* study of the effect of prehistory on thermomechanical behavior. Thermomechanical "fingerprints" of polymer transitions and transformations through the spectrum of mechanical states may be obtained by temperature programing. A schematic description of the author's apparatus is shown in Fig. 4-1, while a commercially available version is shown in Fig. 4-2.

An instrumental innovation(*2*) is the no-drag linear differential optical transducer, which permits the examination of small specimens. Frequency (less than 1 cps) and decay of the freely oscillating pendulum provide information on the modulus and mechanical damping (loss) of the polymer under examination. An electrical analogue of the decaying pendulum oscillation is obtained by attenuating light with a circular transmission disk, which features a linear relationship between light transmission and the displacement angle. The principle involved in using a linear transmission disk is shown in Fig. 4-3, with typical strip-chart records of damped waves being illustrated in Fig. 4-4.

4-2 THEORY AND REDUCTION OF DATA

Two parameters, the real part of the complex shear modulus and the logarithmic decrement, can be calculated(*3*) from the damped waves of a homogeneous rod undergoing free torsional oscillations. The real part of the complex shear modulus, G', is directly proportional to the energy stored in deforming the sample and is given approximately by

$$G' = \frac{2LI}{\pi r^4} \cdot \omega^2 (4\pi^2 + \Delta^2)$$

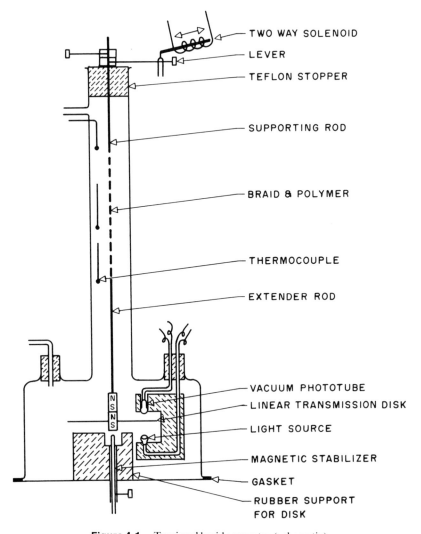

Figure 4-1.   Torsional braid apparatus (schematic).

In this expression, ω is the frequency, Δ is the logarithmic decrement, I is the moment of inertia of the oscillating system, r is the radius, and L is the length of the specimen. The logarithmic decrement is obtained from successive amplitudes (A_n, A_{n+1}) of the decaying wave

$$\Delta = \log_e \frac{A_n}{A_{n+1}}$$

Figure 4-2. Torsional Braid Analyzer. Courtesy: Chemical Instruments Corporation, Bayside, New York.

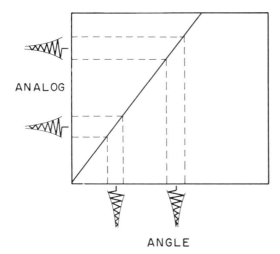

ANGLE

Figure 4-3. Characteristics of a linear transmission disk. The figure shows that the differential output of the analog (intensity of transmitted light) is independent of the neutral position of the mechanical oscillations.

and is related to the imaginary part G'' and real part of the complex shear modulus by the approximate relation

$$\Delta = \pi \frac{G''}{G'}.$$

Storage and loss of energy on cyclic deformation are characterized by the (real part of the shear) modulus and the logarithmic decrement respectively, which are plotted as functions of temperature (and time).

In torsional braid analysis the relative rigidity parameter, $1/p^2$, where p is the period of oscillation, is used as a measure of the modulus and is simply ω^2. This expression implicitly assumes that the contributions of dimensional changes, and changes in the damping characteristics, to the value of the relative rigidity are dominated by changes in the modulus of the polymer. That this is generally true follows by noting that the apparent change in modulus which results solely from a dimensional radial shrinkage of 25% in a homogeneous specimen (i.e., a volume shrinkage and weight loss of 44%) corresponds to a reduction in the relative rigidity parameter by a factor of 3.2.

$$\text{Relative rigidity} = \frac{P_2^{\,2}}{P_1^{\,2}} \approx \frac{r_1^{\,4}}{r_2^{\,4}} = \frac{4^4}{3^4}$$

In comparison, the relative rigidity changes by a large factor in passing

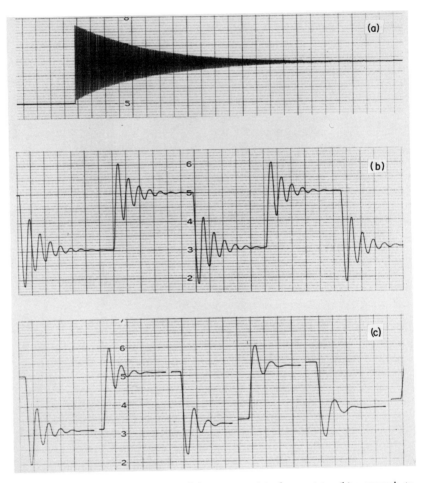

Figure 4-4. Characteristic output of instrument: (a) glassy state, (b) approach to transition, (c) transition region (note drift of neutral position).

through the glass-to-rubber region of most amorphous polymers. The influence of changes in mechanical damping on the value of the relative rigidity is small since Δ is generally considerably less than unity. When large percentages of polymer disappear, as in degradation, caution in interpretation is necessary and the question to be raised is whether or not decreases in the relative rigidity are more than can be accounted for by dimensional changes. As the high-modulus inert substrate does in fact contribute to the modulus of the composite, the expected consequence of dimensional changes which accompany loss of part of the matrix, on the relative rigidity parameter, would be a decrease by less than the factor calculated from weight loss measurements. (Attempts to correct the relative rigidity parameter for decreases in dimensions, by treating the sample as a homogeneous rod and using the proportionality between sample weight and cross-sectional area, provide a limit for the decrease.) Few complications in interpretation arise with systems where there is no loss of weight.

The mechanical damping index $(1/n)$ is used as a measure of the logarithmic decrement, Δ, to which it is directly proportional. It is calculated as $1/n$, where n is the number of oscillations between two arbitrary but fixed boundary conditions in a series of waves.

A multifilament and loose glass braid (formed from yarns taken from heat-cleaned glass cloth) is used as the substrate. The energy used in torsionally deforming the composite specimen of polymer and longitudinal glass fibers is predominantly involved in straining the polymer matrix.

Changes in the relative rigidity and damping index are interpreted as far as is possible in terms of changes in the polymer. Major and secondary relaxations are readily revealed as are the effects of many chemical reactions. Investigation of specific physical and chemical interactions between various substrates and polymers will form the basis of future work.

4-3 EXAMPLES OF THERMOMECHANICAL SPECTRA

Thermomechanical spectra are presented for several classes of polymers: a chemically-modified natural polymer, cellulose triacetate; a denatured biological polymer, gelatin; and an inorganic polymer, a highly cross-linked polysiloxane. Also discussed briefly under subsection D, on di-n-butyl phthalate, are the thermomechanical spectra of low molecular weight and model compounds. The review ends with the application of TBA to an experimental polybenzimidazole system.

Unless stated to the contrary, the experiments described herein were performed in a slow stream of dry nitrogen gas with $\Delta T/\Delta t = 1°C\ min^{-1}$.

A. Cellulose Triacetate (2,4)

A composite specimen of glass braid and cellulose triacetate was prepared from a solution (about 7%) of highly-acetylated polymer in methylene dichloride. Prior to the main experiment, solvent was removed during the process of heating the sample in nitrogen to 150°C at $2°C\ min^{-1}$, then cooling to 25°C at the same rate. Since the glass transition temperature was found to be about 190°C, this treatment was considered not to damage the polymer significantly and to produce only a minor degree of crystallinity.

The thermomechanical spectrum for the specimen is presented in Fig. 4-5 together with the corresponding results for thermogravimetric and differential thermal analyses. The glass transition (T_g) in the vicinity of 190°C is accompanied by a drastic decrease in rigidity, a prominent

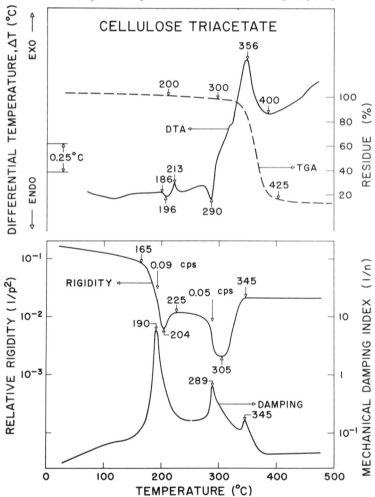

Figure 4-5. Cellulose triacetate; Thermogravimetric analysis, differential thermal analysis and torsional braid analysis.

maximum in damping and an endothermic shift in DTA. The sub-sequent increase in rigidity at temperatures above 200°C is attri-buted to crystallization and/or chain stiffening processes and is accompanied by an exothermic maximum (DTA). The melting transition (T_m) at 290°C is accompanied by an abrupt decrease in rigidity, a maximum in damping, and an endothermic maximum (DTA). The subsequent increase in rigidity, decrease in damping, exotherm (DTA) and weight loss (TGA) are attributed to cross-linking and/or chain stiffening processes.

B. Gelatin (2)

A composite specimen of glass braid and gelatin was prepared from an aqueous solution (about 10%) of limed ossein gelatin. Water was removed during the process of heating the sample to 150°C and then cooling to 25°C at the same rate (1°C min^{-1}). The thermomechanical behavior of the resulting specimen heated at 1°C min^{-1} is presented in Fig. 4-6. The anhydrous gelatin undergoes a major change in the vicinity of 200°C which is revealed by the concurrent decrease in rigidity and maximum mechanical damping at 220°C. Above about 250°C the rigidity is increased by intermolecular cross-linking and/or intramolecular chain stiffening, accompanied by a broad maximum in mechanical damping and an eventual lowering of mechanical damping. The change in the vicinity of 200°C is believed to be due to a transition in the anhydrous gelatin rather than to degradation. This interpretation is in agreement with results previously reported(5), placing the glass transition at about 190°C, for a specimen from the same sample of gelatin. The form of the thermomechanical behavior indicates that the modulus and low damping characteristics are essentially retained to almost 200°C and implies that anhydrous gelatin could be the basis of materials useful structurally to above 150°C.

The neutral position of the inertial mass of the instrument as a function of temperature is shown in Fig. 4-6. Twisting and untwisting of the specimen is a consequence of changing stresses in the composite sample, with the sense of twist determined by the sense of twist in the braid substrate.

C. A Thermoset Polysiloxane (2)

Owens-Illinois Inc. produces a series of liquid prepolymer resins which, by thermosetting condensation reactions, provide glasslike materials (i.e., polysiloxane) of high thermal stability. Infrared spectra of a cured polymer (Glass Resin—type 650) indicated the structural

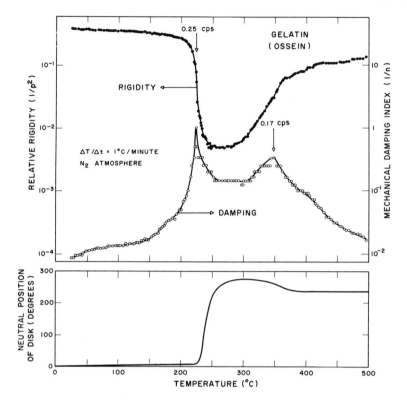

Figure 4-6. Thermomechanical behavior of gelatin.

element to be

$$
\left[\begin{array}{c} CH_3 \\ | \\ -Si-O- \\ | \\ O \\ | \end{array}\right]
$$

A composite specimen of glass braid and prepolymer was prepared from a commercially available alcoholic solution. The solvent was partially removed by passing nitrogen over the specimen overnight at 25°C. The subsequent thermomechanical experiment involved heating to 500°C at 1°C min⁻¹ and then immediately cooling to 25°C at the same rate. The results, presented in Fig. 4-7, show that the rigidity increased to 500°C, whereas on cooling it decreased. Visual examination of the specimen at 25°C showed the colorless resin to be highly

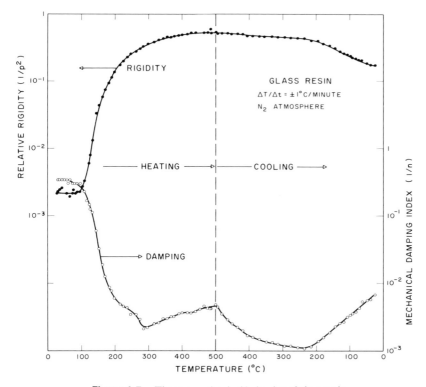

Figure 4-7. Thermomechanical behavior of glass resin.

crazed, suggesting that the treatment of the experiment produces a highly cross-linked resin which, in the composite structure, cannot accommodate the stresses introduced thermally and by the polymerization processes. This represents an example of "overcure" in a thermosetting composite system. One might predict from the behavior of the mechanical damping in Fig. 4-7 that the resin–glass composite would not be structurally useful above 280°C.

D. Di-*n*-butyl Phthalate (6)

A composite specimen of di-*n*-butyl phthalate and glass braid was prepared by using liquid ester. The specimen was cooled to −196°C and the thermomechanical spectrum of Fig. 4-8 was obtained ($\Delta T/\Delta t = 1$°C min^{-1}). Two damping maxima, and concomitant changes in modulus, are apparent. The main glass-to-liquid transition is at about −85°C; another relaxation process is made apparent by the damping maximum at about −170°C. Di-*iso*-butyl phthalate gives rise to a very

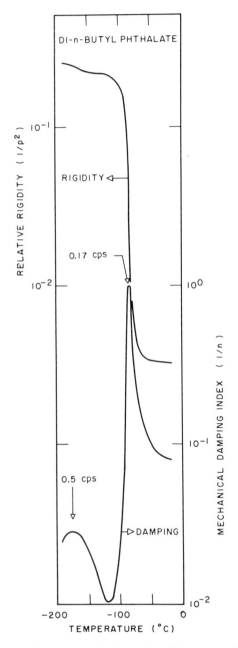

Figure 4-8. Thermomechanical behavior of di-*n*-butyl phthalate.

236

similar spectrum. On the other hand, the mechanical spectrum of dicyclohexyl phthalate displays a major loss maximum (T_g) at $-35°C$, a sharp loss peak at $-95°C$, and a suggestion of a loss maximum peaking below $-190°C$. A more complicated molecule, the diglycidyl ether of bis phenol A, provides two prominent damping maxima, one (T_g) at $-15°C$ and the other at $-150°C$.

A thermomechanical spectrum of a specimen consisting of discrete crystals of diphenyl terephthalate dispersed among the glass filaments appeared (7) to display fine structure. Meaningful results may well be obtained by examination of noncontinuous matrices.

In the current attempt (8) to develop the mechanical spectroscopy of macromolecules by correlating loss maxima with the motions of specific parts of polymer molecules, systematic studies of model and small compounds (7) by TBA should facilitate the interpretation of dynamic mechanical spectra of polymers. Other relaxation techniques (e.g., nuclear magnetic resonance and dielectric) will aid such investigations.

4-4 INVESTIGATION OF A POLYBENZIMIDAZOLE SYSTEM (6)

So complex are the requisites of materials which are being synthesized for application in hostile environments, that to date no organic polymer with satisfactory mechanical properties exists which is capable of withstanding continuous service in air much above 260°C. The lack of success in the field of heat resistance is a consequence of the expensive and time-consuming sequential processes of synthesis, fabrication, and evaluation of new polymers. Polymers are usually evaluated in mechanical terms after their fabrication, so that there is a need for a semimicro method which would permit assessment of the thermomechanical properties of polymers before fabrication (i.e., immediately after synthesis).

Material

Polybenzimidazole prepolymer, formed by partial reaction of 3,3'-diaminobenzidine (formula A) and isophthalamide (formula B), was provided by the Air Force Materials Laboratory and designated AF-R-151. The polymer (formula C) was the culmination in 1965 (9) of an extensive program to provide composite structural materials with significant retention of room-temperature mechanical properties at temperatures above 400°C in nitrogen. According to the technical report(10) on the development, it would appear that the prepolymer (polymer melt temperature, PMT = 180°C) was prepared by heating equal moles of the monomers in melt form for 40 min at 270°C. A pyridine solution (5–7% prepolymer) was used for preparation of the TBA specimens.

$$\text{Prepolymer} \rightarrow C \quad + H_2O + NH_3$$

RESULTS AND DISCUSSION

A. Thermomechanical Behavior (25° to 500°C) of the Polybenzimidazole Prepolymer (Fig. 4-9)

The prepolymer was advanced in order to minimize loss of unreacted monomer in subsequent thermal treatments. This was performed by heating the PBI-prepolymer (PMT = 180°C) – glass substrate preparation to 270°C (solvent being removed during this process) and then heating isothermally at 270°C for 1 hr. According to the data(10) on the prepolymer, a PMT of about 240°C would be expected. The cooled specimen formed the sample for the thermomechanical spectrum displayed in Fig. 4-9, which shows five distinct regions of behavior:

(1) At low temperatures and below 200°C, the prepolymer is a glassy material with low mechanical loss and a modulus which changes little with temperature.

(2) The transition region shows a drastic drop in modulus above 220°C to a minimum at 280°C and a prominent damping maximum at 260°C. Using the latter as an index, the glass transition temperature of the prepolymer may be designated as $T_g = 260$°C.

(3) Above 290°C the modulus increases while the damping passes through a maximum during the polymerization process, presumably leading to the polybenzimidazole. A concurrent total loss of 5% by weight of the sample occurs approximately linearly between 290° and 390°C.

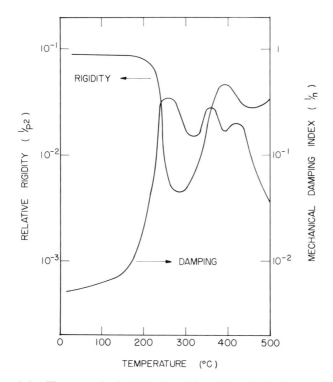

Figure 4-9. Thermomechanical behavior of the polybenzimidazole prepolymer.

(4) The modulus drops above 390°C (through a damping maximum at 420°C) as the result of either a further transition (the glass transition, T_g, of the newly formed polymer) or of degradation. The sample loses, concurrently and approximately linearly, less than 2% of its weight from 390° to 500°C.

(5) Above 460°C the modulus increases in consequence of further chemical reaction while the damping decreases to values characteristic of the glassy state. The product of this last reaction at 500°C could be structurally useful to this temperature.

B. Isothermal (380°C) Behavior of the Polybenzimidazole (Fig. 4-10)

The nature of the process which occurs between 390° and 450°C in the thermomechanical spectrum of Fig. 4-9 is of importance since it might be either degradative or physical (transition). If it is degradative then the development of an optimum cure cycle would have to take this

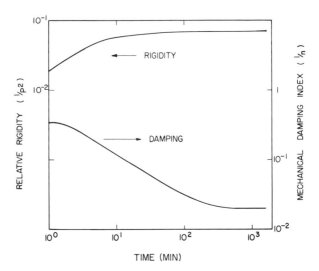

Figure 4-10. Isothermal (380°C) behavior of the polybenzimidazole.

into account. Furthermore, the chemical reaction occurring above 450°C might be expected to give an essentially different product from that formed by heating the prepolymer to 380°C. This, of course, need not be undesirable. If it is nondegradative, then the processes occurring above 450°C may be essentially the same as those occurring below 380°C, in which case the transition (with a damping maximum at 420°C) would presumably be shifted to higher temperatures by heating above 450°C.

The physical or chemical nature of the process might be inferred from the isothermal behavior, monitored at a temperature just below the onset of the decrease in modulus which is due to the process in question. Degradation could lead eventually to a drop in modulus; a transition would not. Figure 4-10 shows that over a relatively long period of 24 hr at 380°C the modulus fails to decrease (the sample had been prepared by heating the prepolymer, $T_g = 260$°C, from 25° to 380°C). It is inferred then that the drop in modulus which occurs immediately above 390°C in Fig. 4-9 is associated with a glass transition, T_g, which may be characterized by the maximum in damping at 420°C.

C. Thermomechanical Behavior (−170° to 500°C) of the Polybenzimidazole (Fig. 4-11)

The same polybenzimidazole–glass braid sample, used to provide Fig. 4-10, was cooled to −190°C and the thermomechanical spectrum

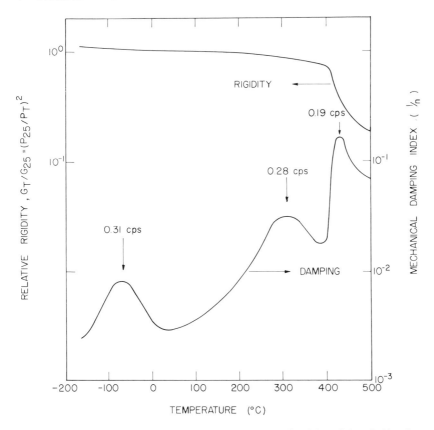

Figure 4-11. Thermomechanical behavior (− 170° to 500°C) of the polybenzimidazole.

of Fig. 4-11 obtained. (The experimental modulus curve is normalized relative to the value at 25°C).

Three distinct transition regions are apparent in the thermome-chanical behavior which may be designated by the temperatures of the damping maxima: − 70°, 310° and 430°C. Distinct changes in the modulus are associated with each of these loss maxima.

From the results one would predict not only that the polymer would be structurally useful to above 380°C, but that resistance to impact above − 130°C would be good. The low-temperature damping maxi-mum is indicative of the presence of a relaxation mechanism which could contribute to mechanical behavior in the same way that the low-temperature dispersion region of polycarbonate resins confers impact properties.

D. Effect of High Temperature on the Thermomechanical Behavior of the Polybenzimidazole (Fig. 4-12)

A polybenzimidazole–glass braid sample was prepared by heating the given prepolymer (PMT = 180°C) isothermally at 400°C for 5 hr before cooling to 25°C. The thermomechanical behavior to 500°C, shown in curve 1 of Fig. 4-12, demonstrates (by comparison with the results of Fig. 4-11) that the differences in prepolymer preparation and cure result in only minor differences in thermomechanical behavior. After the heating cycle the sample was cooled and then recycled successively to give curves 2, 3, and 4 of Fig. 4-12. (The samples from curves 2 and 3 were held at 500°C for 30 min and 200 min, respectively,

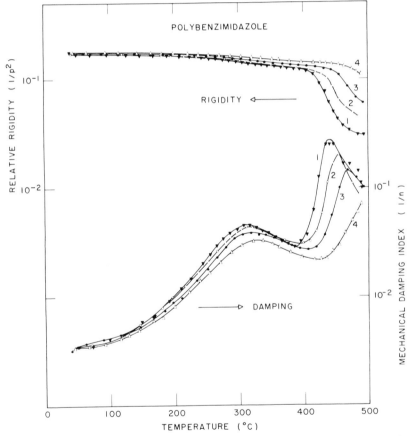

Figure 4-12.   Effect of thermal treatment on the high temperature transition of the polybenzimidazole.

before being cooled.) Such thermal treatments result in a shift of the main glass transition to successively higher temperatures (from 430° to 500°C) as measured by the drop in modulus and by the damping maxima. The intensity of the damping maxima decreases as the transition temperature rises.

These results demonstrate that by suitable thermal treatment a polymer can be formed which would be structurally useful to 500°C. Other results which are not presented herein show that the modulus of the composite polymer–glass specimen is reversible for cycles in which chemical reaction does not occur, demonstrating the excellent adhesion and ductility (sufficient to accommodate stresses arising from the composite nature) in the system.

Several interpretations for the influence of thermal history on the glass-transition temperature of the polybenzimidazole are plausible. Among these are: completion of the ring-closing reactions; dependence of the glass-transition temperature on molecular weight – attainment of high molecular weight in condensation polymers demands a high degree of reaction, besides equivalence in stoichiometry of the reactants; cross-linking – which is compatible with the successive decreases in intensity of the damping maxima; and removal of plasticizing agents by volatilization.

The nature of the relaxation processes which are made apparent by damping maxima at $-70°C$ and $310°C$ is of interest as it is difficult to visualize mobile segments in the pure structure (formula C). Explanations might be found in: the structure not being that represented by formula C; current tendencies(8) to identify damping maxima with specific molecular motions being oversimplifications; specific interactions between polymer and substrate; and the presence of difficult-to-remove foreign entities (e.g., water).

E. Air Oxidation (Fig. 4-13)

Polymer with glass-transition temperature about 500°C was subjected to oxidative attack by air at 400°C. [The sample was that used to obtain the results of Fig. 4-12. After reaching 500°C (Fig. 4-12, curve 4), the specimen was cooled from 500° to 400°C, and the atmosphere was changed from dry nitrogen to air.] The results of Fig. 4-13 show that samples with large surface area-to-volume ratios are oxidatively unstable in air at 400°C.

The results of these TBA experiments on an experimental polymer demonstrate that investigation on less than 0.5 g (of even a polymer precursor) permits a prediction of mechanical behavior which agrees

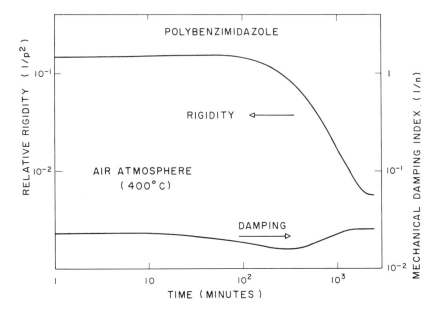

Figure 4-13. Air oxidation (400°C) of the polybenzimidazole.

with and extends the results of much more extensive evaluation of glass cloth-reinforced laminates made from the same polymer system (*10*). The predictions apply to the conditions necessary for preparing the polymer (i.e., the cure cycle), to the thermomechanical behavior of the polymer, to the effect of thermal history on the thermomechanical behavior, and to its oxidative stability. A thermomechanical spectrum (from − 170° to + 500°C) demonstrates the presence of three distinct relaxations at − 70°, 310°, and 430°C. The main glass transition temperature of 430°C can be increased to 500°C by thermal treatment. The process at − 70°C would predictably confer good impact qualities to the polymer above about − 100°C. The results also demonstrate that the adhesive qualities of the polymer to glass from − 170° to 500°C are outstanding and that the polymer has a degree of ductility throughout the same temperature range. Oxidative stability of the thermally treated polybenzimidazole is not good at 400°C in air.

Excellent thermomechanical properties are reported for glass cloth-reinforced laminates made from the prepolymer. For example, the data of Table 4-1 appear on page 147 of ref. (*10*). The particular laminate had been heated in nitrogen at 950°F (510°C) for 6 hr. Its thermomechanical properties were better than those of laminates prepared by

TABLE 4-1

Thermomechanical Behavior of a Glass Cloth-Reinforced Laminate of the
Polybenzimidazole

Test temperature	Flexural strength	Flexural modulus
70°F	117,000 psi	5.0×10^6 psi
700°F (after one hour at 700°F)	91,000 psi	4.5×10^6 psi

curing schedules at 750°F (400°C) for 6 hr. This is readily understood in terms of the work of this present report.

It is evident that the type of development represented by the polybenzimidazole system under discussion could be facilitated greatly by the TBA approach. Thermal transitions and transformations of the solid-state reactions can be monitored in terms of mechanical parameters which have both a theoretical basis (mechanical spectroscopy) and a practical relevance. Since the composite specimen of polymer and glass fibers itself may be considered as being an element of desired gross structures (e.g., glass cloth-reinforced laminates), predictions are direct. It might be emphasized that little material is required in the experiments since the testing is nondestructive. This should be very useful in the early examination of preparations of new polymers.

ACKNOWLEDGMENTS

Appreciation is extended to Interscience Publishers, New York, to the American Chemical Society, and to the Society of Plastics Engineers for permission to reproduce previously published material.

REFERENCES

1. A. F. Lewis and J. K. Gillham, *J. Appl. Polymer Sci.*, **6**, 422 (1962).
2. J. K. Gillham, *Appl. Polymer Symp.*, **2**, 45 (1966).
3. L. E. Nielsen, *Mechanical Properties of Polymers*, Chapter 7, Reinhold Publishing Co., New York, 1962.
4. J. K. Gillham and R. F. Schwenker, Jr., *Appl. Polymer Symp.* **2**, 59 (1966).
5. J. B. Yannas and A. V. Tobolsky, *J. Phys. Chem.*, **68**, 3880 (1964).
6. J. K. Gillham, *Polymer Eng. Sci.*, **7**, No. 4, 225 (1967).
7. J. K. Gillham and A. F. Lewis, *J. Polymer Sci.*, **C6**, 125 (1964).
8. R. F. Boyer (ed.), Transitions and Relaxations in Polymers, *J. Polymer Sci.*, **C14** (1966); and R. F. Boyer, Dependence of Mechanical Properties on Molecular Motion in Polymers, *Polymer Eng. Sci.*, **8**, No. 3, 16 (1968).
9. J. R. Hall and D. W. Levi, Polybenzimidazoles: A Review, *Plastec Rept.*, 28, July 1966.
10. H. H. Levine, *Air Force Materials Lab.* Tech. Rept. 64–365, Part 1, Vol. 1, November 1964.

BIBLIOGRAPHY

1. A. F. Lewis and J. K. Gillham, *J. Appl. Polymer Sci.*, **6**, 422 (1962).
2. J. K. Gillham and A. F. Lewis, *Nature*, **195**, 1199 (1962).
3. A. F. Lewis and J. K. Gillham, *J. Appl. Polymer Sci.*, **7** 685 (1963).
4. J. K. Gillham and A. F. Lewis, *J. Appl. Polymer Sci.*, **7**, 2293 (1963).
5. R. Saxon and F. Lestienne, *J. Appl. Polymer Sci.*, **8**, 475 (1964).
6. J. K. Gillham, *Science*, **139**, 494 (1963).
7. J. K. Gillham and A. F. Lewis, *J. Polymer Sci.* **C6**, 125 (1964).
8. J. K. Gillham, *Encyclopedia of Polymer Sci. and Tech.*, **1**, 760 (1964).
9. J. K. Gillham and J. C. Petropoulos, *J. Appl. Polymer Sci.*, **9**, 2189 (1965).
10. A. Senior, paper presented at 149th Natl. Meeting, American Chemical Society, Detroit, Div. Org. Coatings Plastics Chem. *Preprints*, 25, No. 1,8, 1965.
11. H. W. Holden, *Chem. in Can.*, **17**, 42 (1965).
12. A. Adicoff and A. A. Yukelson, *J. Appl. Polymer Sci.*, **10**, 159 (1966).
13. J. K. Gillham, in *Thermoanalysis of Fibers and Fiber-Forming Polymers* (Applied Polymer Symposia, No. 2), (R. F. Schwenker, Jr., ed.). Wiley-Interscience, New York, 1966, p. 45.
14. J. K. Gillham and R. F. Schwenker, Jr., in *Thermoanalysis of Fibers and Fiber-Forming Polymers* (Applied Polymer Symposia, No. 2), (R. F. Schwenker, Jr., ed.), Wiley-Interscience, New York, 1966, p. 59.
15. J. K. Gillham, *Polymer Engineering and Science*, **7**, No. 4, 225 (1967).
16. S. Nakamura, *High Polymers, Japan*, **16**, 833 (1967).
17. A. Adicoff and A. A. Yukelson, *J. Appl. Polymer Sci.*, **12**, 1959 (1968).
18. S. Nakamura, J. K. Gillham, and A. V. Tobolsky, *Reports on Progress in Polymer Physics in Japan*, **11**, 523 (1968).
19. B. L. Williams and L. Weissbein, *J. Appl. Polymer Sci.*, **12**, 1439 (1968).
20. J. Hakozaki, E. Higashimura, and S. Toyoda, *Kogyo Kagaku Zasshi*, **71**, 887 (1968).
21. J. K. Gillham, G. F. Pezdirtz, and L. Epps, *J. Macromol. Sci. Chem.*, **A3(6)**, 1183 (1969).
22. A. F. Lewis and G. B. Elder, *Adhesives Age*, **12**, No. 10, 31 (1969).
23. A. F. Lewis and L. J. Forrestal, *Treatise on Coatings*, (R. Meyers, ed.), Vol. 2, Part I, Chap. 3, Dekker, New York, 1969.

CHAPTER 5

Thermal Conductivity of Polymers

DONALD E. KLINE

DEPARTMENT OF MATERIALS SCIENCE
PENNSYLVANIA STATE UNIVERSITY
UNIVERSITY PARK, PENNSYLVANIA

DAVID HANSEN

MATERIALS RESEARCH CENTER
RENSSELAER POLYTECHNIC INSTITUTE
TROY, NEW YORK

5-1 MATHEMATICAL ANALYSIS OF HEAT CONDUCTION

A. Fourier's Law and Thermal Conductivity

Phenomenological analyses of heat conduction problems are based on the validity of Fourier's law which may be stated for isotropic systems by the equation (symbols are defined at the end of the text):

$$q_x = -k\frac{\partial T}{\partial x} \qquad (5\text{-}1)$$

This law states that the heat flux is proportional to temperature gradient and defines the thermal conductivity as a material property.

Since polymers are often used in an oriented or anisotropic state, it is pertinent to state the more general form of Fourier's law:

$$q_x = -k_{xx}\frac{\partial T}{\partial x} - k_{xy}\frac{\partial T}{\partial y} - k_{xz}\frac{\partial T}{\partial z} \qquad (5\text{-}2)$$

$$q_y = -k_{yx}\frac{\partial T}{\partial x} - k_{yy}\frac{\partial T}{\partial y} - k_{yz}\frac{\partial T}{\partial z} \qquad (5\text{-}3)$$

$$q_z = -k_{zx}\frac{\partial T}{\partial x} - k_{zy}\frac{\partial T}{\partial y} - k_{zz}\frac{\partial T}{\partial z} \qquad (5\text{-}4)$$

These equations recognize that in an anisotropic material the heat flux in a given direction depends not only on the gradient of temperature in that direction but also on temperature gradients in other directions. The thermal conductivity for an anisotropic material is a tensor property which is specified by the nine components, k_{ij}. Since the Onsager reciprocal relations are generally assumed to apply to the thermal conductivity, the number of distinct components of the conductivity tensor is reduced from nine to six by the relationships:

$$k_{xy} = k_{yx} \qquad (5\text{-}5)$$

$$k_{xz} = k_{zx} \qquad (5\text{-}6)$$

$$k_{yz} = k_{zy} \qquad (5\text{-}7)$$

It can also be shown that when the coordinate directions correspond to the directions of principal conductivity, the cross components of the conductivity tensor are zero, and:

$$q_{x^*} = -k_{x^*}\frac{\partial T}{\partial x^*} \tag{5-8}$$

$$q_{y^*} = -k_{y^*}\frac{\partial T}{\partial y^*} \tag{5-9}$$

$$q_{z^*} = -k_{z^*}\frac{\partial T}{\partial z^*} \tag{5-10}$$

If the three principal conductivities of a material are determined, then all the conductivity coefficients for arbitrary coordinate orientation with respect to the principal conductivities may be calculated. If the principal conductivity directions are known, then the conductivities can be measured by standard methods utilizing one-dimensional heat flow. In single crystals it is generally assumed that the principal conductivity directions coincide with the optic axes of the crystal. For polymers the reported characterizations of anisotropic heat conduction have been concerned with uniaxially oriented (stretched) polymers where it is tacitly assumed that the orientation (stretched) direction is a principal conductivity direction and that the other principal directions are equivalent and may be chosen anywhere perpendicular to the orientation direction. The uniaxially oriented polymer is characterized by two conductivities, $k_{\parallel}$, parallel to the orientation, and $k_{\perp}$, perpendicular to the orientation. Presumably, a biaxially oriented polymer will have three principal conductivities, but no studies of heat conduction in biaxially oriented polymers have been reported.

B. Thermal Diffusivity

The analysis of conduction heat transfer problems typically begins with the insertion of Fourier's conduction law into an energy balance. For simple conduction in an isotropic material with constant properties, this leads to the familiar equation (in Cartesian coordinates):

$$\alpha\left(\frac{\partial^2 T}{\partial x^2} + \frac{\partial^2 T}{\partial y^2} + \frac{\partial^2 T}{\partial z^2}\right) = \frac{\partial T}{\partial t} \tag{5-11}$$

in which α is the thermal diffusivity. It is related to the conductivity by the equation

$$\alpha = \frac{k}{\rho c_p} \tag{5-12}$$

where ρ is the density and c_p is the heat capacity. Whereas the thermal conductivity characterizes the capability of the material to conduct heat, the thermal diffusivity characterizes the capability of the material to transmit a temperature or the time scale required to equilibrate with a temperature field.

5-2 PHYSICS OF HEAT CONDUCTION IN LIQUIDS AND SOLIDS

The physics of heat conduction is concerned with the description of the mechanisms, on a molecular scale, by which thermal energy is conducted through a material. Such description can and does lead to insights on the variations in thermal conductivity with temperature, pressure, and structure of a material. In gases, heat is conducted primarily by the diffusive motion of molecules, which can be quantitatively described by the kinetic theory of gases. In metals heat is conducted primarily by the mobile electrons. In dielectric solids and liquids, which include most polymers, heat is conducted by the interactions of the thermal vibrations of molecules and their component atoms.

A. Conduction in Dielectric Crystals

The theory of heat conduction in dielectrics can be approached most simply by considering first a perfectly ordered atomic crystal. Einstein developed expressions for the heat capacity of such crystals by considering each atom as an oscillator in harmonic motion. This treatment of the heat capacity was extended by Debye who considered the coupling of the oscillations or vibrations. He also introduced the idea that the energy of these vibrations, the thermal energy of the crystal, was quantized. This led to the concept of a quantum of lattice vibrational energy now called a phonon. The crystal lattice then becomes a medium which contains the mobile phonons or lattice energy packets. Analyzing heat conduction in terms of the diffusive motion of an ideal phonon gas leads directly to an equation for the thermal conductivity:

$$k = \tfrac{1}{3} Cu\lambda \tag{5-13}$$

where C is the phonon heat capacity (per unit volume), u is the phonon velocity, and λ is the phonon mean free path. Generally u is equated to the velocity of sound (velocity of propagation of vibrations through the lattice) and C to the heat capacity per unit volume ($C = \rho c_p$). Generally in analyzing heat conduction it is pertinent to consider only those contributions to the heat capacity from vibrations active in the conduction of heat.

In a perfect crystal with perfectly harmonic vibrations, there would be no mechanism for phonon scattering and the thermal conductivity would be infinite. However, the anharmonic aspects of the thermal vibrations lead to a conduction resistance characterized by phonon–phonon scattering. The data of Berman et al.(*1*) reproduced in Fig. 5-1 illustrate the effects of temperature on conduction in dielectric crystals. At temperatures near absolute zero the thermal conductivity is small, reflecting the small heat capacity. As the temperature increases, the conductivity increases in line with the increasing heat capacity. The phonon mean free path, at these low temperatures where the vibrations are very nearly harmonic, is large and is indeed sensitive to the size of the crystals; i.e., the phonon mean free path may be limited by crystal dimensions. As the temperature increases further, the heat capacity increases less rapidly, approaching a nearly constant value, while the lattice vibrations become increasingly anharmonic leading to decreasing phonon mean free path. Consequently the thermal conductivity reaches a maximum with increasing temperature and then declines rapidly. The thermal conductivity of sapphire at 40°K is four orders of magnitude larger than its value at 300°K. Peierls(*2*) has shown

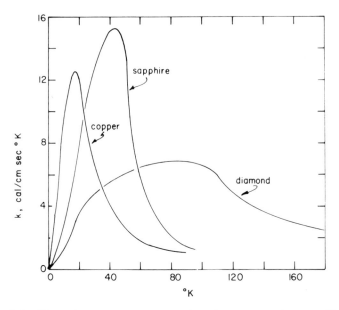

Figure 5-1. Thermal conductivity as a function of temperature for crystalline solids [Berman et al.(*1*) on copper, sapphire, and diamond].

that phonon-phonon scattering depends primarily on phonon concentration and hence is directly proportional to temperature. At higher temperatures, where the heat capacity is often nearly constant, the thermal conductivity is proportional to the phonon mean free path which varies inversely proportional to temperature. A linear relationship between k and $1/T$ has been verified for many dielectric crystals.

B. Conduction in Liquids and Amorphous Solids

The phonon theory of heat conduction is of limited usefulness in analyzing heat conduction in liquids and amorphous solids, inasmuch as the absence of an ordered lattice leaves the concept of a phonon with doubtful meaning. A striking illustration of the difference in heat conduction between crystalline and amorphous dielectrics is provided by the data of Berman et al.(3). The thermal conductivity of quartz crystal was measured as a function of temperature. The quartz crystal was then irradiated to introduce defects into its structure and the thermal conductivity was measured again. This procedure was re-

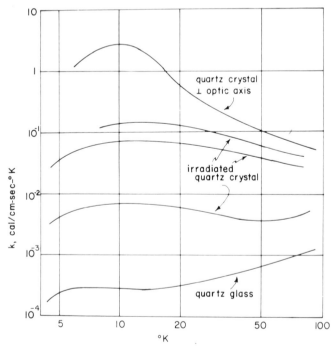

Figure 5-2. Thermal conductivity of quartz crystal, glass, and irradiated crystal [Berman et al.(3)].

peated several times until the quartz crystal had been effectively converted to a glass. Figure 5-2 is a reproduction of the results. The upper curve shows the typical conductivity-vs.-temperature behavior of a crystalline substance, but with increasing doses of radiation the thermal conductivity decreases. The lower curve is for a quartz glass. The conductivity is less than for the ordered crystal, but increases rather than decreases with temperature. Roughly, the temperature dependence of thermal conductivity of a glass can be interpreted as corresponding to a near-constant mean free path whence the thermal conductivity follows the increase in heat capacity with temperature.

In liquids the thermal conductivity is generally less temperature sensitive than in glasses and may decrease with increasing temperature due to thermal expansion. Some materials will show a maximum in the thermal conductivity at the glass transition temperature.

At very low temperatures the wavelengths of phonons become large compared to atomic dimensions, and larger-scale structural features can be factors in heat conductivity. At very low temperatures the simple phonon theory for single crystals or homogeneous amorphous substances predicts conductivity proportional to temperature.

5-3 HEAT CONDUCTION IN POLYMERS

A. Amorphous Polymers

1. TEMPERATURE AND PRESSURE DEPENDENCE

The thermal conductivity of polymethyl methacrylate has been measured from 1°K to 400°K, giving a fairly complete picture of the temperature dependence of thermal conductivity for an amorphous polymer. Reese(4) combined his own measurements at low temperatures with data of Eiermann(5) and Berman(6) to get the results which are summarized in Fig. 5-3. As Reese points out, the general features of these thermal conductivity data are in accord with the theory of heat conduction in glass, proposed by Klemens(7). Over most of the temperature range the phonons are scattered by the disordered, amorphous structure giving a constant mean free path and a thermal conductivity proportional to the volumetric heat capacity. At low temperatures Klemens suggests that the phonon wavelength becomes large compared to the molecular disorder and predicts that mean free path should be proportional to the square of the phonon wavelength, leading to a linear relationship between thermal conductivity and

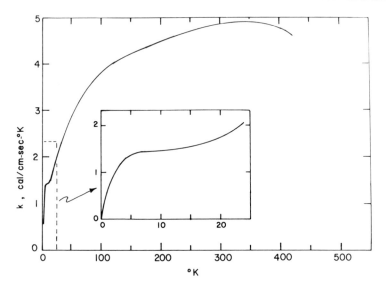

Figure 5-3.   Thermal conductivity of polymethyl methacrylate as a function of temperature [Reese(*4*)].

temperature. Reese's data confirm Klemens' prediction in the region 1°K to 4°K, but the data from 4°K to 25°K diverge from the Klemens theory. Reese was able to eliminate this discrepancy by considering one-dimensional vibrations along the polymer molecule separately from other contributions to the heat capacity, and assigning these vibrations a separate mean free path. In this way Reese fitted a theoretical curve to the experimental data to better than 10% from 1°K to the glass temperature. This agreement is excellent considering the inherent difficulty of obtaining precise thermal conductivity data, and the fact that the data were taken by three different investigators on two different samples. (Reese used Berman's sample for some of his measurements.)

While the phonon theory of heat conductions in amorphous solids, as adapted by Reese for polymers, apparently gives a satisfactory description of the general features of the temperature dependence over a wide temperature range, it does not deal with the effects of transitions, particularly the glass transition. Eiermann and Hellwege(*23*) have indicated that behavior in the vicinity of the transition may be related to thermal expansion effects. The thermal conductivities of polymer melts remain very nearly constant as a function of temperature. The similarity in thermal conductivity behavior in the vicinity of the glass transition has been pointed up by Frisch and Rogers(9) who, by using reduced coordinates, were able to represent data for a number of polymers on a single graph. They also attempted correlation of thermal conductivity with other transport properties, but the limited data available were insufficient to establish the validity or usefulness of these correlations.

In comparing the thermal conductivities of polymer melts, as Shoulberg(10) has done from diffusivity data, one notes that all the data fall in the vicinity of 5×10^{-4} cal/cm-sec-°K, with the exception of polyethylene which is somewhat higher. Shoulberg points out that, for the vinyl polymers, thermal conductivities of the melts apparently decrease with increasing size of substituent groups. However, the data are insufficient to permit refinement of this generalization.

The effect of pressure on thermal conductivity has apparently not been studied except for the experiments of Lohe(11) who recorded approximately a 5% increase in the thermal conductivity of molten polyethylene when the pressure was increased from 1 atm to 300 kg/cm².

A specific, curious temperature effect that has some practical significance was noted by Anderson et al.(12) in their experiments below 1°K. Whereas inorganic glasses have conductivity proportional to temperature in this range, the organic polymers (Teflon, Kel-F, Nylon, epoxy) all showed thermal conductivity decreasing more than linearly with decreasing temperatures. While the reasons for this behavior are not clear, the data indicate that the polymers may be superior thermal insulating materials at very low temperatures.

2. MOLECULAR WEIGHT DEPENDENCE

The first significant study of the effect of molecular weight on the thermal conductivity of a polymer was reported by Ueberreiter and Otto-Laupenmühlen(13) who measured conductivities of polystyrene fractions having molecular weights of 860, 2300, and 3650. Their data, both above and below the glass transition temperature, consistently indicate that the higher molecular weight polymer has the higher thermal conductivity. The authors reasoned that the effect was due to the fact that energy could be transmitted more readily along the polymer molecule than between molecules.

Similar reasoning was incorporated into a theoretical analysis of the molecular weight effect by Hansen and Ho(14). This theory predicts that the thermal conductivity should increase as the square root of the weight average molecular weight at low molecular weights, and become independent of molecular weight at high molecular weights. The data of Hansen, Ho, and Kantayya(*14,15*) on polystyrene and molten polyethylene apparently agree with the general predictions of the analysis. These data are reproduced in Figs. 5-4 and 5-5. For any polymer it is pertinent to know the molecular weight range over which the thermal conductivity varies significantly. Unfortunately, the theory of Hansen and Ho will not predict this *a priori*. Figure 5-4 indicates that the conductivity of polystyrene is independent of molecular weight above a degree of polymerization of 1000, while the polyethylene curve (Fig. 5-5) does not level off until a degree of polymerization greater than 10,000 is reached.

In Hansen and Ho's analysis the thermal conductivity is indicated to be sensitive to the linear extent of a molecule, suggesting that, for branched and linear homologs of equal molecular weight, the linear polymer should have the higher thermal conductivity. Some support for this view comes from data of Tomlinson, Kline, and Sauer(*16*) and Hennig, Knappe, and Lohe(*17*) on melts of linear and branched polyethylene, showing lower conductivity for the branched polymer. When Tomlinson et al. irradiated the branched polyethylene, its melt conductivity increased with increasing radiation dosage to a limiting value of 6.6×10^{-4} cal/cm-sec-°K, essentially the same value determined by Hansen and Ho for molten, high molecular weight, linear polyethylene.

Polymers are frequently used with low molecular weight plasticizers which change thermal as well as mechanical properties. Ueberreiter and Purucker(*18*) first observed this effect in polystyrene blended with hexachlorodiphenyl. Sheldon and Lane(*19*) measured conductivities of polyvinyl chloride blended with dialphanylphthalate, and others have reported data generally showing that the addition of plasticizers will decrease thermal conductivity. (See also Section 5-4.) Hansen and Ho (*14*) have shown that when the thermal conductivity is plotted versus the square root of weight fraction polymer the data of refs.(*18,19*) yield a straight line. They note that this form of plot is equivalent to a graph versus the square root of molecular weight obtained by averaging polymer and plasticizer molecular weights. The thermal diffusivity data of Ueberreiter and Purucker plotted in this way are shown in Fig. 5-6.

All of the experimental data on the effect of molecular weight reported to date have been limited to a fairly narrow temperature range, and there is little data on polymers other than polystyrene and polyethylene. Lohe(*20*) recently reported some molecular weight-conductivity data on polymethylsiloxane and polyethyleneglycol. Several authors

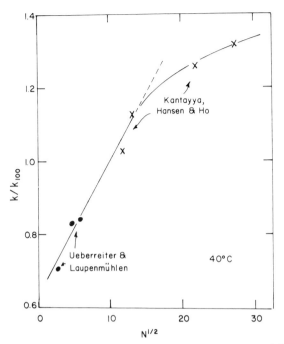

Figure 5-4. Thermal conductivity of polystyrene vs. square root of degree of poly-merization. Conductivities normalized to value at degree of polymerization 100 [Hansen et al.(*15*)].

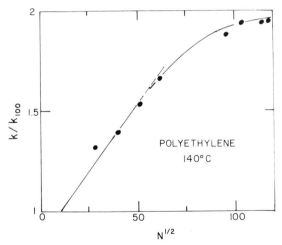

Figure 5-5. Thermal conductivity of molten polyethylene vs. square root of degree of polymerization. Conductivities normalized to value at degree of polymerization 100 [Hansen and Ho(*14*)].

257

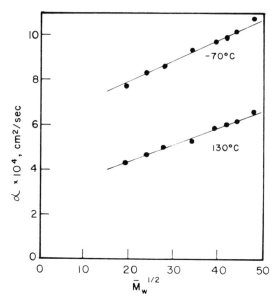

Figure 5-6. Thermal diffusivity of polystyrene blended with hexachlorodiphenyl vs. square root of weight average molecular weight [Ueberreiter and Purucker(*18*)].

have noted wide discrepancies in reported thermal conductivity values of the same polymer. These discrepancies exceed that which would be expected from experimental error alone and may be due to structural differences such as molecular weight and branching. However, more conductivity data on characterized samples covering broader temperature intervals will be necessary to assess the sources of present discrepancies.

3. MOLECULAR ORIENTATION DEPENDENCE

When a polymer is oriented as by stretching or cold-drawing, the anisotropy of structure is reflected in a corresponding anisotropy in properties. One of the earliest characterizations of thermal conductivity in oriented polymers was reported by Tautz(*21*) in 1959. Tautz's data, reproduced in part in Fig. 5-7, showed the thermal conductivity of rubber as a function of degree of stretching and vulcanization. The sensitivity of thermal conductivity to orientation apparently increased and then decreased with further vulcanizing. Most striking was the fivefold increase in thermal conductivity observed by Tautz on a highly oriented specimen.

A comprehensive study of an anisotropic conductivity in oriented

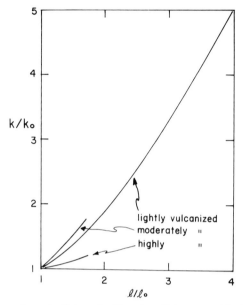

Figure 5-7. Thermal conductivity of rubber (parallel to stretching) as a function of extension ratio [Tautz(*21*)].

polymers has been reported by Eiermann, Hellwege, Hennig, and Knappe in a series of papers(*22–29*). These researchers measured conductivities both parallel and perpendicular to the direction of stretching on a variety of oriented amorphous polymers and elastomers. One set of their data is reproduced in Fig. 5-8, a graph of relative thermal conductivity versus relative extension. These data indicate large differences among different polymers in the magnitude of the orientation effect on thermal conductivity, but all show an increase in conductivity parallel to stretching with a decrease normal to the stretch direction. In polyvinylchloride at 100% extension the ratio of $k_{\parallel}$ to $k_{\perp}$ is almost 2 while in polystyrene at 600% extension the ratio is only 1.5. Eiermann and co-workers(*22–29*) have analyzed the conductivity of oriented polymers in terms of a model comprising low thermal resistances (intramolecular bonds) and high thermal resistances (intermolecular, van der Waals bonds). Stretching the polymer orients the low resistances preferentially parallel to the stretching direction and the high resistance preferentially perpendicular to the stretching direction. From this model of high and low resistances acting in series and parallel, they derived the following equation

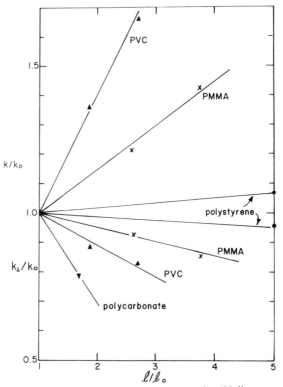

Figure 5-8.   Thermal conductivity as a function of extension [Hellwege et al. (24)].

relating the anisotropy in thermal conductivity to the conductivity of the unoriented polymer:

$$\frac{1}{k_{\parallel}} + \frac{2}{k_{\perp}} = \frac{3}{k_0} \tag{5-14}$$

The data on a variety of amorphous polymers were found to agree with this relationship, including data on polymethyl methacrylate from −190°C to 50°C. While Eq. (5-14) very successfully correlates the anisotropy in conductivity of oriented, amorphous polymers, it does not say anything of the difference in magnitude of the anisotropy among different polymers. However, Eiermann and co-workers(22–29) have also successfully applied their model analysis to other properties such as thermal expansion and compressibility. From this they predict relationships between the properties such as the following equations, relating thermal conductivities and the coefficients of linear thermal expansion:

$$\frac{k_0}{k_{\parallel}} = \left(0.8 \times \frac{\beta_{\parallel}}{\beta_0}\right) + 0.2 \tag{5-15}$$

$$\frac{k_0}{k_{\perp}} = \left(0.8 \times \frac{\beta_{\perp}}{\beta_0}\right) + 0.2 \tag{5-16}$$

Their experimental verification of these relationships is summarized in a graph of their data reproduced in Fig. 5-9.

Hansen and Ho(14) also applied their analysis of the thermal conductivity of polymers to a prediction of the orientation effect, obtaining the relationship,

$$\frac{k_0}{k_{\perp}} = \left(\frac{k_{\parallel}}{k_0}\right)^{1/2} \tag{5-17}$$

They also predicted that, barring a transition, the change in conductivity with stretching should be linear with the molecular orientation. While Eq. (5-17) is very different in form from Eiermann's Eq. (5-14), it does not predict very different numerical results within the bounds where experimental data are available.

Recently, Washo(30) has extended the analysis of Hansen and Ho and predicts a relationship between molecular weight and orientation

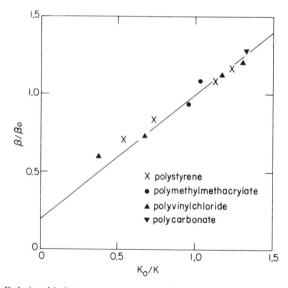

Figure 5-9. Relationship between anisotropy in thermal conductivity and linear thermal expansion [Hellwege et al.(24)].

sensitivity of the thermal conductivity. However, only limited data are given showing a low molecular weight polymethyl methacrylate to be more orientation sensitive than a specimen of higher molecular weight.

As all of the reported data indicate, orientation can induce a significant anisotropy in the thermal conductivity of polymers, which must be considered in analysis of heat transfer in these materials. Presumably, in biaxially oriented materials, three principal conductivities are needed to characterize the material. The derivation of Eqs. (5-14) and (5-17) can be modified to consider biaxial orientation, but no experimental data are available.

Processes such as extrusion generally require heat transfer to a polymer melt, under shear, which may be significantly oriented. While the effects of orientation on conductivity of a melt are expected to be similar to the effects on a solid, amorphous polymer, there have been no reports of experimental characterization of anisotropic conductivity in a polymer melt.

B. Crystalline Polymers

In comparison with the amorphous polymers, crystalline polymers are characterized by a more ordered, denser structure which, in general, yields a higher thermal conductivity. The difference between the amorphous and crystalline polymers with respect to heat conduction may be characterized as a lower resistance to intermolecular transfer in the crystalline polymer. Hence, it might be expected that the conductivity of crystalline polymers would be less sensitive to a parameter such as molecular weight. Indeed, Hansen and Ho(14) observed a significant molecular weight effect in the conductivity of molten polyethylene, but discerned no difference in thermal conductivity among crystalline polyethylenes of different molecular weights. For the same reasons, one would expect less effect of molecular orientation on the conductivity of a crystalline polymer than is observed with amorphous polymers. On the other hand, the crystal structure of polymers is itself highly anisotropic and when oriented could yield significant anisotropy in heat conduction properties. No experimental or theoretical characterization of the thermal conductivity of oriented, crystalline polymers has been reported.

The most extensive studies on heat conduction in crystalline polymers have been reported by Eiermann(31), who measured thermal conductivity of polyethylene, polyoxymethylene, polypropylene, and polyethylene terephthalate from $-190°C$ to $+100°C$. He found the thermal conductivity–temperature relationship to be sensitive to density. For example, an annealed, linear polyethylene ($\rho = 0.982$ gm/cm³) has a conductivity of 2.8×10^{-3} cal/cm-sec-°C at -190°C which decreases to 1.1×10^{-3} at $+100$°C. A low density, branched polyethylene ($\rho = 0.918$) has a conductivity of only 0.75×10^{-3} cal/cm-sec-°C at -190°C, which increases slightly with temperature to a maximum of 0.9×10^{-3} at about -50°C from which it declines to 0.6×10^{-3} at $+100$°C. However, Eiermann(32) found that some of the wide differences in thermal conductivity of different specimens of the same crystalline polymer could be correlated on the basis of a simple model. Considering the polymers to consist of a composite of amorphous and crystalline material, Eiermann analyzed his data on the basis of a hypothetical conductivity k_c of a perfectly crystalline polymer, and k_a, the thermal conductivity of completely amorphous polymers. The volume fraction or "per cent crystallinity" was assigned in the usual way from density data, and Maxwell's equation was used to calculate k_c and k_a from data on the real polymers(32). When treated in this way, Eiermann's data showed k_a to be proportional to temperature and k_c to the reciprocal of temperature. This is the behavior predicted from phonon theory for amorphous and crystalline dielectrics. Hansen and Ho(14) and Sheldon and Lane(33) have analyzed their data on polyethylene in similar fashion, and confirm Eiermann's findings.

Other studies on heat conduction in crystalline polymers include the observations of Hsu, Kline, Tomlinson, and Sauer(16,34,35), Hattori (36), and Sheldon and Lane(33) on the effects of nuclear radiation. These are discussed in Section 5-4,O. Effects of crystal morphology have not been studied, per se, with respect to heat conduction in polymers. Also lacking is any extensive study of thermal conductivity of crystalline polymers at very low temperatures.

In addition to the general trends in conductivity–temperature graphs for crystalline polymers, one sees local bumps or discontinuities. These may reflect various transitions, and indeed Tomlinson, Kline, and Sauer (16) have related them to dynamic mechanical spectra observations on the same samples. Steere(37) has even suggested the use of thermal conductivity measurements to study polymer transitions, and has demonstrated the potential of the technique with some observations on transitions in polyethylene terephthalate, polytetrafluoroethylene, and polypropylene.

5-4 POLYMER CONDUCTIVITY DATA

In this section a general discussion of thermal conductivity data will be presented. Where sufficient data have been accumulated on a given polymer, it will be discussed separately. It is intended that the discussion be reasonably extensive, realizing that space limitations prevent discussion of every existing reference. The work cited will hopefully provide a core from which the reader can consult the literature in further detail and locate references on a given subject or material. For convenience, thermal conductivity unit conversion factors are given in Table 5-1.

A. Polymethyl Methacrylate (PMMA)

Polymethyl methacrylate has been a primary material for investigation of the process of thermal conduction in amorphous polymers. Studies have included the low temperature behavior, the effect of the glasslike transition, effects of chain orientation, and behavior of the conductivity in the melt. Thermal conductivity data for PMMA have been reported by Reese(4,38), Hattori(39), Eiermann and co-workers (22,23,40), Berman(6), Lohe(11,42), Shoulberg and Shetter(44), Eiermann and Hellwege(23), Holzmüller and Münx(45), Kirichenko, Hennig, and Knappe(46), and Knappe(47). Orientation effects have been investigated by Eiermann(26) (for stretched and unstretched materials), Hellwege et al.(24), and Hansen and Ho(14). Thermal diffusivity data have been presented for temperatures from 25° to 325°C by Shoulberg(10) and, for some temperatures above room temperature, by Chung and Jackson(48).

A combination of Reese's low temperature data with that of others [Eiermann(22) and Berman(6)] were summarized in Fig. 5-3 in a previous section. The conductivity increases from a near-zero value

TABLE   5-1
Thermal Conductivity Unit Conversion Factors

g-cal/cm²-sec	w/cm²	w/in.²-°C/in.	Btu/ft²	kg-cal/m²-hr	Btu/ft²-hr
1.0	4.19	10.63	242.0	360.0	2903.0
0.239	1.0	2.54	57.8	86.0	694.0
0.094	0.394	1.0	22.8	33.9	273.0
4.13×10^{-3}	0.0173	0.0440	1.0	1.488	12.00
2.788×10^{-3}	0.0116	0.0295	0.672	1.0	8.06
0.344×10^{-3}	1.442×10^{-3}	3.66×10^{-3}	0.0833	0.124	1.0

slightly above 0°K to 1×10^{-4} cal/cm-sec-°K at 2.5°K and to 4×10^{-4} cal/cm-sec-°K near 125°K. Values continue to increase with increasing temperature to a maximum near 350°K followed by a slight downward trend. Data of Shoulberg and Shetter(44) have shown that the conductivity typically is independent of temperature up to the glasslike transition temperature, and then decreases with temperature up to 160°C (Fig. 5-10). A discussion of the implications of the PMMA data thus far reported was given in Section 5-3.

B. Polystyrene (PS)

Various aspects of thermal conductivity in polystyrene have been studied. Ueberreiter and co-workers(13,18,49,50) reported data for k, α, c_p, and v concerning the effect of molecular weight, the effect of plasticizing, and the effect of cross-linking via divinyl benzene. Reese and Tucker(51) reported data at low temperatures (below 5°K); Holzmuller and Munx(45) from 20° to about 130°C; Hattori(36,52,53) (k and α) from 20° to 120°C; Kirichenko et al.(46) from 30° to 75°C; Cherkasova(54) from 25° to 95°C; Kline(55) from room temperature to about 100°C; and Lohe(42) from 100° to 250°C (in the melt). Shoulberg(10) has also presented diffusivity data from near the glass temperature to about 300°C.

Hellwege, Hennig, Knappe, and Semjonow(24,47,56) have presented data for c_p and k, including the effect of orientation by stretching. The studies of Hansen, Kantayya, and Ho(15) included molecular weight dependence in polystyrene and molten polystyrene (some PS data are given in Fig. 5-4).

Much of the data reported in the literature has been compiled and

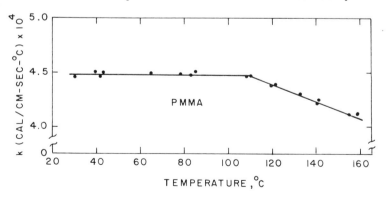

Figure 5-10. Thermal conductivity of polymethyl methacrylate [Shoulberg and Shetter(44)].

evaluated in a study by Carwile and Hoge(57). A summary of their findings is given in Fig. 5-11 where they have also drawn a line representing their selection of probable thermal conductivity values as a function of temperature. For the most part data reported by investigators so far tend to exhibit an increase in conductivity with temperature but an identifiable maximum may also occur. For solid PS the maximum would appear to occur near the glass temperature while this value would appear to be exceeded by a further rise in conductivity with increasing temperature in the melt. It should be noted that all results thus far reported apparently concern atactic PS. No results have been reported for isotactic crystalline PS.

C. Polyurethane

Thermal conductivity data for polyurethanes have been reported by Knappe(47) and Cherkasova(54). These investigators have not described in detail the preparation and analysis of their materials. Their results differ in that Cherkasova's(54) data exhibit an increase from about 3.4×10^{-4} cal/cm-sec-°C at 25°C to about 4.6×10^{-4} cal/cm-sec-°C at 90°C (Fig. 5-12), and results of the Knappe(47) investigation using a partly crystalline material show a decrease from about 7.5×10^{-4} cal/cm-sec-°C at 15°C to 6.2×10^{-4} cal/cm-sec-°C at 100°C. If the material used by Cherkasova was almost completely amorphous rather than appreciably crystalline in nature, as that reported by Knappe, it could conceivably account for the difference in results obtained by the two investigators.

D. Polyvinyl Chloride (PVC)

Polyvinyl chloride is usually considered to be a primarily amorphous polymer. Quantitative estimates of the per cent crystallinity are difficult to obtain. Eiermann, Hellwege, and Knappe(58) reported thermal conductivity data for PVC showing a gradual increase from 3×10^{-4} cal/cm-sec-°K at −180°C to a maximum of slightly greater than 4×10^{-4} cal/cm-sec-°K near 40°C and decreasing only slightly to 90°C. Knappe(47) reported a relatively temperature-independent value of 4×10^{-4} cal/cm-sec-°K from 10°C to 100°C. In this temperature range, Knappe(47) also reported an over-all decrease in conductivity with increasing plasticizing concentration. Holzmüller and Münx(45) presented results from the range 25° to 75°C which showed a small peak followed by a small dip at 45°–55°C superimposed on a nearly-constant thermal conductivity level.

Sheldon and Lane(19) measured thermal conductivity of the PVC

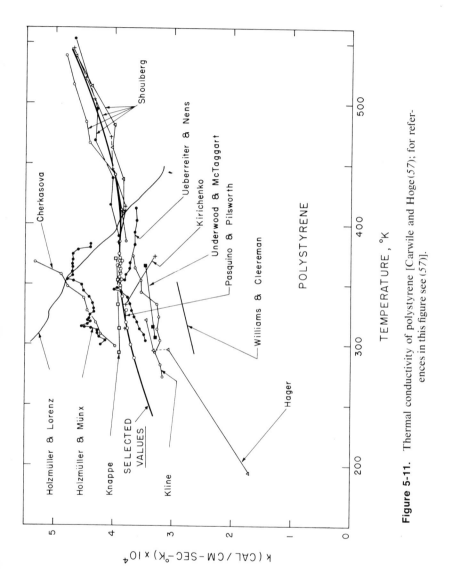

Figure 5-11. Thermal conductivity of polystyrene [Carwile and Hoge(57); for references in this figure see (57)].

267

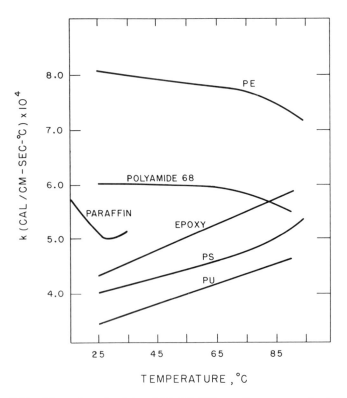

Figure 5-12.   Thermal conductivity of PS, PE, PU, paraffin, epoxy, and polyamide 68
[Cherkasova(*54*)].

specimens with varying plasticizer content (0, 20, 26, 30, 36, 40%) from 15°–98°C and found the conductivity of the unplasticized sample (Fig. 5-13) to increase gradually up to the glass temperature and then to begin to decrease. Maximum values were about 4×10^{-4} cal/cm-sec-°K. With the addition of plasticizer, the glass temperature of PVC decreases and this is apparently reflected in the thermal conductivity; i.e., the maximum in the thermal conductivity shifts to lower temperatures with increasing plasticizer concentration. Near 100°C the conductivity of the 40% plasticized sample was reduced to about 3.4×10^{-4} units. Extrapolations of the thermal conductivity were also made to 0% and 100% plasticizer concentrations for data at 25°C from plasticized specimens and these values (Fig. 5-14) were compared to other measurements and calculations.

Others have also observed changes in thermal conductivity with

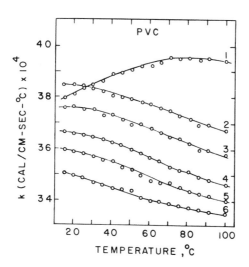

Figure 5-13. Thermal conductivity of polyvinyl chloride as a function of temperature [Sheldon and Lane(*19*)].

increasing plasticizer content. Hellwege, Knappe, and Semjonow(*56*) presented data for PVC (20, 40, and 60% plasticizer) from −150° to +100°C. The sample with least plasticizer exhibited a slight broad peak $(4.2 \times 10^{-4}\,\text{cal/cm-sec-}°\text{K})$ near −65°C, while the sample containing 40% plasticizer exhibited a smaller peak $(3.2 \times 10^{-4}\,\text{cal/cm-sec-}°\text{K})$ at −40°C, and a sample containing 60% plasticizer exhibited no peak but merely decreased from 2.5×10^{-4} units at −130°C to 2.2×10^{-4} units at 100°C. Increased plasticizer decreased the conductivity at all temperatures.

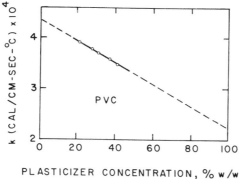

Figure 5-14. Thermal conductivity of polyvinyl chloride as a function of plasticizer concentration [Sheldon and Lane(*19*)].

Eiermann's(22) results for −190° to 90°C appear to differ from the above. With increasing plasticizer content (0, 10, 20, 40%) the conductivity peak shifts from the highest temperatures to −50°C. While increasing the percentage plasticizer causes a decrease in conductivity above the peak, it results in an increase in conductivity below the peak. This behavior is very similar to that observed by Sheldon and Lane(19). The reference of Eiermann and Hellwege(23) repeats these data. Steere(37) has also presented data for plasticized PVC.

Hellwege et al.(24) have measured the effects of stretching in the conductivity of PVC in directions parallel to and perpendicular to the stretch direction. (See also Fig. 5-8 of Section 5-3 for typical orientation results.) Diffusivity measurements of unplasticized PVC from 120° to 200°C can be found in Shoulberg's(10) work.

E. Polyethylene (PE)

Thermal conductivity behavior of polyethylene has been investigated extensively by Eiermann and co-workers(17,22,23,31,32,41, 47,58,59) from −190° to about +100°C although an appreciable number of the publications apparently present repetitious data. Hattori(36,52,53,60) has reported k and α data for PE over the −60° to 120°C temperature range including studies of molecular weight. Cherkasova(54) reported results from 25°–95°C; Kirichenko et al.(46) reported results from 30° to 80°C; Hansen and Ho(14) reported results for k, including the effect of molecular weight, for the temperature range 50° to 160°C; Kline(55) reported results from 0° to ~100°C; and Steere (62) has reported results from −50° to +30°C for α, k, and c_p.

Data of Eiermann(32) are given in Fig. 5-15 illustrating the increase in conductivity with increasing density of PE. Sheldon and Lane(61) obtained similar results, which illustrate the effect of increased density resulting primarily from increased crystallinity, as did Hansen and Ho (14), Tomlinson, Kline, and Sauer(16), and others. By a calculation based on the Maxwell equation for conduction in mixtures, Eiermann (32) has resolved the conductivity of PE into contributions from the amorphous and crystalline regions. The amorphous conductivity (Fig. 5-16) rises from about 3×10^{-4} cgs units at −190°C to a maximum of about 4.3×10^{-4} cgs units at −25°C. This behavior is somewhat similar to the conductivity behavior of amorphous PMMA cited earlier and is very similar to the results obtained on atactic (amorphous) polypropylene, as shown in Fig. 5-16. The conductivity of the crystalline regions (Fig. 5-17) follows approximately the T^{-1} behavior typical of molecular crystals.

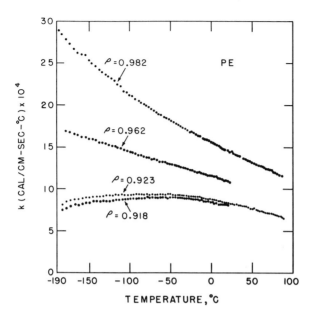

Figure 5-15. Thermal conductivity of polyethylenes (ρ = 0.982, 0.962, 0.923, 0.918) as a function of temperature [Eiermann(*32*)].

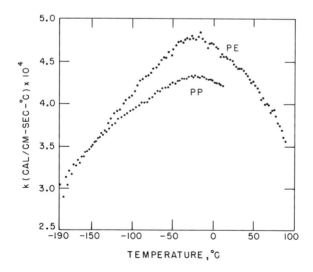

Figure 5-16. Thermal conductivity of atactic polypropylene and calculated thermal conductivity of amorphous polyethylene [Eiermann(*32*)].

271

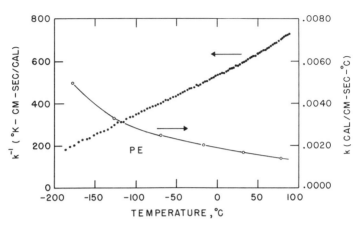

Figure 5-17. Calculated thermal conductivity and reciprocal conductivity of crystalline polyethylene [Eiermann(*32*)].

Reese and Tucker(*51*) have reported thermal conductivity data for PE below 5°K, showing that the conductivity tends towards zero with decreasing temperature. Shoulberg(*10*) has presented diffusivity data at high temperatures and in the melt. Hansen and Ho(*14*), Lohe(*20*), and Tomlinson, Kline, and Sauer(*16*) have measured the conductivity of polyethylene in the melt. The latter group obtained results by inducing slight cross-linking between molecular chains using nuclear radiation. Results indicate that the conductivity rises slightly with temperature in the melt and that the conductivity is higher for linear PE as compared to branched PE. Effects of radiation on the conductivity of polyethylene are discussed elsewhere. (See also Fig. 5-18.)

F. Polypropylene (PP)

Figure 5-19 is a plot of Eiermann's(*31*) data for isotactic partially crystalline PP ($\rho = 0.911$ gm/cm³) and atactic amorphous PP. Tomlinson and Kline(*35*) have reported data for isotactic PP ($\rho = 0.907$) showing that the conductivity decreases rather rapidly with temperature, similar to PE at higher temperatures, and approaches the conductivity value of the melt near the crystalline melting temperature (see Fig. 5-28 later in this section). Data on PP have been reported in other articles by Eiermann(*32,41*), Knappe(*47*), and Steere(*37*). The latter gives values of α, and c_p and the k data exhibit an increase from about 3.2×10^{-4} cal/cm-sec-°C at -100°C to about 7×10^{-4} cal/cm-sec-°C near $+100$°C.

Polypropylene data generally parallel PE data in that values for the

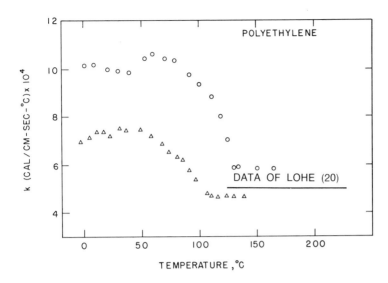

Figure 5-18. Thermal conductivity of polyethylenes at high temperatures [○, △, Tomlinson et al. (*16*); — Lohe(*20*)].

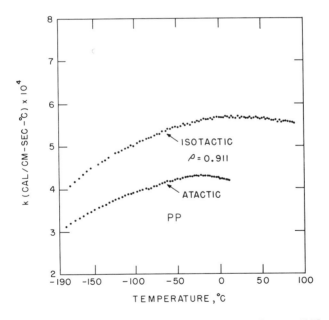

Figure 5-19. Thermal conductivity of polypropylene [Eiermann(*31*)].

amorphous material increase at increasing temperature to a maximum near the temperature of a glasslike relaxation (Fig. 5-16); the conductivity increases upon crystallization of the polymer; and at higher temperatures the conductivity decreases with increasing temperature as the crystallites melt, reaching the value of the molten polymer at the crystallite melting temperature.

Eiermann(31) has separated the conductivity of PP into amorphous and crystalline contributions by an analysis similar to that discussed for PE(32). The amorphous conductivity was similar to that for atactic PP; however, the conductivity was found to increase with increasing temperature contrary to that observed in PE.

G. Polyamides

Polyamides or nylons have been studied by a number of investigators including Hattori(63) (nylon 6, see Fig. 5-20); Kline(55) (nylon 66 from 0° to 100°C); Cherkasova(54) (nylon 68 from 25° to 95°C); Knappe(47) (nylon 6 and 610 from 20° to 100°C); and Holzmüller and Münx(45) (25° to 130°C). Reese and Tucker(51) obtained data on a nylon from 0.2° to 5°K, and Lohe(42) obtained data on nylon 6 in the melt from 210° to 240°C. In the melt the value was observed to be nearly temperature independent (5.2×10^{-4} cgs).

H. Polyoxymethylene

Data for polyoxymethylene have been reported by Eiermann(31) from $-190°$ to $+90°$C and diffusivity data have been presented by Shoulberg(10) for Delrin in the melt. Eiermann's(31) results are shown in Fig. 5-21 for two materials ($\rho = 1.441$ gm/cm³ and $\rho = 1.432$ gm/cm³).

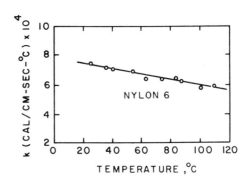

Figure 5-20. Thermal conductivity of nylon 6 as a function of temperature [Hattori (63)].

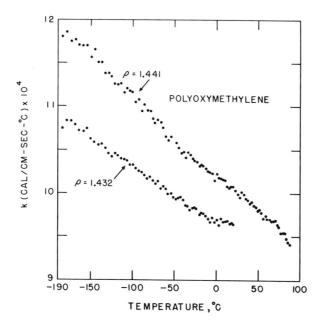

Figure 5-21. Thermal conductivity of polyoxymethylene as a function of temperature [Eiermann(*31*)].

The data show that the conductivity level is relatively high, that it decreases monotonically over the temperature range, and that it differs for materials of different density, the densities probably indicating different percentages of crystallinity.

I. Polyethylene Terephthalate (PETP)

PETP has been investigated by Eiermann and Hellwege(*23*) from −190° to +80°C and by Steere(*37,62*) from −150° to 120°C. Data of Eiermann and Hellwege(*23*), which are essentially repeated in references(*22,31,41,58*), are shown in Fig. 5-22 indicating that the thermal conductivity rises toward a maximum over the temperature range covered, and that the higher density material ($\rho = 1.409$) exhibits higher values of conductivity than the lower density material ($\rho = 1.337$). As in other partially crystalline polymers, this is probably a reflection of increased crystallinity.

Results of Steere(*37,62*) also show an increase in conductivity with increasing temperatures. Data for higher temperatures and for PETP in the melt are not reported.

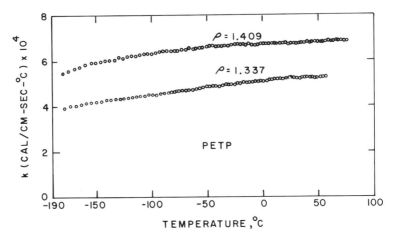

Figure 5-22. Thermal conductivity of polyethylene terephthalate [Eiermann and Hellwege(*23*)].

J. Polytetrafluoroethylene (PTFE)

The thermal conductivity behavior of PTFE has been studied by a number of investigators. It is considered to be especially interesting because, in addition to other known relaxations, it undergoes crystal–crystal transitions near 19° and 30°C, respectively. Steere's(*37*) conductivity data obtained by a dynamic technique (Fig. 5-23) show a

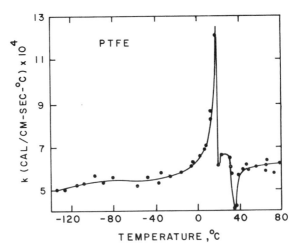

Figure 5-23. Thermal conductivity of polytetrafluoroethylene as a function of temperature [Steere(*37*)].

276

sharp rise above 0°C and an abrupt drop near 19°C. Following a slight recovery the data again show an abrupt drop near 30°C. Values (37) for α and C also exhibit dramatic changes with temperatures in the regions of the transition.

Eiermann and Hellwege (23) reported a drop in conductivity near 19°C. This work by Eiermann and associates can also be found in references (22,31,41,47,58). Hsu, Kline, and Tomlinson (34) also found changes occurring in the conductivity values in this temperature region. Results generally suggest that the conductivity tends to rise with increasing temperature below room temperature and that it is rather temperature independent from RT to about 120°C. At higher temperatures, it then decreases with temperature. Reese and Tucker (51) have reported a reasonably sharp increase in conductivity with temperature below 5°K, much as in other polymers. Powell et al. (64) have presented data for an investigation of PTFE from 5° to 90°C. Hattori (65) reported data for the 20°–100°C temperature region. Kirichenko et al. (46) reported data for the 30°–160°K range and Vasilev and Surkov (79) have presented c_p, k, and α data.

Conductivity studies of Hsu, Kline, and Tomlinson (34) suggest that relaxations present in PTFE may also affect the conductivity. Their data further indicate that, although quenching and annealing procedures changed the thermal conductivity, the conductivity level of both the quenched and annealed material was less than that of the as-received material. Furthermore, although the per cent crystallinity increased after a slight nuclear radiation dose, the conductivity decreased. Radiation effects data are discussed in another part of this section.

K. Polychlorotrifluoroethylene (PCTFE)

Reese and Tucker (51) investigated the thermal conductivity of PCTFE from ~0.2° to 5°K; Hattori (65) has reported data from 20° to 110°C for specimens of different percentages of crystallinity and has plotted conductivity vs. crystallinity for some percentages. Data of Eiermann (31) given in Fig. 5-24 show an increase in thermal conductivity from rather a low value of ~2.4×10^{-4} cal/cm-sec-°C at −190°C to a maximum of about 3.5×10^{-4} cal/cm-sec-°C near 75°C. Differences between the results for the two materials of different densities ($\rho = 2.097$ and $\rho = 2.112$ gm/cm³) are slight; but, above about −50°C, the conductivity of the denser material appears to be less than that of the less dense material. This is in contrast to Hattori's (65) results and results for many polymers which exhibit higher conductivity as the density increases.

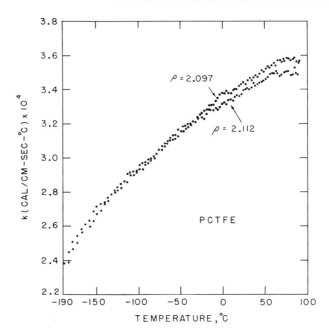

Figure 5-24. Thermal conductivity of polychlorotrifluoroethylene as a function of temperature [Eiermann(*31*)].

L. Thermosetting Polymers; Epoxies

Data on the thermal conductivity of epoxy systems and other thermosetting polymers have been reported by Cherkasova(*54*) for RT to ~95°C, by Frielingsdorf(*66*), by Hertz and Haskins(*67*), by Eiermann and Knappe(*68*) as a function of filler; by Knappe(*47*) from 0° to 100°C, by Tsetlin, Yanova, Sibirskaya, and Rebinder(*69*) (bakelite and graphite system) as a function of filler concentration; and by Kline(*55*) for aluminum-filled epoxy systems from 0° to near 100°C. Data of Kline(*55*) are given in Fig. 5-25.

For the unfilled epoxy, diglycidyl ether of bisphenol A hardened with *m*-phenylene diamine(*55*), the conductivity rises slightly with temperature over the range studied. This is much as expected for an amorphous crosslinked polymer and is similar in character to results of Cherkasova in Fig. 5-12 (material specifications are not given) and not too different from the results of Knappe(*47*) which indicated a relatively constant conductivity of 4.8×10^{-4} cal/cm-sec-°C over the 0°–100°C temperature range.

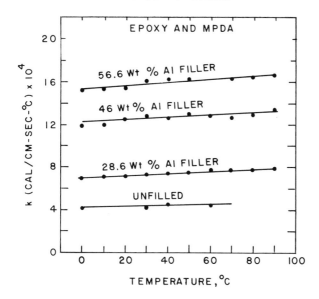

Figure 5-25. Thermal conductivity of aluminum-filled epoxy systems as a function of temperature [Kline(55)].

Addition of aluminum powder filler increased the conductivity but, as expected, the increase was not a simple arithmetic average of the conductivities of the aluminum and epoxy separately. The conductivity increased with filler content more rapidly than predicted by the Rayleigh–Maxwell equation for a dilute dispersion of spherical particles in a continuous medium. At all concentrations the epoxy apparently isolated the aluminum particles and maintained appreciable thermal resistance. From Fig. 5-25 it is noted that the conductivities of the filled systems increased slightly with temperature and there was some evidence that the data did not lie on straight lines but that there was some finer detail imposed on the over-all behavior.

M. Rubbers

Rubbers mentioned herein include both natural and synthetic forms although not nearly all the forms will be discussed. Carwile and Hoge (70) have studied conductivity data of the available literature to arrive at selected values for natural rubber. Their work provides an excellent source of references on the subject including the graphing of much of the data. Also, Anderson(71) has included rubber and cellular materials in a recent review discussing thermal conductivity in polymers.

Schallamach(72) has presented rubber data over the temperature range 100°–300°K while Eiermann and co-workers(22,23,29,40,41,56) have reported data from −190° to +90°C. Data of Eiermann and Hellwege(23) are given in Fig. 5-26, and it should be noted that some of the other references are only repeat data. Cherkasova(54) reported results for 25°–95°C, and Shoulberg(10) reported diffusivity data up to ~300°C.

Eiermann and Hellwege's(23) results indicate that data for natural rubber, crosslinked polyester-urethane, polyisobutylene, and silicone

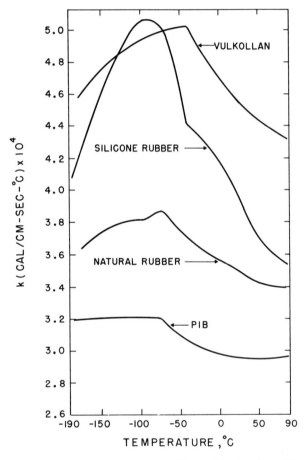

Figure 5-26. Thermal conductivity of natural rubber, polyisobutylene, silicone rubber, and Vulkollan (crosslinked polyester-urethane) as a function of temperature [Eiermann and Hellwege(23)].

rubber have a similar character in that for the most part the conductivity rises with increasing temperature up to the glass–rubber transition, then the values decrease with temperature, somewhat as in the case of the glass–liquid transition (PMMA). Actual conductivity levels depend upon the particular molecular structure. At higher temperatures it seems probable that the conductivity again rises with temperature. One would expect the results to be generally similar in some respects to those for polymer melts and epoxy systems at higher temperatures. Filled rubber systems have been studied, and data on some of these can be found in references(70,71).

N. Other Polymers

Some other polymers which have been studied but will not be treated separately include a polyester studied by Hattori(36,39); cellulose acetate and cellulose acetate butyrate studied by Knappe(47) from RT to 100°C; chlorosulfonated PE reported by Hennig and Knappe(29); vinyl chloride acetate copolymer reported by Hattori (52,74); and polybutene studied by Boggs and Sibbitt(75). Cherkasova (54) also reported data (25°–95°C) on miscellaneous other materials not heretofore discussed, including paraffin (see Fig. 5-12). Knappe(47) gave conductivity data for polyvinyl carbazol and polycarbonate (~20° to 100°C). Polycarbonate data are also presented by Hellwege, Hennig, and Knappe(24) and Steere(37), and diffusivity data are reported for polycarbonate in the melt by Shoulberg(10). Penton data are reported by Lohe(42) at temperatures into the melting region.

O. Irradiated Polymers

Changes in thermal conductivity resulting from nuclear radiation have been studied by Tomlinson et al.(16) for PE, Hsu, Kline, and Tomlinson(34) for PTFE, and Tomlinson and Kline(35) for PP. Hattori (36) has reported diffusivity results for γ-irradiated PE. Results(16) indicate that reactor radiation tends to break up the crystallites in PE, leading to decreased conductivity at lower temperatures, as can be observed in Fig. 5-27. Crosslinking occurs as a result of the irradiation but at lower temperatures this does not appear to compensate for the loss in crystallinity even though the crosslinking/scission ratio is relatively high. At higher temperatures, for instance above 100°C (see Fig. 5-27), higher doses result in an increase in conductivity level, probably resulting primarily from radiation-induced crosslinking.

Isotactic polypropylene is rather similar to PE in structure and typically has a relatively large percentage crystallinity. The crosslinking

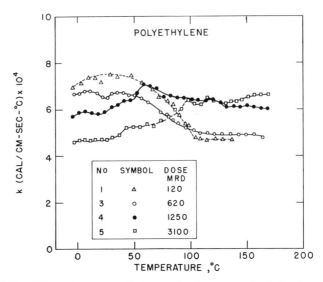

Figure 5-27. Effect of reactor radiation on the thermal conductivity of polyethylene [Tomlinson *et al.*(*16*)].

to scission ratio is much lower than in the case of PE. Upon γ-irradiation(*35*) the over-all conductivity level (0°–160°C) decreases, probably primarily as a result of disordering of crystallites. Results are given in Fig. 5-28. Differential scanning calorimeter data indicate that as the crystallites are increasingly disordered the temperature range of melting process broadens. The melting temperature shifts to lower temperatures with increasing radiation dose. It is interesting to note that, although radiation-induced crosslinking occurs in PP, the conductivity did not increase with dose, presumably largely because of the relatively small crosslinking/scission ratio.

Data for PTFE(*34*) showed that the thermal conductivity behavior following gamma irradiation differed substantially from both PE and PP (see Fig. 5-29). PTFE is relatively sensitive to radiation and the percentage crystallinity, as indicated by infrared measurements, increased with dose. However, the conductivity level decreased with increasing radiation dose.

5-5 CONDUCTIVITY MEASUREMENTS

Thermal conductivity measurement techniques can be conveniently divided into steady-state methods, where the conductivity measurement parameters are not changing significantly with time, and into

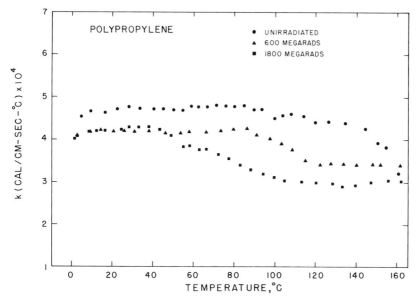

Figure 5-28. Thermal conductivity of γ-irradiated polypropylene as a function of temperature [Tomlinson and Kline(*35*)].

transient methods, where measurement parameters change rather rapidly with time. In the former it is customary to calculate the thermal conductivity of, say, a slab directly from an equation of the form

$$k = \frac{q \cdot d}{A \cdot \Delta T}$$

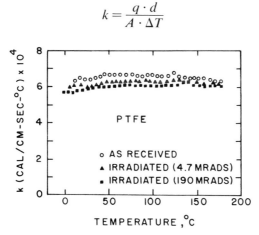

Figure 5-29. Thermal conductivity of γ-irradiated polytetrafluoroethylene as a function of temperature [Hsu *et al.*(*34*)].

where A is the area of the sample and d is the thickness. In the latter method the diffusivity α is usually the basic quantity calculated from the measurements because the thermal diffusivity is the property which determines time-dependent heat flow through the polymer material. Using the relation

$$k = \alpha \rho c_p$$

k is then deduced if α, ρ, and c_p are known. As will be pointed out in the following discussion, some types of apparatus have been designed to operate utilizing both techniques.

A. Steady-State Techniques

1. ASTM METHOD

Perhaps the best-known standard for measuring the thermal conductivity by steady-state techniques is that given by the American Society for Testing Materials (76). This method will be discussed first, then variations used by many research groups will be discussed along with some possible reasons for the variations employed.

Figure 5-30 is a diagram illustrating the basic features of the ASTM Designation C177-63 for the metal-surfaced hot plate. The heating section is composed of a round or square central heater A and similarly-shaped central surface plates B into which permanently installed thermocouples are set in grooves or just below the working surface. A guard section, composed of a guard heater C and guard surface plates D, surrounds the heating section and is isolated by a gap $\frac{1}{8}$ in. or less. The radial heat flow in the sample is minimized by adjusting the power inputs to heaters A and C such that the temperature differential between plates B and D is nearly zero. The detection system for this is required to be sufficiently sensitive to assure that the variation in conductivity due to gap temperature imbalance is restricted to less than 0.5%. Heat losses from the outer edges of the guard section and specimens are restricted by edge insulation or by governing the surrounding air temperature. Identical test specimens are placed between the central sections and the cooling units. Rigid and hard specimens are required to have parallel flat surfaces to within 0.003 in./ft, and all plates involved require similar flatness. Working surfaces of the heating unit and cooling plates are required to be smoothly finished and checked periodically for defects. Surfaces are to be treated to have a total emittance greater than 0.8 at all operating temperatures.

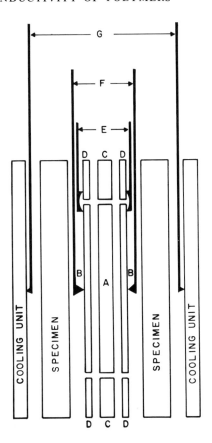

Figure 5-30. Schematic diagram for guarded hot plate cell: A, central heater; B, central surface plate; C, guard heater; D, guard surface plate; E, differential thermocouples; F, heating surface thermocouples; G, cooling unit surface thermocouples. [ASTM(76)].

A reproducible constant pressure is maintained between the plates and specimens to promote good thermal contact. The temperature differential between hot and cold plates is specified to be 10°F or more and, for good insulators, the minimum recommended gradient is 40°F/in. Fluctuations or changes in temperatures of the hot plate surfaces must not be more than 0.5% during a 1-hr test period. Temperatures of the cold plate surfaces are subject to the same limiting conditions.

Typical sample sizes can range from about 1-in. max. thickness with a central linear dimension of 4 in. and a 2-in. wide guard ring to a 4-in. max. thickness with a central linear dimension of 12 in. and a 6-in.-wide guard ring. The specification designates that, for practical purposes, the method is limited to specimens having thermal conductances of not more than 10 Btu/hr-ft^2-°F and thickness conforming to the above. It would appear that the conductance limitation would very seldom affect most polymer systems.

ASTM Designation C177-63 described above provides for accurate repeatable thermal conductivity measurements for stable polymer systems. Woodside and Wilson(77) have reported on imbalance errors in the use of guarded hot plate measurements. If the conductivity is not changing with temperature or time and contact at the specimen surfaces is adequate, the measurements are absolute; however, the rather large specified temperature differential tends to average any rapid fluctuations of material conductivity with temperature, and the stringent conditions regarding the long-time steady-state conditions for measurement tend to obscure any conductivity changes occurring as a function of time. Using this method, heat losses are minimized and can be largely accounted for and measurements can be made over a rather wide temperature range (from near −100°F to values approaching 1300°F) according to the designation.

In studies of thermal conductivity which are primarily related to research, deviations from the ASTM method are often utilized for several reasons. New and/or special polymers and related materials are typically available only in relatively small quantities and multiple specimens may be required for experiments; thus the sample size must be small. Furthermore, measurements at extreme temperatures (for instance, below liquid nitrogen or liquid helium temperatures) may be of primary interest and small samples and small over-all dimensions tend to reduce some problems associated with measurements because losses are less and the entire system may be easily enclosed by a Dewar vessel or equivalent. In studies of variations of conductivity with a given parameter, such as with regard to temperature for instance, the temperature differential must be minimized if rather rapid changes are to be detected and analyzed. This too suggests that specimens should be rather thin. Since a very large number of experimental points are desired in most research, and specimens with varying histories and treatments are of interest, it is of the utmost importance to decrease the time per measurement to a point where the over-all time required for a given experiment is manageable and practicable. Thus very large times required for equilibrium are sometimes reduced at the expense of accuracy in attaining absolute values.

2. TUBULAR GEOMETRY VARIATION

For thermal conductivity measurements of polymers above room temperature, a variation of the steady-state method reported by Kline (55) utilizes tubular samples formed from stock or molded to size. The volume of material per specimen is relatively small (~6 cc). Heat is supplied to a central copper rod by an imbedded heater and flows radially through the sample to an outside copper tube which is maintained at the desired temperature by a circulating coolant. Thermocouples in the inner and outer copper surfaces are used to measure the temperature drop across the specimen and the energy supplied to the heater is determined from voltage and current measurements.

3. PLATE METHOD FOR SMALL SPECIMENS

Eiermann and Knappe(68) and co-workers have described an apparatus in which a thin foil heater about $\frac{1}{100}$ mm is used as a resistance source to supply heat to dual samples which are about $80 \times 80 \times 3\text{-}5$ mm $(3.2 \times 3.2 \times 0.12\text{-}0.20$ in.). This sample size corresponds to ~19 cc minimum sample volume. For many polymers one can reach steady-state values to within 1% in 10 min when the power is turned on abruptly in the heater and the cold plates act as infinite heat sinks. Thus with proper controls one can obtain a reasonable number of data points per unit time in research studies. In the Eiermann and Knappe reference(68) metal blocks grip the heating foil at each end and supply electrical power evenly to the foil. Operation to satisfactory accuracy levels does not require the use of a guard ring.

Eiermann and Knappe(68) report results from −180° to +50°C which demonstrate the extreme importance of good thermal contact in obtaining reliable results, especially at lower temperatures. In another reference, Eiermann et al.(58) describe an apparatus in which the temperature rises slowly with time while thermal conductivity data are obtained. Heat input is measured by noting the rate of temperature rise of a copper disk whose mass and heat capacity are known.

Kreahling and Kline(78) have developed an apparatus similar to that of Eiermann and co-workers which utilizes samples which are typically 0.080 in. thick and 3 in. in diameter. However in this case heat is supplied by a foil which has a weaving conduction pattern etched into shape and requires only simple wire electrical connections. The temperature range is about −190° to +100°C.

4. LOW TEMPERATURE METHODS

For thermal conductivity measurements of polymers in the general range of liquid helium temperatures and above, Berman(6) has described an apparatus which utilizes relatively small samples. Powell et al.(64) also have reported an apparatus and data for use at low temperatures. In this case a relatively long sample is used and a system of guard rings is utilized along the length of the specimen to reduce losses to acceptable values. Reese and Tucker(4,51) have presented data in the helium temperature range obtained with an apparatus which has features somewhat similar to those of the Berman(6) apparatus and the Reese and Tucker(51) apparatus. Thermal contact is made with a threaded copper plug screwed into the end of the sample.

Anderson(71) has recently presented a review article on the thermal conductivity of polymers along with some discussion of apparatus. A split-bar method which may be particularly convenient for measurements of conductivity in materials with relatively large k values is noted with other various methods which are useful in certain applications. The reader is referred to the Anderson(71) paper for further details.

B. Transient Techniques

A number of investigators have reported methods for obtaining thermal conductivity data of polymers by transient techniques. Vos (73) considered heat flow characteristics in cylindrical geometry for the determination of k. Jaeger(8) considered heat conduction in an infinite region bounded internally by a circular cylinder of a perfect conductor to propose techniques for determination of k and α. In Shoulberg's(10) work, diffusivity of polymer melts were obtained in experiments involving a constant rate of temperature rise of a metal block which enclosed the samples. Techniques are also noted in the review paper by Anderson(71) and others(54,56). Chung and Jackson(48) reported a rapid, versatile, simple and inexpensive technique for the determination of the diffusivity in cylindrical geometry. For use on such materials as PMMA and rocket propellents, cylindrical samples with length-to-diameter ratios greater than 8 closely approximated infinitely long samples for test purposes. From room temperature to below steam temperatures, temperature data as functions of time were taken following an abrupt change in ambient temperature of the specimen. From these data the diffusivity was calculated. Chung and Jackson(48) emphasized that heat exchange losses with the surroundings were rather unimportant in their method and that the technique was especially valuable for badly warped or distorted samples. At a later date Hattori(*36*) also reported the usefulness of a transient method involving cylindrical geometry in the determination of diffusivity in polymers.

Harmathy(*43*) has reported on transient methods for the determination of thermal properties of solids which offer the advantage of producing a very small thermal disturbance in the material during measurement. Using flat specimens, a hot or cold pulse is applied to the surface of the sample. [A similar radial heat flow method has been described by Vasilev and Surkov(*79,80*).] By measuring the temperature–time behavior of points elsewhere in the material, data can be obtained from which k and α can be calculated. Using these and the density, the specific heat can also be deduced. Harmathy's(*43*) work is a valuable reference for previous related work by others as well.

An important part of the basic Harmathy technique is the use of a very thin foil electrical resistance heater between two flat specimens. Also, the specimens can be composed of layers of film material. When the electrical power to the heater is abruptly turned on or turned off, the heat flux to the specimens responds almost immediately because the mass of the foil can be largely neglected. In two important papers by Steere(*37,62*) further refinements of the method are presented along with conductivity, diffusivity, and specific heat data for several polymers over the approximate temperature range of $-180°$ to $+120°C$. Steere(*62*) reported the use of 0.00025 in. constant heating foil in providing a constant heat flux, the reduction of measurement time from 400 sec to 4 sec, and the application of 0.005 edge welded copper-constantan foil thermocouples. With refinements typical sample dimensions of Steere's(*62*) work might be $3 \times 6 \times 0.4$ cm, a total sample volume of 14.4 cm^3. The small sample volume is clearly an important advantage of his method.

ACKNOWLEDGMENTS

The authors are indebted to R. P. Kreahling and B. D. Washo for assistance in surveying the literature.

Research on polymer thermal conductivity at The Pennsylvania State University and at Rensselaer Polytechnic Institute has been supported by the National Aeronautics and Space Administration.

SYMBOLS

C	heat capacity per unit volume, cal/cm^3-°C
c_p	heat capacity, cal/gm-°C
k	thermal conductivity, cal/cm-sec-°C

q	heat flux, cal/cm^2-sec
T	temperature, °K or °C
t	time, sec
u	velocity of sound, cm/sec
v	specific volume
x, y, z	coordinate directions
x^*, y^*, z^*	principal axes directions
α	thermal diffusivity, cm^2/sec
β	linear thermal expansion coefficient
ρ	density, gm/cm^3
λ	phonon mean free path, cm
$\parallel$	subscript denoting direction parallel to stretching in an oriented polymer
$\perp$	subscript denoting direction perpendicular to stretching in an oriented polymer
0	as subscript denotes value for unoriented polymer
l	length, cm

REFERENCES

1. R. Berman, F. E. Simon, and R. L. Wilks, *Nature*, **168**, 277 (1951).

2. R. Peierls, *Ann. Physik*, **3**, 1055 (1929).

3. R. Berman, P. G. Klemens, F. E. Simon, and T. M. Fry, *Nature*, **166**, 864 (1950).

4. W. Reese, *J. Appl. Phys.*, **37**, 3227 (1966).

5. K. Eiermann, *Kunststoffe*, **51**, 512 (1961).

6. R. Berman, *Proc. Roy. Soc.*, **A208**, 90 (1951).

7. P. G. Klemens, *Proc. Roy. Soc.*, **A208**, 108 (1951).

8. J. C. Jaeger, *Australian J. Phys.*, **9-2**, 167 (1956).

9. H. L. Frisch and C. E. Rogers, *J. Polymer Sci.*, **C12**, 297 (1966).

10. R. H. Shoulberg, *J. Appl. Polymer Sci.*, **7**, 1597 (1963).

11. P. Lohe, *Kolloid Z. Z. Polymere*, **205**, 1 (1965).

12. A. C. Anderson, W. Reese, and J. C. Wheatley, *Rev. Sci. Instr.*, **34**, 1386 (1963).

13. K. Ueberreiter and E. Otto-Laupenmühlen, *Z. Naturforsch.*, **8a**, 664 (1953).

14. D. Hansen and C. C. Ho, *J. Polymer Sci.*, **A3**, 659 (1965).

15. D. Hansen, R. C. Kantayya, and C. C. Ho, *Polymer Eng. Sci.*, **6**, 260 (1966).

16. J. N. Tomlinson, D. E. Kline, and J. A. Sauer, *SPE Trans.*, **5**, 44 (1965).

17. A. Hennig, W. Knappe, and P. Lohe, *Kolloid Z. Z. Polymere*, **189**, 114 (1963).

18. K. Ueberreiter and S. Purucker, *Kolloid Z.*, **144**, 120 (1955).

19. R. P. Sheldon and K. Lane, *Polymer*, **6**, 77 (1965).

20. P. Lohe, *Kolloid Z. Z. Polymere*, **204**, 7 (1965).

21. H. Tautz, *Exper. Tech. Phys.*, **7**, 1 (1959).

22. K. Eiermann, *Kunststoffe*, **51**, 512 (1961).

23. K. Eiermann and K. H. Hellwege, *J. Polymer Sci.*, **57**, 99 (1962).

24. K. H. Hellwege, J. Hennig, and W. Knappe, *Kolloid Z. Z. Polymere*, **188**, 121 (1963).

25. K. Eiermann, *Kolloid Z. Z. Polymere*, **198**, 5 (1964).

26. K. Eiermann, *Kolloid Z. Z. Polymere*, **199**, 125 (1964).

27. J. Hennig, *Kolloid Z. Z. Polymere*, **196**, 136 (1964).

28. J. Hennig, *Kolloid Z. Z. Polymere*, **202**, 127 (1965).

29. J. Hennig and W. Knappe, *J. Polymer Sci.*, **C6**, 167 (1964).

30. B. D. Washo, Ph. D. Thesis, Rensselaer Polytechnic Institute, 1967.

31. K. Eiermann, *Kolloid Z. Z. Polymere*, **201**, 3 (1965).

32. K. Eiermann, *Kolloid Z. Z. Polymere*, **180**, 163 (1962).
33. R. P. Sheldon and K. Lane, *Polymer*, **6**, 205 (1965).
34. K. L. Hsu, D. E. Kline, and J. N. Tomlinson, *J. Appl. Polymer Sci.*, **9**, 3567 (1965).
35. J. N. Tomlinson and D. E. Kline, *J. Appl. Polymer Sci.* **2**, 1931 (1967).
36. M. Hattori, *Kolloid Z. Z. Polymere*, **202**, 11 (1965).
37. R. C. Steere, *J. Appl. Polymer Sci.*, **10**, 1673 (1966).
38. W. Reese, *J. Appl. Phys.* **37**, 864 (1966).
39. M. Hattori, *J. High Polymer Chem. (Japan)*, **19-201**, 32 (1962).
40. K. Eiermann, *Kolloid Z. Z. Polymere*, **198**, 5 (1964).
41. K. Eiermann, *J. Polymer Sci.*, **C6**, 157 (1964).
42. P. Lohe, *Kolloid Z. Z. Polymere*, **203**, 115 (1965).
43. T. Z. Harmathy, *J. Appl. Phys.*, **35**, 1190 (1964).
44. R. H. Shoulberg and J. A. Shetter, *J. Polymer Sci.*, **6-23**, 532 (1962).
45. W. Holzmüller and M. Münx, *Kolloid Z.*, **159**, 25 (1958).
46. Y. A. Kirichenko, B. M. Oleinik, and T. Z. Chadovich, *Inzh. Fiz. Zh., Akad. Nauk. Belorussk SSR*, **7** (5), 70 (1964).
47. W. Knappe, *Kunststoffe*, **51**, 707 (1961).
48. P. K. Chung and M. L. Jackson, *Ind. Eng. Chem.*, **46**, 2563 (1954).
49. K. Ueberreiter and S. Nens, *Kolloid Z.*, **123**, 92 (1951).
50. K. Ueberreiter and E. Otto-Laupenmühlen, *Kolloid Z.*, **133**, 26 (1953).
51. W. Reese and J. E. Tucker, *J. Chem. Phys.*, **43-1**, 105 (1965).
52. M. Hattori, *Bull. Univ. Osaka Prefecture*, **A9-1**, 51 (1960).
53. M. Hattori and O. Kamiike, *J. High Polymer Chem. (Japan)*, **15-157**, 285 (1958).
54. L. N. Cherkasova, *Zh. Fiz. Khim.*, **33**, 1929 (1959).
55. D. E. Kline, *J. Polymer Sci.*, **50**, 441 (1961).
56. K. H. Hellwege, W. Knappe, and V. Semjonow, *Z. Angew. Phys.*, **11-8**, 285 (1959).
57. L. C. K. Carwile and H. J. Hoge, *Tech. Rep.* **66-27-PR**, U.S. Army Natick Laboratories, Natick, Mass., (April 1966).
58. K. Eiermann, K. H. Hellwege, and W. Knappe, *Kolloid Z.*, **174**, 134 (1961).
59. K. Eiermann, *Kolloid Z. Z. Polymere*, **198**, 96 (1964).
60. M. Hattori, *J. High Polymer Chem. (Japan)*, **17-183**, 432 (1960).
61. R. P. Sheldon and K. Lane, *Polymer*, **6**, 205 (1965).
62. R. C. Steere, *J. Appl. Phys.*, **37**, 3338 (1966).
63. M. Hattori, *J. High Polymer Chem. (Japan)*, **19-201**, 35 (1962).
64. R. L. Powell, W. M. Rogers, and D. O. Coffin, *J. Res. NBS*, **59**, 349 (1957).
65. M. Hattori, *Kolloid Z. Z. Polymere*, **185**, 27 (1962).
66. H. Frielingsdorf, *Chem. Ingr. Tech.*, **32**, 291 (1960).
67. J. Hertz and J. F. Haskins, *Adv. Cryogenic Eng.*, **10**, 163 (1965).
68. K. Eiermann and W. Knappe, *Z. Angew. Phys.*, **14**, 484 (1962).
69. B. L. Tsetlin, L. Yanova, G. K. Sibirskaya, and P. A. Rebinder, *Proc. Acad. Sci., USSR, Phys. Chem. Sect.*, **114**, 281 (1958).
70. L. C. K. Carwile and H. J. Hoge, *Tech. Rep.* **66-49-PR**, U.S. Army Natick Laboratories, Natick, Mass., June 1966.
71. D. R. Anderson, *Chem. Rev.*, **66-6**, 677 (1966).
72. A. Schallamach, *Proc. Phys. Soc. (London)*, **53**, 214 (1941).
73. B. H. Vos, *Appl. Sci. Res.*, **A-5**, 425 (1955).
74. M. Hattori and O. Kamiike, *J. High Polymer Chem. (Japan)*, **15-156**, 215 (1957).
75. J. H. Boggs and W. L. Sibbitt, *Ind. Eng. Chem.*, **47**, 289 (1955).
76. American Society for Testing Materials, Designation C177-63.

77. W. Woodside and A. G. Wilson, *ASTM, STP*, **217**, 32 (1957).
78. R. P. Kreahling and D. E. Kline (Unpublished).
79. L. L. Vasilev and G. A. Surkov, *Inzh. Fiz. Zh., Akad. Nauk. Belorussk SSR*, **7** (6), 20 (1964).
80. L. L. Vasilev, *Inzh. Fiz. Zh., Akad. Nauk. Belorussk SSR*, **7** (5), 76 (1964).

CHAPTER **6**

Electrothermal Analysis of Polymers

D. A. SEANOR†

CHEMSTRAND RESEARCH CENTER
DURHAM, NORTH CAROLINA

6-1 INTRODUCTION

Electrothermal analysis of polymers involves the measurement of the electrical current passing through a polymer sample as a function of temperature. It is the purpose of this chapter to discuss the experimental techniques of electrothermal analysis and to review some examples of its application. That is, we are to be concerned with the kind of information which can be obtained by looking at the variation in the electrical current flowing through a polymer sample as a function of

†*Present address:* Chemical Research Laboratories, Xerox Corporation, Webster, New York.

293

temperature. This is then related to the physical or chemical processes likely to be occurring within the polymer. While these processes bear an obvious relationship to mechanisms of conduction in polymers, several reviews of semiconduction in polymers have appeared in recent years(1–8) and this subject will be only briefly touched upon. However where electrothermal analysis yields information about conduction mechanisms it will be pointed out.

Electrothermal analysis of polymers is defined as an investigation of the current flowing through the polymer sample under a fixed potential, as a function of temperature.

Since the current flowing through the sample depends upon the applied electrical potential, it is implicitly assumed that Ohm's law is obeyed. This may not be correct since space charge(9) and other electrode effects(10,11) may be present in insulators. However, for the moment we assume Ohm's law to hold, i.e.,

$$i = \frac{V}{R} = \sigma V \qquad (6\text{-}1)$$

where i amperes is the current flowing under an applied potential V volts and σ ohm^{-1} cm^{-1} is the specific conductivity equal to $1/R$ where R ohm cm is the specific resistivity. We also assume that the polymer sample has not been polarized prior to experiment. However the effects of such prior polarization, when present, can be studied systematically using the electrothermal technique.

There are three types of experiments which can be carried out:

(i) *Static Electrothermal Analysis* in which the sample temperature and the current flowing through the sample are allowed to reach equilibrium before measurement.

(ii) *Dynamic Electrothermal Analysis* in which the sample is heated under an applied potential at a predetermined rate. The current and the sample temperature are recorded simultaneously.

(iii) *Thermally Stimulated Current Analysis* in which the release of electrical charge stored in the sample is studied as a function of temperature. Electrical charge is stored within the sample at low temperatures by the prolonged application of an electric field or by illumination of the sample while under an applied potential field. Then the current is recorded while the sample is heated at a linear rate. This experiment presupposes that trapping of the charge carriers occurs and that at a particular temperature they acquire sufficient thermal energy to escape from the traps. The detrapped charge carriers are then swept out of the sample giving rise to the thermally stimulated current.

In the static electrothermal experiment(I) equilibrium effects are studied. The kinetic processes occurring as the system approaches equilibrium may also be investigated by electrical methods. In dynamic electrothermal analysis the charge carriers and the matrix are not in equilibrium. Consequently static and dynamic experiments yield different but complementary data. Each of the methods and the information they give will be discussed in relation to one another and to specific problems.

The information which can be obtained by electrothermal analysis can be related to:

(1) determination of transition temperatures and the onset of molecular motion,
(2) studies of decomposition and pyrolysis,
(3) studies of polymerization,
(4) studies of crystallization,
(5) studies of charge carrier trapping,
(6) determination of conductivity and activation energy of conduction,
(7) studies of diffusion and ionic conductivity.

It must be emphasized that interpretation of the observed phenomena is seldom unambiguous. However some effects may be observed in more than one type of experiment. For example, the onset of molecular motion may be shown by the release of trapped charge carriers in dynamic electrothermal analysis experiments, by a change in the gradient of the current-vs.-temperature curve in static electrothermal analysis experiments, and by dielectric or mechanical loss measurements. Wherever possible cross checking experiments should be carried out. Often this can be relatively simple. For example, in pyrolysis studies simultaneous electrothermal, differential thermal, and thermogravimetric analysis can be carried out on similar samples. On the other hand, electrothermal analysis is very sensitive to effects which may not be easily seen by other methods.

In studying electrical properties of materials results are generally given in terms of specific resistivity, R ohm cm, specific conductivity, σ ohm^{-1} cm^{-1} or current i amperes. These terms are simply obtained from the experimental measurement of current, applied potential, and sample dimensions shown in Fig. 6-1. Bearing in mind that the conductivity is equal to the current flowing through a 1-cm cube under a

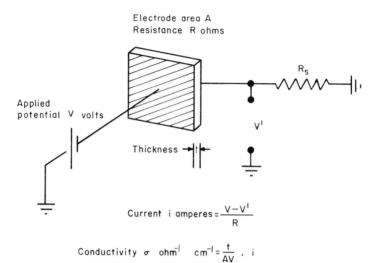

Figure 6-1.   Typical high resistance circuit with sample dimensions.

potential of 1 volt the conductivity is given by

$$\sigma = \frac{t}{AV}i \qquad (6\text{-}2)$$

Other circuit parameters of interest are R_s the series resistance, C_s the circuit capacitance, and, in measurements using amplifiers in negative feedback mode, R_f and C_f the resistance and capacitance of the feedback loop. The time constant of the circuit τ, given by $\tau = R_s C_s$, may be important. In most circuits the resistance is sufficiently small that the time constant is low and the equilibrium current is reached almost immediately after the potential is applied. However in high resistance circuits the time constant is high, and it may be many seconds before the equilibrium current is attained. This should be borne in mind when electrical circuits are being designed for dynamic electrothermal analysis, since a slowly responding circuit could cause displacement of current peaks to misleadingly high temperatures.

The conductivity is given by

$$\sigma = \sum_i q_i n_i \mu_i \qquad (6\text{-}3)$$

where q_i is the charge, μ_i cm^2 V^{-1} sec^{-1} ($\equiv$ cm/sec per V/cm) is the mobility, and n_i is the number of each charge-carrying species. The charge carriers may be ions, electrons, positive holes, or any combination of these. Usually there will be one positive charge carrier and one negative charge carrier. The term *positive hole* originated in solid-state physics where it is used to describe the absence of an electron in the valence band of the solid. In the case of solids with well-defined, long-range order, the charge carriers can remain in the conducting state for long periods of time. Most polymers, however, have no long-range order. Consequently the charge carriers can be rapidly and efficiently trapped. If the charge carrier spends most of its time in traps its motion consists of a number of thermally activated jumps or "hops" from trap to trap. On a molecular basis this is equivalent to saying that the charge carrier can hop from an ionic site to a neutral site leaving the initial site neutral and creating a new ionic site. The process may be represented as $A^+ + A \rightarrow A + A^+$ for positive holes or $B + B^1 \rightarrow B^1 + B$ for electrons. This is not the same as ionic conduction since no transfer of matter is involved.

In general it is necessary to know both μ and n for each charge-carrying species, to know how each varies with temperature and, in the case of mobility, the direction of measurement in relation to the crystal axis. We can write

$$\mu(T,z) = \mu_0 \exp\left(\frac{-E_\mu}{kT}\right) \qquad (6\text{-}4)$$

or

$$\mu(T,z) = \mu_0 T^{-n} \quad (1 < n < 3) \qquad (6\text{-}5)$$

depending upon the particular model adopted. The number of charge carriers is given by

$$n(T) = n_0 \exp\left(\frac{-E_n}{kT}\right) \qquad (6\text{-}6)$$

E_μ and E_n are activation energies of mobility and charge carrier generation, respectively.

The conductivity $\sigma(T,z)$ is given by

$$\sigma(T, z) = \sum_i q_i \mu_0 n_0 \exp\left(\frac{-E_\mu}{kT}\right) \exp\left(\frac{-E_n}{kT}\right)$$

$$= \sigma_0 \exp\left(\frac{-E_a}{kT}\right) \qquad (6\text{-}7)$$

$$\therefore E_a = E_n + E_\mu \qquad (6\text{-}8)$$

Should $E_\mu = 0$ then E_n can be easily adjusted for changes in T^{-n} as would be required for accurate calculation.

At the present time, measurements of mobility and the number of charge carriers have not been made on polymers mainly because of the experimental difficulties. This presents a major hurdle to be overcome in studies of polymers. However once this is accomplished it should be possible to relate the number of charge carriers and their mobility to properties of the polymer such as molecular structure, molecular motion, and morphology as has been done in the case of metals and semiconductors. This would be a great step forward in understanding how polymers behave and in our ability to design and synthesize materials for specific ends. Electrothermal analysis can contribute to our understanding of the conduction process and also give information not readily obtainable by other methods.

6-2 EXPERIMENTAL CONSIDERATIONS

Simply speaking, in an electrothermal analysis experiment the current passing through the sample is measured as a function of time during which the temperature is continuously changing. This means that there are four key units in any electrothermal analysis system:

(1) the sample which consists of polymer, electrodes, leads, and sample holder;

(2) the heating unit which should be designed to give a variable but linear heating rate over a wide range of temperatures;

(3) the current detector which typically should be capable of measuring currents from as small as 10^{-13} A to as large as 10^{-4} A (the power source for applying potential to the sample should be considered part of this unit);

(4) the recording unit which will record temperatures and currents (this may be an $X - Y$ recorder or a two-channel strip-chart recorder, or they may be recorded manually).

Static electrothermal systems are essentially the same as those used in dynamic electrothermal analysis. Apart from substitution of the programmed heater by a variable temperature thermostat all the problems of sample preparation, electrodes, ambient atmosphere, and current measurement are the same. A typical block diagram of an electrothermal analysis is shown in Fig. 6-2. Each part of the system will be discussed separately and the necessary precautions mentioned as the need arises.

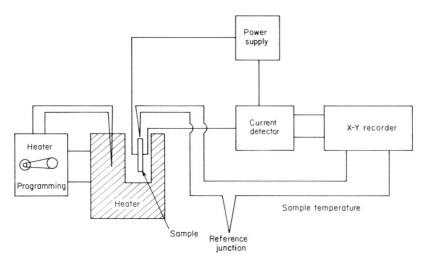

Figure 6-2. Block diagram of a typical electrothermal analysis system.

A. The Sample and Electrodes

When studying the electrical properties of materials it goes without saying that the materials themselves must be well characterized. This has not been the case in many studies of polymers. Ideally the polymer should be as well characterized as possible. The molecular weight, the molecular weight distribution, the purity, the morphology, and the thermal history should be specified. If possible the effect of variation in these parameters should be studied systematically since any of these factors may play a critical role in determining the electrical properties of a particular polymer.

The electrode–polymer interface and the preconditioning of the polymer sample play a key role in determining the electrical properties of the polymer. Good contact between the electrode and polymer must be achieved and maintained during the experiment. It is also necessary to control the atmosphere surrounding the sample.

Control of the ambient atmosphere is easily effected using conventional vacuum systems(*12*) which are routinely capable of attaining pressures of 10^{-5} Torr or less. Humidity or water vapor pressure can be controlled by alteration of the temperature of a water source or by the use of salt solutions(*13,14*).

It is often necessary to condition the samples by repeatedly heating and cooling the material under vacuum until reproducible current vs.

temperature curves are obtained(*15,16*). Any changes in conductivity during conditioning can be studied systematically with time, temperature, and ambient atmosphere as variable parameters. In this way it is possible to make a number of inferences regarding the effect of moisture loss, changes in morphology, or degradation on conductivity.

Good thermal equilibrium between the sample and heater is also required. This can be accomplished by using an inert gas atmosphere (helium) or massive copper block electrodes. The thermocouple must be sufficiently close to the sample to ensure that the temperature recorded is in fact that of the polymer. The gas surrounding the sample should in most instances be dry or of known water vapor content since the conductivity of most polymers is notoriously sensitive to traces of moisture. The most effective method of drying the gas is to pass it slowly through a liquid nitrogen trap. Measurement of electrical conductivity in air is not recommended since the adsorption of oxygen or water vapor will affect the conductivity of the polymer being studied.

The problem of electrode attachments to polymers has not been solved satisfactorily, particularly where large changes in temperature are involved. Ideally the electrical contact to the polymer should be electrically "invisible." That is, it should introduce a negligible impedance in series with the sample impedance, there should be no contact potential at the polymer–electrode interface, the electrode should not inject charge carriers, and there should be no bending of energy levels at the polymer–electrode interface. Such an ideal electrode is termed "Ohmic." An Ohmic electrode–polymer system subjected to a voltage pulse should show a current response which can be analyzed in terms of a single resistance shunted by a single capacitance. Ohmic contacts are also characterized by a linear dependence of current on applied potential over a large range of voltage. Poor contacts are manifested by irreproducible current–voltage characteristics, susceptibility to vibration, high noise level, and poor agreement between results from different samples of the same material.

While many different electrode systems have been studied(*11*) the most convenient are evaporated metal films. The coating is carried out in the same type of vacuum evaporator as is used for shadowing samples for electron microscopy. Usually the recommended technique is to clean the polymer surface and, after drying and evacuation, to evaporate a metal such as silver, gold, or chromium onto the surface. For photostimulation the thickness of the metal film can be controlled in order to allow light through the electrode onto the polymer. Our experience has shown that evaporated films do not hold too well on polymer films but are quite adequate for compressed polymer powders. At other times colloidal graphite suspensions or a liquid alloy of indium, thallium, and mercury† have been used successfully. The liquid alloy electrodes suffer from the drawback that rigid mounting is difficult to achieve. The use of silver paints using organic solvents or cellulosic bases is not recommended since modification of the surface is usually observed.

The sample may be mounted in between the lead wires using conductive epoxy cement for adhesion between the leads and evaporated metal electrodes as shown in Fig. 6-3a. Alternatively it may be held between spring-loaded metal plates as in Fig. 6-3b, or between electrodes relying on the weight of a massive metal block to ensure good electrical contact as in Fig. 6-3c. More complex systems based on

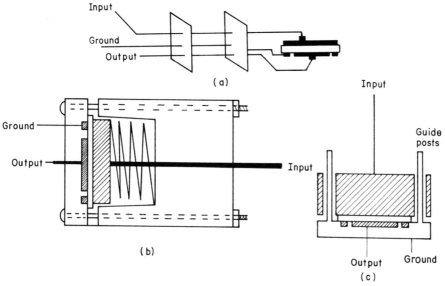

Figure 6-3. Electrode systems. (a) Simple supported sample. (b) Spring loaded. (c) Gravity maintained.

variations of these techniques can be found in the literature of organic semiconductors since each investigator tends to design his own cell. More complicated cells are required if photoeffects are to be studied since transparent conducting electrodes are required. Depending upon the spectral range to be studied the electrodes are usually made of

†Viking alloy. Victor King Laboratories, Inc., Palo Alto, California.

quartz coated with a thin layer of tin oxide (NESA) or a metal such as chromium or gold. In order to minimize surface conduction, guard rings should be used since surface currents can swamp the bulk current in certain ambient and temperature ranges. The electrodes should be frequently examined for signs of fracture and peeling because the difference in thermal expansion between the electrode and the polymer may be large. Nonadhesion of the electrode on cooling can be a serious problem and can lead to quite misleading results such as an abnormally high resistivity. Reestablishment of broken electrode contacts may also give rise to spurious effects. A high noise level would also be indicative of poor contacts. Two further complications arise in pyrolysis experiments: the products of decomposition may force the electrode away from the surface, or if the decomposition products are reactive they can combine with the electrode to create injecting or non-ohmic electrodes. There is no simple answer to these problems except to remember their existence and to minimize their effects.

The sample may be in the form of fiber, film, or a compacted disk of precipitated polymer powder. Each has its own particular problems.

In the case of fibers, contact between electrode and polymer presents serious difficulties, particularly if the sample is in the form of a yarn rather than monofilament as shown in Fig. 6-4. Surface conductivity may be much greater than the bulk conductivity and cannot be eliminated by the use of guard rings since the surface-to-bulk ratio is large. One convenient system we have used for fiber studies is shown in Fig. 6-5. This is based on a multistrip copper jumper cable. The advantage of this system is that many turns of the fiber can be used in order to boost the current to more easily detectable levels. Fibers of different denier can be used to separate the surface and bulk conductivities.

The total current i passing through the fiber consists of bulk and surface contributions, i_b and i_s, respectively, i.e.,

$$i = i_b + i_s \qquad (6\text{-}9)$$

For a given radius r and length l

$$i_b = \sigma_b \frac{\pi r^2}{l} \quad \text{and} \quad i_s = \sigma_s \frac{2\pi r}{l} \qquad (6\text{-}10)$$

where σ_b and σ_s represent the bulk and surface conductivities.

$$\therefore \frac{i}{\pi} \frac{l}{r} = \sigma_b r + 2\sigma_s \qquad (6\text{-}11)$$

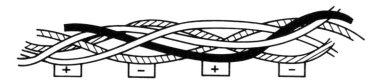

Figure 6-4. Contact problems when studying the electrical properties of yarns.

Therefore if we plot (i/r) vs. r for different diameter fibers, σ_s and σ_b can be obtained. In practice this is not as easy as it seems since there is usually a wide scatter of points.

Another commonly used technique involves the pressing of a pellet from precipitated polymer powder using a KBr pellet press. 100–200 mg of powder are required to press a pellet 1 cm in diameter and 1–2 mm thick. The pressures required to give good homogeneous pellets vary from material to material and can be discovered only by experiment. Humidity is often a key parameter when pressing pellets. Under some conditions of relative humidity the polymer may stick to the die face. The use of commercial mold-release sprays is not recommended as they may affect the polymer surface, but thin teflon sheets cut to

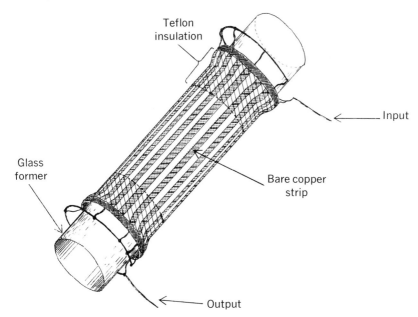

Figure 6-5. Electrode system for measurement of the electrical properties of fibres.

the size of the die often help to eliminate the problem of sticking. The conductivity may also depend upon the pressure used to press a particular pellet. This should be checked. Measurements carried out while the sample is under pressure show a strong dependence of both conductivity and activation energy of conductivity on the applied pressure($17,18$). Unless the ambient atmosphere is controlled and triboelectric and local heating effects are eliminated, the interpretation of the experiment is open to question. In some cases decomposition or further polymerization has been observed with samples under high pressure(19). Extruded or cast films present the least complicated systems to study. They have an important advantage in having a large area A and small thickness t (Fig. 6-1). This means that larger currents will be observed for a given conductivity. This is particularly helpful when studying high resistance materials.

Even in the case of films a number of elementary precautions must be observed. The thermal history of a sample may be important. If an extruded film is rapidly cooled the crystalline/amorphous ratio may be completely different to that of a slowly cooled sample. The film may be spherulitic or oxidation may have taken place. Cast films should be free from solvent. Removal of solvent can present problems particularly if high boiling point solvents such as dimethyl acetamide (DMAc) are involved. Spurious peaks may be introduced into the electrothermal analysis curves as unremoved solvent begins to evaporate. Films cast from DMAc often show a break in the vacuum electrothermal analysis curve between $140°$ and $150°C$ as solvent is lost. This can be correlated with peaks in the differential thermal analysis or thermogravimetric analysis curves. Films cast onto glass plates often have visibly different surface characteristics which may be reflected in their electrical properties by rectification phenomena. Peeling a cast film off the casting plate may create a triboelectric charge which must be dissipated before reliable measurements can be obtained. All these points can be and should be checked by independent methods such as differential thermal analysis, thermogravimetric analysis, X-ray scattering, and other techniques. They are illustrated to show the care required in sample preparation before unambiguous interpretation of the observed phenomena can be made.

B. The Heating Unit

The second key block in the electrothermal analysis system is the programmed heating unit.

In the case of the static type of experiment, temperature control presents little problem. Any type of thermostat which is capable of being controlled over a wide range of 0.02°C or better will suffice. Liquid thermostat baths or air thermostats have been used in many cases.

However for dynamic electrothermal analysis some means of varying the temperature at a linear rate is necessary. The linear rate of temperature change with time is particularly desirable if quantitative estimates of the number of trapped charge carriers or the depth of the traps are required. Not only should the change of temperature be linear with time but the rate should also be variable. Control over a wide range of temperature − say, from liquid nitrogen temperatures to 500°C − is required. Ways in which control of the heating rate can be accomplished and commercially available units have been discussed in Volume 1 of this series (20).

The most desirable unit would be a proportional current temperature controller in which the zero control may be altered at a linear rate. This minimizes electric noise associated with an on/off type of controller. The rate at which the temperature changes is altered by using different gear drives on the synchronous motor driving the controller. Electrical noise must be reduced by electrical shielding and noninductive heater coils when possible. Such systems are described in the literature (21–24) and a block diagram is shown in Fig. 6-6. When operating at low temperatures better control of the heating rate can be obtained by driving the heater against cold nitrogen evaporating from a liquid nitrogen source. If the heat capacity of the sample is small and that of the system large the heating rate can be regulated

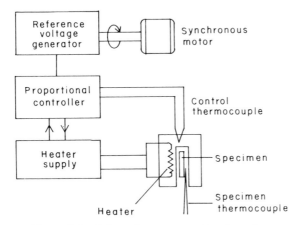

Figure 6-6. Schematic programmed heating unit.

more precisely by embedding the controlling thermocouple in a copper block to which the sample is attached. It is then desirable to use a separate thermocouple to record the sample temperature.

C. The Current Detector

The current detector should be designed to measure currents which may range from 10^{-13} to 10^{-3} A. This means that high impedance electrometers are required in the very low conductivity ranges. It is mandatory that the impedance of the measuring device be higher than that of the sample. The electrometer may be used to measure the potential drop across the sample in series with an approximately equal resistance as shown in Fig. 6-7. When used in circuits similar to Fig. 6-7 the resistance of the electrometer must be greater than the resistance of the sample R and the comparison resistance R_s. If the electrometer resistance R_E is lower than R or R_s the potential drop across the sample is a function of R_E. This must be allowed for in calculating R. At higher conductivities and low sample capacitance the circuit shown in Fig. 6-7 has the advantage of stability, speed, and freedom from noise since the amplifier operates at zero gain. The primary amplifier can be a cathode follower(25), an operational amplifier(26), or an electrometer amplifier. For still higher conductances ($10°$–10^{-5} ohm^{-1} cm^{-1}) conventional bridge methods are generally applicable(27).

If the sample resistance is high the RC time constant of the circuit is high. For a sample of resistance 10^{13} ohms cm and capacitance of 10

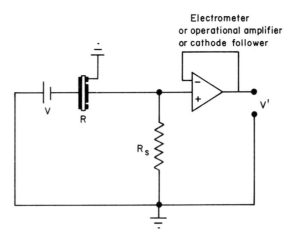

Figure 6-7. Voltage follower circuit: $V'/V = R_s/(R+R_s)$; $R = R_s(V-V')/V'$; $i = V'/R_s$.

pF the circuit time constant is $10^{13} \times 10 \times 10^{-12} = 10^2$ sec. In order to reduce the time constant of the circuit it is often more convenient to use an electrometer with an inverting output in the negative feedback mode(14). As shown in Fig. 6-8 the negative output V' is fed back through an external resistance R into the circuit at a common point A. The current in the external circuit i_f equals the current flowing through the sample i. Then we have

$$i = \frac{V}{R} = i_f = \frac{V'}{R_f} \qquad (6\text{-}12)$$

$$R = \frac{V}{V'} R_f \qquad (6\text{-}13)$$

The negative feedback system shown in Fig. 6-8 has a number of advantages for electrothermal analysis in high resistance circuits. First, the current flowing through the sample is readily obtained from the measured output voltage and the feedback resistance as in Eq. 6-12. Since the output voltage can be recorded directly changes in current are readily visualized from the recorder trace. Second, the resistance of the measuring circuit is essentially zero. This means that the response time of the circuit is limited by the electrometer characteristics rather than the RC time constant of the circuit. Third, when used in the feedback mode, the common point A in the feedback and sample circuits is virtually at ground potential. Consequently,

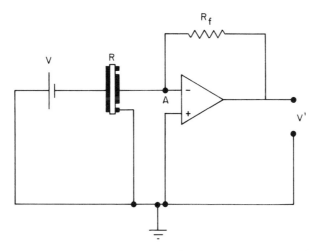

Figure 6-8. Use of feedback circuit for high resistance measurement: $i = V/R = V'/R$: $R = VR_f/V'$.

grounding of the guard ring ensures that the field lines are parallel and are also perpendicular to the input electrode. In addition there is no current flow between the guard ring and the output electrode.

One drawback of the system used in this manner is that the feedback loop consists of a series of resistors each differing by a factor of 10 over the range 10^{13}–10^{4} ohms. The electrometer output (V') is limited to a full-scale output of 10 V. Consequently, each time the current passing through the sample changes by an order of magnitude, the feedback resistor must be changed. In each decade of resistance there may be changes in zero setting of the electrometer which need to be taken into account when plotting the current vs. temperature curve. One way of avoiding this problem would be to use a logarithmic transconductor, i.e., a transistor device in which the current is an exponential function of the applied potential. When used as shown in Fig. 6-9, the potential across the feedback loop V' is a logarithmic function of the current flowing through the sample. In this case

$$V' = -E_0 \log \frac{i_s}{I_0} \qquad (6\text{-}14)$$

therefore, from Eq. (6-2)

$$V' = -E_0 \log \frac{AV\sigma}{I_0 t} s \qquad (6\text{-}15)$$

where E_0 and I_0 are characteristic parameters of the transconductor. Since σ_s is usually an exponential function of temperature (Eq. 6-8),

$$V' = E_0 \left(\frac{E_a}{2.303kT} - \log \frac{AV\sigma_0}{tI_0} \right) \qquad (6\text{-}16)$$

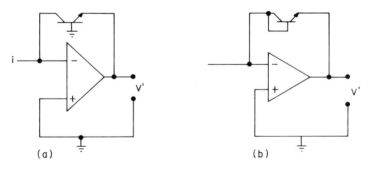

Figure 6-9.   Use of logarithmic feedback modules: (a) transdiode connection. $V' = -E_0 \log (i/I_0)$; (b) diode connection. $V' = -E_0 \log (i/I_0)(1 - 1/\beta)$.

in which E_a is the activation energy of conduction, i.e., the output should be linear in $(1/T)$. The main interest in electrothermal analysis lies in deviations from this equation. The transconductor device is particularly useful in electrothermal analysis experiments since the output can be recorded directly without any need to change the feedback resistor. The device is used at the loss of a decade or more in sensitivity in low current regions.

A number of precautionary suggestions concerning measurements in high impedance circuits can be made at this stage. First, the time constants of high resistance circuits are long. The capacitance of a normal polymer sample is about 10^{-11} F. Stray capacitances in the circuit can easily boost this by a factor of 10 unless precautions are taken to reduce them. This involves keeping the leads short and ensuring good soldered joints. Even so, time constants of the order of seconds are not unusual. The feedback system reduces the time constant since the resistance to point A of the circuit is effectively zero. Time constants of electrometers usually range from 10^{-3} sec to seconds with 10^{12} or 10^{13} ohms in the circuit. Since the sample is in fact a capacitance, there will be a transient-charging current in addition to the resistive current. The charging current becomes apparent only with high resistance samples and may persist for minutes to months. The prolonged charging current is called the dielectric absorption current. Its effect will appear in the dynamic electrothermal analysis studies of polarization. Thus after the potential is applied to a sample the current decreases because of the two contributions: the dielectric absorption current and the finite time constant of the electric circuit. Such effects are observable in static electrothermal analysis experiments. They exist in dynamic electrothermal analysis but are not readily observed. Electrical noise presents problems in making measurements of low currents or high resistances. The noise may be caused by faulty connections, pickup from electrical appliances, or ripple on power supplies. A number of precautions will help to reduce the noise level. All soldered connections should be checked — the solder must wet both parts being joined. It is essential to use shielded cables at all points, otherwise the electrical pickup from just one 40-W fluorescent lamp would swamp the electrometer. A common ground lead should be used, that is, all points to be grounded should be connected to one common lead; this also minimizes stray capacitance. The length of the leads from the power supply to the sample, from the sample output to the electrometer and the leads in the feedback loop, should be minimized. Often noise can be reduced by using battery power supplies for both the sample and amplifier. All these precautions can be taken without tremendous effort and all help to obtain more reliable measurement. Figure 6-10 shows a brass cell designed to study photoconductivity which has been successfully operated from 25° to 180°C. This cell has the amplifier attached directly to it from which the shielding has been removed to show the amplifier circuits. The sample is held by spring-loaded optically transparent electrodes as in Fig. 6-3b.

D. Commercially Available Instruments

Many amplifiers, electrometers, and power supplies are commercially available. The final selection depends upon the degree of accuracy desired, the range of conductivity to be studied, and speed of response of the electrometer necessary. However there is only one complete electrothermal analysis system on the market. This is the

Figure 6-10. Photoconductivity cell showing operational amplifier for fast response.

duPont 900 Electro-Thermal Analyzer. This instrument is designed as a plug-in unit for use with the duPont 900 Thermal Analyzer† described in Chapter 1 of Volume 1 of this series(20). The block diagram of the electrothermal analyzer is shown in Fig. 6-11. The programmed

†E. I. duPont de Nemours & Co.. Inc.. Instrument Products Division. Wilmington. Delaware.

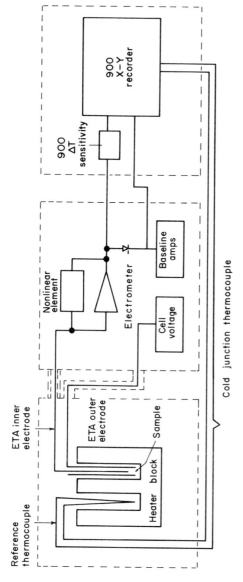

Figure 6-11. Block diagram of the duPont Electrothermal Analyzer.

311

heater and recorder are required in addition to the electrometer unit. If these units are available, considerable saving in time can be achieved by using the complete unit. However there are two drawbacks to this particular system.

First, the rather high minimum current which can be measured means that many interesting phenomena occurring at low current levels may not be observed. The low limit of detection is a consequence of the way in which the logarithmic feedback module is used. There are two ways of using the logarithmic unit, as shown in Figs. 6-9a,b. In Fig. 6-9a the unit is used in the transdiode configuration which enables smaller currents to be measured. However connections for the reversed polarity are not possible in the transdiode mode and current reversals cannot be studied. In the diode connection shown in Fig. 6-9b current reversals can be studied but there is a loss of a decade in the current which can be accurately measured. In the duPont system the lower level of conductivity has apparently been sacrificed for the versatility associated with the ability to study current reversal. For measurements on high resistance polymers this is a serious disadvantage, particularly at low temperatures. For instance, a glass transition is observed at about 110°C in nylon 66(*14,15*) where the conductivity is about 10^{-11} ohm^{-1} cm^{-1}. Consequently a meaningful current ($\sim 10^{-8}$ A) would be observed only if the surface area-to-thickness ratio of the sample were 100 or more, and in fact in Chiu's electro-thermal analysis curve for nylon 66(*24*) no such transition is observed. This brings us to the second disadvantage of the duPont electrothermal analysis system—the sample holder.

As we have discussed previously, contact between the sample and the electrodes, packing of the polymer, and conditioning of the sample are all important factors in obtaining meaningful measurements. So far none of these points has been satisfactorily solved in the duPont sample cell. This is shown in Fig. 6-12. The cylindrical cell is designed to fit in the heater block of the duPont 900 Differential Thermal Analyzer. The outer electrode is placed in the cell, the polymer is introduced, and the insulating spacer and center electrode are placed in position. The polymer is then compacted by pressing down the spacer. It is not possible to use this cell to make measurements on films.

While only one complete electrothermal analysis unit is available, there is a wide variety of components for electrothermal analysis systems on the market. The Keithley Company† has a variety of in-

†The addresses of the manufacturers cited are, respectively:
Keithley Instruments, Inc., 12415 Euclid Avenue, Cleveland, Ohio 44106

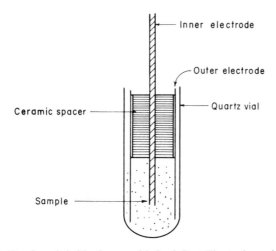

Inner electrode

Outer electrode

Ceramic spacer

Quartz vial

Sample

Figure 6-12.   Sample holder for use with the duPont Electrothermal Analyzer.

struments ranging from picoammeters to versatile high impedance electrometers. The Keithley 610 and 603 electrometers are very frequently used instruments. For very high resistance samples the Cary Vibrating Reed electrometers are useful.† Many companies, of whom Kepco† and Sorenson† are well known, have stabilized power supplies available, the price depending on the range of potential, ac ripple, and current desired. In the long run it is more satisfactory to buy the separate units and to design an in-house sample holder since no commercially available sample holder will adequately cover the wide temperature range desired. In this way many of the potential pitfalls can be minimized.

Many recorders are also available, depending upon the time scale involved. $X–Y$ recorders give traces which are perhaps the easiest to interpret, particularly if they incorporate a wide range of full scale readings. However it is often necessary to plot $\log i$ vs. T or $\log i$ vs. $1/T$ so that unless the logarithmic feedback loop is incorporated into the electrometer circuit, considerable computation may be involved. In this case a two-channel strip chart recorder would be adequate. On occasions more information can be obtained from the differential curve of di/dT or di/dt. The di/dt may be calculated graphically or

Cary Instruments, 2724 South Peck Road, Monrovia, California 91016
Kepco, 131–38 Sanford Avenue, Flushing, New York 11352
Raytheon Company, Sorenson Operation, Richards Avenue, Norwalk, Connecticut 06856

electronically if desired. Commercial units for differentiation are available but the noise level of the imput signal must be low. Suitable electronic modules for differentiation, logarithmic feedback units, and current-measuring devices are readily obtainable from the manufacturers of operational amplifiers.†

6-3 TYPES OF EXPERIMENTS AND THEIR INTERPRETATION

Electrothermal analysis can be used to investigate a number of different but often related phenomena. In particular we will discuss:

(a) Pyrolysis and decomposition of polymers by electrothermal analysis. This can be correlated to thermogravimetric analysis, differential thermal analysis, and studies of gas evolution from the polymer. However electrothermal analysis is more sensitive to small changes than most of the other techniques. This gives the technique a definite advantage in sensitivity if the correct interpretation of the observed phenomena can be made.

(b) Transition temperatures. In many cases electrothermal analysis will enable studies of glass transitions to be made, particularly of copolymers. It is quite a sensitive technique for detecting glass transitions and can be used in conjunction with dielectric and mechanical measurements. Smaller samples can be studied and measurements can be made at high pressures.

(c) Depolarization phenomena and electrets can be studied by electrothermal analysis which can again give some information about molecular rotation and glass transitions.

(d) Charge-carrier trapping and detrapping and their relationship to molecular structure.

Applications of static electrothermal analysis which will be mentioned but not discussed at length are:

(a) Studies of kinetics under isothermal conditions — polymerization, crystallization, decomposition, adsorption, and desorption. In some of

†Details of operational amplifiers, logarithmic feedback modules, and other components may be obtained from
Nexus Research Laboratory, Inc., 480 Neponset Street, Canton, Massachusetts 02021
Analog Devices, 221 Fifth Street, Cambridge, Mass. 02142
Burr-Brown Research Corporation, International Airport, Industrial Park, Tuscon, Arizona 85706
Philbrick Researches, Inc., Allied Drive at Route 128, Dedham, Massachusetts 02026

these cases ETA will give information which is hard to obtain in other ways.

(b) Conductivity and activation energy of conductivity, non-ohmic behavior, and photoconduction. In fact all the techniques necessary to understand the conduction process could be classified under this heading.

(c) Studies of diffusion and ionic conductivity can also be made in order to understand such factors as local viscosity (as opposed to microscopic viscosity).

A. Pyrolysis

Studies of pyrolysis provide an excellent example of the way in which electrothermal analysis supplements other methods of analysis and of how the technique can be used to detect changes which are too small to be seen by more conventional methods. The pyrolysis of polymers has been studied for many years in order to understand thermal degradation or to produce semiconducting organic materials(2.28–32). It is also reviewed in Chapter 1 of this volume. Most materials which have been studied appear to go through a number of well-defined stages. There is an initial loss in weight and increase in unsaturation as shown in Fig. 6-13. The first stage is accompanied by a decrease in resistivity (33) and an increase in the electron spin resonance signal(34). The

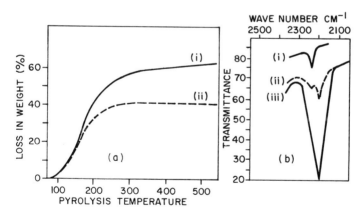

Figure 6-13. (a) Weight loss of poly-α-chloracrylonitrile as a function of pyrolysis temperature: (i) observed (ii) calculated from chlorine content. (b) Increase in infrared absorption due to $+CH=C+_n$
$$\text{CN}$$
as chlorine is lost: (i) 40.2% Cl (ii) 30.3% Cl (iii) 1.6% Cl. [After Kubishiro et al.(39)].

electron spin resonance increases to a maximum for a pyrolysis temperature in the region of 600°C (*35,36*) as shown in Fig. 6-14. As the temperature of pyrolysis increases the resistivity and activation energy of conductivity continue to decrease, ultimately approaching those of graphite as shown in Fig. 6-15 (*37–39*). These changes are accompanied by weight losses up to about 1000°C, above which temperature graphitization begins to take place with no further reduction in weight.

It is suggested that the loss of more thermally unstable groups leads to both broken σ bonds and to conjugation. The broken σ bonds give rise to the electron spin resonance signal. As the number of broken σ bonds increases they eventually begin to react with each other to form new covalent bonds. At higher temperatures this is accompanied by the motion of large segments of the polymer to form extensive networks of conjugated double bonds and aromatic rings. This may also involve the simultaneous breaking and reformation of covalent bonds in order, as these processes take place, to decrease the free energy of the system.

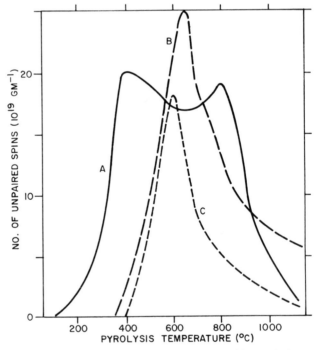

Figure 6-14. The variation of esr signal of polymers with pyrolysis temperature: A. polyvinylidine chloride; B. polyfurfuryl alcohol; C. polyvinyl chloride. [After C. Jackson and W. F. K. Wynne-Jones (*36*).]

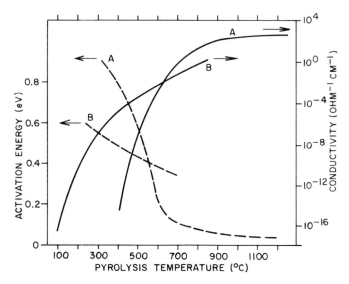

Figure 6-15. The effect of heat treatment on the conductivity and the activation energy of polymers: A. petroleum cokeo (37,38); B. poly α chloracrylonitrile (39).

As the extent of conjugation and aromatization increases, charge-carrier creation becomes easier and the charge carriers can move through the system more easily. In this way the conductivity increases and the activation energy of conductivity decreases with increasing pyrolysis temperature.

Generally this type of pyrolysis experiment has been carried out under static conditions, particularly when other experiments are involved. The static measurement is usually an experimental necessity since dynamic measurements are not feasible. For instance the effect of dehydrochlorination on the length of conjugated chains in poly(α-chloracrylonitrile) has been studied spectrophotometrically (39) and correlated with the loss in weight on pyrolysis. The dielectric constant (40) and activation energy of conduction have each been studied in static systems. The sample being pyrolyzed is allowed to reach equilibrium before the measurement is made. Few kinetic studies of pyrolysis have been made by either electrothermal analysis or thermogravimetric analysis.

Simultaneous or complementary electrothermal and thermogravimetric measurements have enabled the course of pyrolysis to be followed and interpreted in a meaningful way. For instance the pyrolysis of polyacrylonitrile is thought to occur in two steps.

$$\text{CH}_2\text{—CH(CN)—CH}_2\text{—CH(CN)—CH}_2\text{—CH(CN)} \xrightarrow[\text{Step 1}]{200°C} \text{CH}_2\text{—CH(C=N)—CH}_2\text{—CH(C=N)—CH}_2\text{—CH(C=N)}$$

$$\text{Step 2} \Big\downarrow \quad 350°C \text{ or } O_2$$

Step 1 occurs with the little loss of weight or change in conductivity, but a decrease in the —CN absorption and the appearance of IR bands corresponding to —C=N— are observed. Step 2 occurs with the loss of hydrogen and is accompanied by large changes in both σ and E. The values of σ and E are very dependent upon the pyrolysis temperature (41–43).

Similarly the pyrolysis of polyvinylidene chloride has been explained in terms of the two-stage elimination of HCl combined with cross-linking and coalescence of aromatic rings (33). While the mechanisms of degradation are plausible they are obviously oversimplified since they leave no room for broken σ bonds.

$$\xrightarrow[\text{heat}]{\text{—HCl}} \qquad \xrightarrow[\text{heat}]{}$$

$$\xleftarrow[\text{heat}]{\text{—HCl}}$$

Bruck(*44*) has studied aromatic polyimides by similar techniques, making measurements of the electron spin resonance, conduction, weight loss, density, and composition to give him an insight into the degradation processes. He found that in the region of maximum ESR signal (575°–620°C) there was a sharp increase in conductivity and density but little weight loss. This he related to internal rearrangement within the pyrolyzed material. The rearrangement was calculated to have an activation energy of 25 kcal/mole. A mechanism of degradation was proposed. However all these measurements (apart from the thermogravimetric experiments) have been in static systems. Dynamic electrothermal measurements have been made of some decomposition reactions and have proved to be extremely sensitive to small changes.

Pope(*45*) has carried out dynamic ETA experiments on coals and unplasticized polyvinyl chloride. His solution to the problems of removing gases from the sample and the electrodes was to use a relatively thick sample and blow dry nitrogen through the pyrolysis cell(*46*). His results on coals are shown in Figs. 6-16 and 6-17. The significant points are (1) the detail which is present in the curves and (2) the way in which the detail is enhanced by plotting the derivative (*di/dT*) against temperature. The observable detail enabled differences between coals to be characterized. When used in conjunction with other methods a fairly good interpretation of the carbonization mechanism was possible(*47*). This involved the loss of water at low temperatures, the loss of low molecular weight alkyl aromatic compounds between 150° and 350°C. The onset of primary carbonization

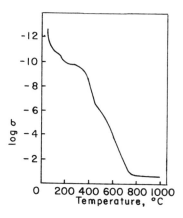

Figure 6-16. The logarithm of conductivity of Markham black shale plotted as a function of temperature of carbonization. [After Pope(*45*).]

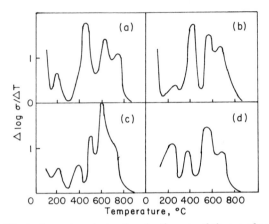

Figure 6-17. Electrothermal analysis of coals: the rate of change of conductivity with temperature of variously treated Markham black shales ($d \log \sigma/dT$) plotted as a function of temperature: (a) untreated. (b) methylated. (c) dehydrogenated. and (d) brominated. [After Pope(*45*).]

occurred between 400° and 500°C. Above 600°C peripheral material such as $-CH_3$ and $-H$ was lost and the condensation of aromatic nuclei took place growing into sheets similar to but smaller than those in graphite. These reached their steady state at about 800°C and little structural change occurred above 1000°C. This fits in with our previous picture with the maximum ESR signal at about 600°C and the major weight loss occurring between 400° and 500°C with its associated decrease in resistance.

It was also possible to detect the changes in carbonization brought about by chemical reaction as shown in Fig. 6-17.

The same technique was also applied to unplasticized polyvinyl chloride. Figure 6-18a shows $\log \sigma$ plotted against temperature while Fig. 6-18b shows the differential plot $d(\log i)/dT$ vs. temperature. Once again the detail showing up in the differential plot is considerably more than in the original curves. These curves indicate a two-stage reaction in agreement with other work(*48*). Stage I is endothermic accompanied by the loss of HCl only(*49*). Stage II is an exothermic reaction(*33*) accompanied by the evolution of simple hydrocarbons. Above 500°C hydrogen is the predominant product of decomposition.

Other examples of dynamic electrothermal analysis carried out by Chiu(*24*) have shown the sensitivity of the technique when compared with other techniques such as differential thermal analysis or thermogravimetric analysis, particularly if the derivative di/dT or $d(\log i)/dT$ is

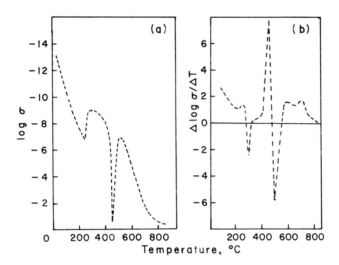

Figure 6-18. Dynamic electrothermal analysis of unplasticized polyvinyl chloride: (a) Log conductivity vs. temperature; (b) $(d \log \sigma / dT)$ vs. temperature. [After Pope (45).]

used. In Chiu's original paper (24) a number of curves were shown in which there was no indication of anything unusual in the differential thermal analysis curve. Figure 6-19 shows the differential thermal analysis and electrothermal analysis curves for the glass beads

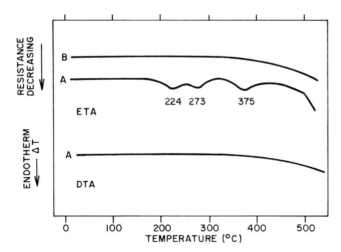

Figure 6-19. Differential thermal analysis and dynamic electrothermal analysis of glass beads : A, initial curves; B, after heating. [After Chiu (24).]

commonly used as references for differential thermal analysis. The differential thermal analysis curve shows no sign of any unusual occurrence whereas three peaks are observed in the electrothermal analysis curve. Since these have disappeared on reheating it is supposed that they were caused by the volatilization of impurities in the glass beads not detectable by other methods. Similarly the electrothermal analysis curve for an aromatic polyimide film (Fig. 6-20) shows that a considerable change in electrical conductivity starts at 280°C. The differential thermal analysis curve shows that about 2% weight loss occurs on heating between 270° and 400°C. The break is thus associated with the slight amount of decomposition. However it is hard to see why there is no exponential increase in current observed in the second experiment unless the current is below the limit of detection. Our experience with similar high resistance materials has been that decreases in conductivity do occur on thermal cycling (presumably caused by loss of solvent). However in repeated experiments the conductivity increases reproducibly with temperature to values of 10^{-9} ohm^{-1} cm^{-1} at about 350°C. Amborski's data(50) indicate that similar behavior is observed in *H*-film* another aromatic polyimide. However these results do show the sensitivity and broad applicability of the electrothermal technique to studies of pyrolysis.

B. Determination of Glass Transition Temperatures

Most amorphous polymers undergo a glass transition during which changes in the temperature coefficients of various physical properties

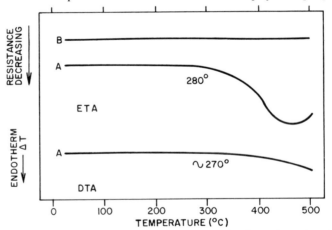

Figure 6-20. Differential thermal analysis and dynamic electrothermal analysis of polyimide films: A, initial curves; B, after heating. [After Chiu(24).]

*Trade Mark: E. I. du Pont de Nemours & Co., Inc.

associated with the free volume take place. Usually there is no abrupt change in volume or thermodynamic properties and no latent heat is associated with the transition. This is in contrast to a first-order transition with which discontinuous thermodynamic properties are associated. One way of defining the glass transition temperature T_g is that temperature below which the main-chain configurations are "frozen in." The T_g is the temperature above which the low frequency motions of the main chain can be observed. Usually the glass transition is studied thermodynamically or by mechanical and dielectric methods. Many of these techniques have been discussed in other chapters of this series. Electrothermal analysis presents yet another method of studying glass transition temperatures.

The term "electrothermal analysis" was originally used by Warfield (7) in relation to his studies of the steady-state current passing through polymers as a function of temperature. In his work (51,52) changes in the slope of the log σ vs. $1/T$ curves were used to indicate the transition temperature. Some of his typical curves are shown in Fig. 6-21. It is generally observed that the activation energy of conductivity is lower at temperatures above the glass transition temperature. This

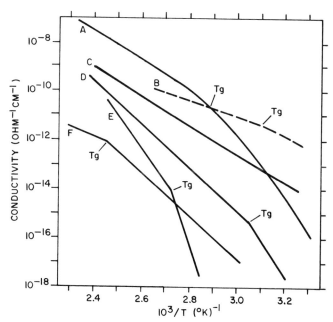

Figure 6-21. Static electrothermal analysis curves of various resins indicating T_g by the change in gradient curve: A. polyamide epoxide; B. polyurethane; C. diallyl phthalate; D. epoxide; E. epoxide; F. polyester. [After Warfield (51).]

observation has often been used to infer that ionic conduction takes place above the glass transition temperature, particularly if the activation energy of conduction is above 0.5 eV (53). Eley and Spivey (16) have obtained the glass-transition temperature of a series of polyamides given in Table 6-1 using static measurements to obtain T_g.

TABLE 6-1
Glass Transition Temperatures Obtained by Electrical
Methods

Polyamide	E_2 (eV)[a]	E_1 (eV)	R 400. ohm cm.	T_g. °C
45	1.83–2.89	1.14	3.8×10^9	112
47	1.84–2.96	1.17	3.0×10^9	111
48	1.96–2.43	1.13	2.6×10^9	116
49	2.34–3.05	1.06	1.9×10^8	100
410	1.68–2.22	1.12	3.7×10^9	111
2Me66	2.18–3.06	1.07	6.5×10^8	101
66	1.95–2.64	1.12	2.6×10^{10}	115
68	2.05–2.80	1.17	1.6×10^9	98
69	2.31–3.01	1.08	2.2×10^8	91
610	2.20–2.96	1.27	8.1×10^8	82
Polyglycine		2.99/2	3.5×10^{13}	

[a]Upper and lower limits given.

The alternative method using dynamic electrothermal analysis can also give some indications of the glass transition temperature, although the precise temperature at which changes are observed depends upon the rate at which the sample is heated.

Shim(54) has reported anomalous breaks in the current vs. temperature curves for a number of polymers and copolymers. These were often observed in temperature regions at which the glass transition was obtained by other methods. Two of his curves for polyvinyl butyral and polyvinyl acetate are shown in Fig. 6-22.

Table 6-2 shows his results compared with literature values of the transition temperature. Some of his curves showed increases in the current followed by decreases in the neighborhood of the glass-transition temperature. This was probably caused by polarization of the sample at low temperatures. As the polymer was taken through the glass-transition temperature the trapped charge was released causing the current increase.

Somewhat similar phenomena have been reported for nylon 66 (55) preirradiated with UV light at 25°C. On heating, the anomalous

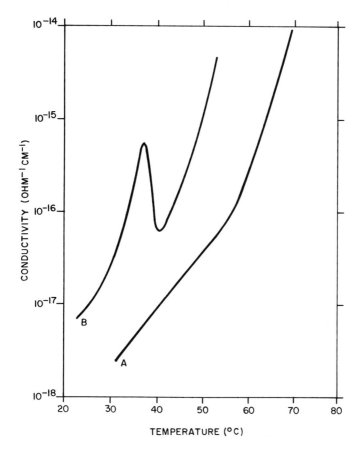

Figure 6-22. Dynamic electrothermal analysis curves of: A, polyvinylbutral; B, poly-vinylacetate. [After Shim(*54*).]

current decrease shown in Fig. 6-23 was observed. Preirradiation at 52°C gave rise to a current decrease at 69°C. These results show that anomalous effects are observed at temperatures of 35°, 48°, and 70°C which correspond closely to temperatures at which breaks in the log σ vs. T curves are observed(*14,56*) and to transition temperatures recorded by Billmeyer(*57*). It is suggested that irradiation creates or fills traps within the polymer. As the state of the polymer changes the trapped charges become mobile and recombine causing a decrease in current.

Experiments involving trapping and detrapping of charge carriers

TABLE 6-2
Glass Transition Temperatures (T_g) and Electrical Behavior in Region of T_g (54)

Polymer	T_g, °C Expt.	T_g, °C Lit.	Activity	Transition zone °C
PMMA	104	105	Sharp inflection	104
PVButyral	50	49	Gradual inflection	50–59
PStyrene	85	100	Inflection	85
PVAc	28	29	Inversion, 37°C	28–40
85/15 VCL-VAc	58	59	Inversion, 65°C	58–69
PEMA	47	47, 65	Inversion, 51°C	47–61
PBMA	20	21	Inversion, 20°C	20–31
PIBMA	42	48	Inversion, 52°C	42–60
2/1 MMA-ST	104	103	Inversion, 103°C	103–110
92/8 VCL-VAc	52, 64	67	Step	52–70
Plasticized PMMA	−15	—	Step	−15–+3

similar to those above are also important in the next two applications of electrothermal analysis—the study of electrets and charge-carrier trapping, and determination of the role played by molecular structure and molecular motion in these phenomena.

C. Electrets

If a dielectric material such as a polymer is heated to above its glass transition and then cooled under an applied potential field the result is a permanently polarized dielectric. That is, the material has acquired a more or less permanent electric field at its surface. The slab of polarized dielectric is called an electret. In the electret state the material has a number of uses such as reducing static in electrical instrumentation, providing permanent electric fields, and in electro-photography. Electrothermal analysis can be used to analyze the decay of charge from the electret under isothermal or dynamic conditions. Usually studies of depolarization are carried out as the sample is heated after it has been polarized. Studies of the reverse effect, polarization during cooling, do not appear to have been made. The cause of this probably lies in a sharp decrease in current which would be expected with the onset of polarization.

Two good reviews of electrets have been published. The first, *Photoelectrets and the Electrophotographic Process*, deals with the development and use of electrets up to 1960(*58*). The second publica-

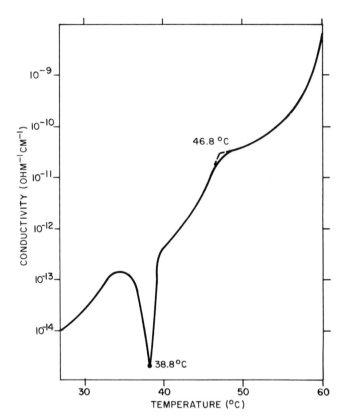

Figure 6-23. Anomalous dark conductivity in nylon 66 after irradiation at 25°C. [After Pilling (55).]

tion is a collection of research papers presented at the Electrochemical Society Meeting in October 1967 (59).

The electret state is thought to be made up of two types of polarization—the "homocharge" and the "heterocharge." The homocharge consists of trapped charge carriers whereas the heterocharge is caused by the alignment of the permanent dipoles under the electric field or by ionic migration. Studies by electrothermal analysis can prove very useful in determining how the electret is formed and the relative part played by charge carrier trapping or dipole alignment in creating the electret. Short-lived increases in current would be anticipated as the trapped charge carriers were released. Disalignment of the oriented dipoles should give rise to a higher effective potential field, and so a larger current should be observed. While studies have been carried out on organic materials(*60,61*) few experiments have been made on polymers. The observations of Shim(*54*) and Pilling(*55*) described in the preceding section are obviously related to the topic of electret discharge. Miller and Murphy(*62*) have studied the depolarization of electrets formed from polystyrene, poly(methyl methacrylate), and copolymers of styrene and various acrylates. They found that the greatest release of charge on heating their previously polarized materials occurred in the neighborhood of the glass-transition temperature. Typical electrothermal analysis curves are given in Fig. 6-24 and details of their results in Table 6-3. The total stored charge was estimated by integrating the area under the peak. Typically this was 10^{-9} to 10^{-8} C/cm^2 for samples some $\frac{1}{2}$-mm thick. They also mention that in poly(methyl methacrylate) and styrene/methyl methacrylate copolymers, two peaks were usually observed in the electrothermal analysis curve. The peak occurring at the lower temperature was related to the glass transition which could be observed in differential thermal analysis experiments. However the second peak was observed when the sample began to soften and there was no corresponding peak in the differential thermal analysis curves.

Thus it seems that increases in current are observed in the region of the glass-transition temperature but further studies are required before a differentiation between charge-carrier detrapping and dis-alignment of the dipole can be made. One way of carrying out experiments to do this will become apparent in the next section which deals exclusively with charge-carrier trapping.

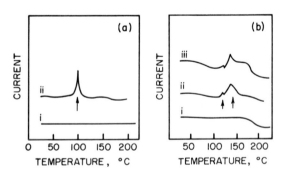

Figure 6-24. Dynamic electrothermal analysis curves of electrets: (a) polystyrene (i) before and (ii) after electret formation; (b) poly(methyl methacrylate) (i) before polarization (ii) polarized by cooling under potential (iii) polarized by deformation. [After Miller and Murphy(*62*).]

TABLE 6-3

Glass Transition Temperatures Estimated from Depolarization Curves for
Copolymers of Styrene (M_1) and a Second Monomer (M_2) (62)

Monomer M_2	Proportion M_2, wt%	T_g of Homopolymer of M_2, °C.	T_g of Copolymer, °C		ΔT_g, °C.
			From depolarization curve	Computed[a]	
4-Chlorostyrene tert-	20	110	103	97	6
butylacrylate	50	40	68	66	2
Methyl α-chloroacrylate	30	120	103	110	−7
Methyl methacrylate	40	105	80	76[b]	4
Poly(methyl methacrylate)	100	105	100–110	100	−5–4
Polystyrene	100	93	99	93	6

[a]On the basis of a value for T_g (polystyrene) of 93°C and assuming a linear relationship between T_g and composition.
[b]Measured by differential thermal analysis.

D. Studies of Charge-Carrier Trapping by Electrothermal Analysis (Thermally Stimulated Currents or Conductivity Glow Curves)

Most polymers contain polar groups at some point in the backbone chain. In addition they are usually disordered and little long-range order is observed. The effect of the polar groups and disorder is to provide many points at which charge carriers (holes, electrons, or ions) can be trapped. The relationship between the number of traps and the energy required to escape from the traps to the physical and molecular structure of the polymer is of great interest. However this is still a relatively unexplored field of research in polymers since it has only recently been acknowledged that trapping could play an important role in determining the electrical properties of polymers(4,63). There are a number of ways of attacking the problem of trapping, such as studying space-charge-limited currents(9), studying the decay characteristics of transient charge pulses(64), observing the transient current on reversal of potential(65), and studying the thermal- or radiation-stimulated release of trapped charges(66). Study of the thermal release of trapped charge carriers presents another application of dynamic electrothermal analysis.

The technique consists of cooling the sample to low temperatures (90°K), creating and trapping the charge carriers either by illumination (67,68) or prolonged application of potential(69), and measuring the current as the temperature of the sample increases. The method is the electrical analog of the thermoluminescent glow curve technique frequently used when studying trapping and electroluminescence in inorganic semiconductors(70–72). It is assumed that at a certain temperature a trapped charge carrier acquires sufficient thermal energy to escape from the trap and contributes to the current flowing through the sample. The fate of the charge carrier will depend upon the number and state of the traps still remaining in the solid. It may be retrapped, it may be swept out of the sample. or it may recombine with a trapped charge carrier of opposite sign. The last process is often accompanied by the emission of light of a characteristic wavelength corresponding to the depth of the trap. or in the case of organic molecules to an excited molecular state. The current measured in such an experiment, which is in excess of the normal dark current, is called the "thermally stimulated current." Considerable information can be extracted from the thermally stimulated current vs. temperature curve.

(a) The depth of the trap (or the energy required to escape from the trap) can be obtained from the temperature at which the thermally stimulated current is at its maximum level. The trap depth may also be obtained from the initial rate of detrapping, i.e., the initial rise in thermally stimulated current vs. temperature curve.

(b) The number of traps can be obtained from the area under the thermally stimulated current vs. time.

(c) The capture cross section of the trap can be obtained from the detailed shape of the thermally stimulated current.

However the precise interpretation of the data is difficult and there is considerable discussion in the literature of inorganic semiconductors as to the detailed meaning of this type of experiment. In many cases thermally stimulated current curves alone cannot distinguish between different models(73), although claims are often made in which theoretical curves for a particular model have been fitted to the experimental data(74–77).

At the present time it is suggested that the Garlick–Gibson method, in which the activation energy of the initial rise in the thermally stimulated current is equated to the trap depth, is the most reliable method of obtaining the depth of the trap. A variant of this method which is particularly useful when using the Garlic–Gibson approach is the decayed thermally stimulated current method. A preliminary heating is used to partially empty the trap and completely remove all traps of lower energy(75). Schematic thermally stimulated current curves obtainable in this way are shown in Fig. 6-25.

The Garlick–Gibson method of analysis assumes that both retrapping and recombination can take place(68). It is assumed that there are N traps within the solid of which n are filled at any given instant. Therefore there will be $(N-n)$ empty traps and n recombination centers. The current at any time is then determined by the rate at which the charge carriers escape from the traps minus the fraction which are

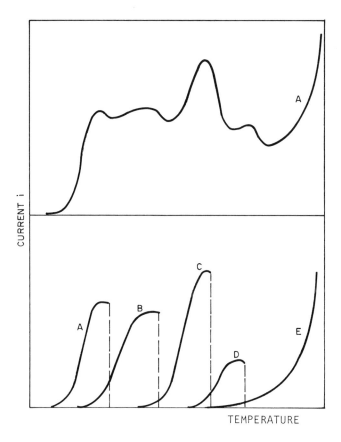

Figure 6-25. Schematic dynamic electrothermal glow curves and "cleaned" glow curves: A, initial curves; B–E, cleaned curves.

retrapped or which recombine, i.e.,

$$i_{stim} = -\frac{dn}{dt} = \frac{n^2}{N} s \exp\left(\frac{-E}{RT}\right) \tag{6-17}$$

where $s \exp(-E/RT)$ is the probability per unit time that an electron escapes from its trap of depth E. For a uniform rate of temperature increase β

$$i_{stim} = -n_0{}^2 s \exp\left(\frac{-E/kT}{N}\right)\left[1 + \frac{n_0}{N}\int^T \frac{s\exp(-E/kT)\,dT}{\beta}\right]^2 \tag{6-18}$$

where n represents the initial trap filling.

The characteristics of thermally stimulated current curves when analyzed in this way show the following:

(a) For fixed s, N_0, and β the maximum current is observed at a temperature proportional to the trap depth E.

(b) For fixed values of E and N_0 the temperature of maximum current varies with s and with β.

(c) The area under the i_{stim} vs. temperature curve is proportional to N_0. This assumes that all the released charge reaches the electrodes.

(d) The initial increase in thermally stimulated current is given by

$$i_{stim} = \left(\frac{n_0{}^2}{N}\right) s \exp\left(\frac{-E}{RT}\right) \tag{6-19}$$

from which the trap depth E can be obtained.

The model used assumes that retrapping and recombination take place and that a single trapping level exists. Simpler(67) or more complicated models(76) have been discussed but from our point of view the Garlick–Gibson model suffices.

While the thermally stimulated current technique has been applied to a number of organic compounds(69,78) particularly anthracene (78–81), its application to polymers has been rather limited. Some similar types of experiment have been mentioned in the discussion of electrets and glass-transition temperatures. The only reported study on polymers is a rather sketchy report by Sysmanski and Kryszewski(82) on the thermally stimulated currents observed in p-polyphenyl. Values of the trap depth and the number of traps are given in Table 6-4.

One application of the glow curve method of analysis in polymers has been in the study of the thermoluminescence of polyethylene(83–85). No studies of the thermally stimulated current have been reported although polyethylene would seem to be an excellent material

TABLE 6-4

Characteristics of p-Poly Phenyls (82)

Substance:	p-Terphenyl		p-Quaterphenyl		p-Polyphenyl	
Characteristic	Crystal	Layer	Crystal	Layer	In polystyrene	In p-terphenyl
Thickness t	15μ	20μ	20μ	5μ	40μ	65μ
No. of Traps[a]	6×10^{14}	—	3×10^{13}	3×10^{15}	—	—
E_T, eV[b]	—	0.5	—	0.2	0.6	0.02–0.08
		1.1–1.7		0.7–1.0		0.3–0.6
E_a, eV[c]	1.0	1.15	—	0.83	0.35^d	0.6
					0.70^e	

[a]Calculated from current–voltage characteristics.

[b]Calculated from thermally stimulated current curves by the Garlick-Gibson method (68).

[c]Calculated from the $\log i$ vs. $(1/T)$ curves.

[d]Low temperature range.

[e]High temperature range.

with which to work, since its conductivity may well be trap-limited (4,86,87). It has been suggested that the polymer chains could act as traps and that the multiple thermoluminescent peaks are caused by different degrees of molecular motion in different structural regions of the polymer(88). On irradiation, photoionization of "luminescence-centers" takes place. At low temperatures the ejected charge carrier, presumably an electron, is trapped in a polar region of the polymer which may be a dipole, an impurity, or a region of strain within the polymer chain. On warming the sample, segments of the polymer begin to move releasing the trapped charges. If this is the case then it must be concluded that the release of trapped carriers is associated with molecular motion rather than thermal detrapping. This is certainly in agreement with the studies of electret depolarization previously discussed in which there was a close correspondence of peaks in the electrothermal analysis curves and glass-transition temperatures. If this conclusion is correct then the value of the activation energy obtained from T_{max} in the glow curve has little meaning in terms of a trap depth. The T_{max} is more likely to be related to the onset of a molecular motion. However a study of the initial rise in current (Garlick–Gibson method) should give some indication of the trap depth. The conclusion that the onset of molecular motion is responsible for major peaks in the electrothermal curve suggests that normal conduction may also be controlled by molecular motion, a suggestion previously hinted at(*3*) but not yet substantiated. It still remains to be proven which mechanisms control the conductivity and electrothermal properties. Electrothermal analysis combined with light-stimulated detrapping experiments could give clear indications of the factors involved.

E. Other Applications of Static Electrothermal Analysis

Other applications of static electrothermal analysis have been mentioned in passing. Essentially they measure approaches to equilibrium, i.e., they are rate processes and no detailed discussion will be given. Activation energies of the processes can be obtained by studying the rate of the process at different temperatures. Among the studies which have been made are (1) studies of polymerization and curing kinetics (*7,52,88–91*), (2) studies of crystallization and spherulitic formation (*92–95*), (3) adsorption and desorption kinetics(*96*), and (4) plasticization(*97*). These processes are of great importance in understanding the electrical behavior of polymers but a detailed discussion is beyond the scope of this chapter.

6-4 SUMMARY

In summary, we can say that the technique of electrothermal analysis has led to the observation of very interesting phenomena, some of which cannot be observed by other techniques. We can also say that its use as a technique to improve our understanding of the basic phenomena involved in charge transfer through polymers will also increase. While there are experimental difficulties associated with the method there are ways in which they can be overcome and meaningful results can be obtained.

REFERENCES

1. J. E. Katon (ed.), *Semiconducting Organic Polymers.* Marcel Dekker, New York, 1968.
2. D. W. Weiss and B. A. Bolto in *Physics and Chemistry of the Organic Solid State* (D. Fox et al., eds.), Vol. 2, p. 68, Interscience, New York, 1965.
3. D. A. Seanor. *Adv. Polymer Sci.*, **4**, 317 (1965).
4. D. A. Seanor. *Charge Transfer Mechanisms in Polymers.* 1967 Conf. on Elec. Insulation and Dielectric Phenomena. NAS/NRC publication. 1968.
5. A. Rembaum, J. Moacanin, and H. A. Pohl, *Progr. Dielectrics*, **6**, 41 (1965).
6. H. A. Pohl in *Modern Aspects of the Vitreous State* (J. D. MacKenzie, ed.), Chap. 2, p. 108. Butterworths. London. 1962.
7. R. W. Warfield in *Testing of Polymers* (J. V. Schmitz, ed.), Chap. 8, p. 271, Interscience, 1965.

8. A. Rembaum and R. F. Landel (eds.). *Electrical Conduction Properties of Polymers*, Interscience, New York, 1967. [*J. Polymer Sci.*, Part C. No. 17.]
9. M. Lampert, *Repts. Progr. Phys.*, **27**, 329 (1964).
10. L. E. Lyons in *Physics and Chemistry of the Organic Solid State* (D. Fox et al., eds.). Vol. 1. Chap. 13. Interscience. New York. 1963.
11. F. Gutmann and L. E. Lyons. *Organic Semiconductors*. p. 185. Wiley. New York. 1967.
12. S. Dushman. *Scientific Foundations of Vacuum Technique*. Wiley. New York. 1962.
13. *Handbook of Physics and Chemistry*, Vol. 46, Chemical Rubber Co., 1966.
14. J. F. Young. *J. Appl. Chem.*. **17**. 241 (1967).
15. D. A. Seanor. *Electrical Conduction Properties of Polymers* (A. Rembaum and R. F. Landel, eds.), p. 195, Interscience, New York, 1967.
16. D. D. Eley and D. I. Spivey. *Trans. Faraday Soc.*. **57**. 2280 (1961).
17. G. A. Samara and H. G. Drickammer. *J. Chem. Phys.*. **37**. 471 (1962).
18. H. A. Pohl. A. Rembaum. and A. Henry. *J. Am. Chem. Soc.*. **84**. 2699 (1962).
19. W. H. Bentley and H. G. Drickammer. *J. Chem. Phys.*. **42**. 1573 (1965).
20. E. M. Barrall and J. F. Johnson, in *Techniques and Methods of Polymer Evaluation* (P. J. Slade and L. T. Jenkins. eds.). Vol. 1. p. 1. Marcel Dekker. 1966.
21. S. Galarneau and G. W. Green. *J. Sci. Instr.*. **42**. 749 (1965).
22. G. Johansson. *J. Sci. Instr.*. **41**. 382 (1964).
23. D. McSweeny. P. W. Levy. and A. D. Townsend. *Rev. Sci. Instr.*. **36**. 1324 (1965).
24. J. Chiu. *J. Polymer Sci.*. **C8**. 27 (1965).
25. P. J. Reucroft. O. W. Rudj. and M. M. Labes. *Molecular Crystals*. **1**. 429 (1966).
26. W. H. Wing and T. M. Saunders. *J. Rev. Sci. Instr.*. **38**. 1341 (1967).
27. W. C. Dunlop, Jr.. *Methods of Experimental Physics*. (K. Lark-Horowitz and V. A. Johnson. eds.). Vol. 6. Part B. Chap. 7. Academic Press. New York. 1959.
28. *Proc. Carbon Conf.:* Vols. 1 and 2, Buffalo Univ. Press, Buffalo, New York, 1956; Vol. 3, Pergamon, 1959; Vol. 4, Pergamon, 1960; Vol. 5, Pergamon, 1963.
29. *Carbon*. Vols. 1 to date. Pergamon Press. 1963.
30. L. E. Lyons and F. Gutman. *Organic Semiconductors*. p. 473. Wiley. New York. 1967.
31. S. D. Bruck. *Ind. Engng. Chem.*. **59**(7). 18 (1967).
32. A. Armington in *Organic Semiconductors* (Y. Okamoto and J. Brenner. eds.). Chap. 7. Rheinhold. New York. 1964.
33. F. H. Winslow, W. O. Baker, and W. A. Yager. *J. Am. Chem. Soc.*, **77**, 4751 (1953); *Proc. 1st. 2nd Carbon Conf.*. Buffalo Univ. Press. Buffalo. 1953.
34. L. S. Singer, *Proc. 5th Carbon Conf.*, *1961*, Vol. 2, p. 37. Pergamon, London, 1963.
35. D. E. G. Austen. D. J. E. Ingram. and J. G. Tapley. *Trans. Faraday Soc.*. **54**. 400 (1956).
36. C. Jackson and W. K. F. Wynne-Jones. *Carbon*. **3**. 227 (1964).
37. H. Hirabayashi and H. Toyoda, *J. Phys. Soc. (Japan)*, **7**, 337 (1952).
38. H. T. Pinnick, *Proc. 1st, 2nd Carbon Conf.*, p. 3, Buffalo Univ. Press, Buffalo, 1953.
39. J. Kubishiro, M. Hatano, and S. Kambara, *Intern. Chem. Eng.*, **5**, 384 (1965).
40. L. K. H. vanBeek. *J. Appl. Polymer Sci.*. **9**. 553 (1965).
41. A. V. Topchiev. M. A. Geiderikh. B. E. Davidov. V. A. Kargin. B. A. Krentsel. I. M. Kustanovich. and L. S. Polak. *Chem. Ind. Dok. Akad. Nauk USSR*. **128**. 312 (1959).

42. M. A. Geiderikh, B. E. Davidov, B. A. Krentsel, I. M. Kustanovich, L. S. Polak, A. V. Topchiev, and R. M. Voitrenko, *J. Polymer Sci.*, **54**, 621 (1961).

43. W. D. Brennan, J. J. Brophy, and H. Schonhorn, in *Organic Semiconductors* (J. Buttery and J. J. Brophy, eds.), MacMillan, New York, 1962.

44. S. D. Bruck, *Polymer*, **6**, 319 (1965).

45. M. I. Pope, *Polymer*, **8**, 49 (1967).

46. M. I. Pope and S. J. Gregg, *Brit. J. Appl. Phys.*, **10**, 507 (1959).

47. M. I. Pope, *Proc. 2nd Conf. Ind. Carbon Graphite, Soc. Chem. Ind. London* p. 474, (1965).

48. J. Chiu, *Appl. Polymer Symp.* No. **2**, p. 25 (1966).

49. C. B. Murphy, J. A. Hill, and G. P. Sacher, *Anal. Chem.*, **32**, 1374 (1960).

50. L. E. Amborski, *Ind. Engng Chem.* (Prod. Res. Devel.), **2**, 189 (1963).

51. R. W. Warfield and M. C. Petrie, *Macromol. Chem.*, **58**, 139 (1962).

52. R. W. Warfield, *Soc. Plastics Eng. J.*, **14**, 39 (1958); *ibid.* **17**, 364 (1961).

53. J. H. Kallweit, *Koll. Z. und Z. Polymere*, **188**, 97 (1963).

54. B. K. Shim, *J. Polymer Sci.*, Part **C17**, p. 221 (1967).

55. B. Pilling, unpublished.

56. T. Nakajima and Y. Matsumoto, *Rept. Progr. Polymer Phys. (Japan)*, **6**, 241 (1963).

57. F. W. Billmeyer, Jr., *Textbook of Polymer Science*, 1st ed., Wiley, New York, 1958.

58. V. M. Fridkin and I. S. Zheludev, Photoelectrets and the Electrophotographic Process, Van Nostrand, New York, 1966.

59. L. M. Baxt and M. M. Perlmann (eds.), *Electrets and Related Electrostatic Charge Storage Phenomena*, Electrochem. Soc., New York, 1968.

60. B. Gross, *J. Chem. Phys.*, **17**, 866 (1949).

61. M. Campos, G. L. Ferreira, and S. Mascarenhas, *J. Electrochem. Soc.*, **115**, 388 (1968).

62. M. L. Miller and J. R. Murphy, *J. Polymer Sci.*, **A2, 4**, 697 (1966).

63. M. Kryszewski and A. Szymanski, *Plaste und Kautschuk* **12**, 1025 (1965).

64. S. Z. Weisz, R. C. Jarnagin, M. Silver, M. Simhony, and J. Balberg, *J. Chem. Phys.*, **40**, 3365 (1964).

65. W. Helfrich and P. Mark, *Z. Phys.*, **168**, 495 (1962).

66. R. H. Bube, *Photoconductivity in Solids*, Wiley, New York, 1960.

67. J. T. Randell and M. H. F. Williams, *Proc. Royal Soc. (London)* **A184**, 347, 365, 390 (1945).

68. G. F. T. Garlick and A. F. Gibson, *Proc. Phys. Soc.*, **60**, 574 (1948).

69. P. Devaux and M. Schott, *Phys. Stat. Solidi*, **20**, 301 (1967).

70. F. Urbach, *Sitzber. Math.-Naturw. Kl. Bayr. Akad. Wiss. Muchen, Abt.* **11A**, 139, 363 (1930).

71. G. F. Garlick, *Luminescent Materials*, Oxford Univ. Press, Oxford, 1949.

72. E. C. Avery and L. I. Grossweiner, *J. Chem. Phys.*, **21**, 372 (1953).

73. P. Braunlich and A. Scharmann, *Phys. Stat. Solidi*, **18**, 307 (1966).

74. G. A. Dussel and R. H. Bube, *Phys. Rev.*, **155**, 764 (1967).

75. K. H. Nicholas and J. Woods, *Brit. J. Appl. Phys.*, **15**, 783 (1964).

76. T. A. T. Cowell and J. Woods, *Brit. J. Appl. Phys.*, **18**, 1045 (1967).

77. H. J. Dittfield and J. Boigt, *Phys. Stat. Solidi*, **3**, 1941 (1963).

78. A. Bree, P. J. Reucroft, and W. G. Schneider, in *Symposium on Electrical Conductivity in Organic Solids*, (H. Kallman and M. Silver, eds.), p. 113, Interscience, New York, 1961.

79. F. J. Bryant, A. Bree, P. E. Fielding, and W. G. Schneider, *Disc. Faraday Soc.*, **28**, 48 (1959).
80. H. Kokado and W. G. Schneider, *J. Chem. Phys.*, **40**, 2938 (1964).
81. P. Toma and G. Vaubel, *Phys. Stat Solidi.*, **16**, 663 (1966).
82. A. Sysmanski and M. Kryszewski, *Intern. Union Pure Appl. Chem. Preprints* (Brussels) Paper 5/38 (1967).
83. A. Charlesby and R. H. Partridge, *Proc. Royal Soc. (London)*, **A271**, 170 188 (1963).
84. A. Charlesby and R. H. Partridge, *Proc. Royal Soc. (London)*, **A283**, 312 329 (1965).
85. R. H. Partridge, *J. Polymer Sci.*, **A3**, 2817 (1965).
86. G. Stetter, *Koll. Z. und Z. Polymere*, **215**, 112 (1967).
87. H. J. Wintle, *Photochem. Photobiol.*, **6**, 683 (1967).
88. V. I. Bukhgalter, L. N. Pirozhnaya, B. I. Sazhin, and N. I. Sergeyeva, *Polymer Sci., USSR*, **6**, 139 (1964).
89. R. W. Warfield and M. C. Petree, *J. Polymer Sci.*, **37**, 305 (1959).
90. J. A. Aukward, R. W. Warfield, and M. C. Petree, *J. Polymer Sci.*, **27**, 199 (1958).
91. L. J. Gough and I. T. Smith, *J. Appl. Polymer Sci.*, **3**, 362 (1960).
92. V. A. Kargin, N. G. Podosenova, G. P. Andrianova, and B. I. Sazhin, *Polymer Sci., USSR*, **9**, 323 (1967).
93. K. Arizana, K. Tsuge, and J. Wada, *J. Appl. Phys. (Japan)*, **4**, 138 (1965).
94. B. I. Sazhin and N. G. Podosenova, *Polymer Sci., USSR*, **6**, 162 (1964).
95. L. E. Amborski, *J. Polymer Sci.*, **62**, 331 (1962).
96. Y. L. Frankevich, L. I. Busheva, Y. I. Balavanov, and L. G. Cherkashina, *Polymer Sci., USSR*, **6**, 1132 (1964).
97. J. H. Kallweit, *J. Polymer Sci., Part A1*, **4**, 337 (1966).

Author Index

Numbers in parentheses are reference numbers and indicate than an author's work is referred to although his name is not cited in the text. Numbers in italics show the page on which the complete reference is listed.

341

Subject Index

353